Cosmometry

Exploring the HoloFractal Nature of the Cosmos

Marshall Lefferts

A Unified Model of Cosmic Geometry, Physics, Music and Consciousness

Foreword by Foster and Kimberly Gamble

Cosmometria Publishing

ISBN-13: 978-1-7336977-0-5

Library of Congress Control Number: 2019903120

Images and excerpts from *Synergetics*, Synergetics Dictionary, and picture of Buckminster Fuller courtesy of The Estate of R. Buckminster Fuller.

Images and excerpts from *INTERFERENCE – A Grand Scientific Musical Theory* courtesy of and copyright by Richard Merrick.

Cymatics images courtesy of and copyright by Erik Larson (except on page 277 and top of page 278).

Universal Mind Lattice image and text excerpt courtesy of and copyright by Alex Grey and Allyson Grey.

Images from *Thrive: What On Earth Will It Take?* courtesy of and copyright by Thrive Movement.

3D graphics by Andy Day and Marshall Lefferts.
Cover design by Daniel VanTassell , Teresa Collins and Marshall Lefferts.
Book design by Lynda Rae, Aurora Design Studio.

Printed in the United States of America.

Published by
Cosmometria Publishing
PO Box 5613
Santa Cruz, CA 95063 USA
connect@cosmometry.com

Visit **www.cosmometry.com** for additional resources related to each chapter of this book.

TABLE OF CONTENTS

FOREWORD

In his *Operating Manual for Spaceship Earth*, Buckminster Fuller warned of the risk of human extinction through over-specialization. He said what was needed was more "comprehensivists" — individuals dedicated to thinking in terms of the whole. Marshall Lefferts is a paragon of what Bucky had in mind.

As close friends and colleagues for over two decades, we have witnessed Marshall synthesize a lifetime's work into this beautiful, profound and very useful book. Combining pattern recognition with astute insight, he offers an unprecedented perspective that coheres physics, geometry, math, music and consciousness to provide a star map for those on the ultimate journey to discover how to live in harmony with the cosmic life force so that humanity can truly thrive. As a master musician himself, he reminds us that "Uni-verse" means "one song", and that music holds the keys to accessing the healing, the power and the wisdom of a Unified Field.

Cosmometry shows us that everything we experience is the result of vibration, at various frequencies and degrees of resonance. Every molecule, every mountain, every star, everything we experience as matter is energy vibrating at a particular frequency and interacting within a greater field of resonance. Understanding these dynamics unlocks a new paradigm of science, including guidelines for how to access new sources of energy for electricity, gravitational control and healing our bodies.

Lefferts' commitment to deeper truth takes him to the principles beyond the phenomena, to the whole, the Synergy, that is greater than the sum of the parts. He has humbly and ceaselessly apprenticed his mind to the likes of Bucky Fuller, David Bohm, Nassim Haramein, Walter Russell, Arthur Young, Richard Merrick, Robert Grant and others. He's also integrating his own unique insights, especially the role of the intrinsic boundary conditions of the Phi Double Spiral, the Phi Scaling Angle, and the "hologramic field of light," that confirm and extend the work of other masters.

Fasten your seatbelts and relish the journey!

Foster & Kimberly Gamble, Co-creators – THRIVE and the Thrive Movement

PREFACE

Cosmometry is a word that has been in the English language for a few centuries, though it has never been in popular use. When I first thought of the word in 2005 as a substitute for the currently popular name for this field of interest, Sacred Geometry, I thought I had made it up. I also thought it sounded a little funny, having the word "mom" in the middle of it. When I did an online search on the word, I was amazed to find that, out of thousands of search results, there were only two uses of cosmometry in scientific papers and about a half-dozen references to it in channeled writings by Masters from the Sirian star system (who, by the way, appear to really understand the importance of cosmometry as a field of knowledge). The rest were either dictionary definitions or strangely jumbled sets of words on otherwise blank web pages that included cosmometry in the list.

"The art of measuring the world or universe" is its formal definition, which while it's evident what it means, it is also very generalized. And as well, how could you measure the world *or* the universe when the world is clearly an integral aspect *of* the universe? Seemed like a strange and limited definition to me. I am proposing, therefore, an expanded definition of cosmometry as being the study of fundamental patterns, structures, processes and systems that are inherent in manifestation at all scales within the cosmos.

There is a rapidly emerging understanding of the Unified Field in which all things exist, the foundation of which appears to rest upon an integral synthesis of cosmic geometry, physics, music and consciousness that arises through the study of the patterns that unify them as a coherent system. Cosmometry is a name for this pursuit that fits the inclinations of both artists and spiritual teachers (who tend to refer to Sacred Geometry as the label for this field) and scientists (who are definitely not going to use that term as a context for their research in this field).

One of my great guides and teachers on this path of discovery, Buckminster Fuller (whose work is foundational to cosmometry), said that we are all "artist-scientists" by nature, born to explore, learn, develop skills and express talents through both artistic inspiration and scientific investigation. Over my 40 years of pursuing what I now call cosmometry, I've generally considered myself to be more on the artist side of the equation, looking for patterns in nature and seeking creative ways to visually reveal the implicit energy dynamics that inform them. It became obvious to me that until I could visually show others what I was seeing, it would be too challenging for them to understand what I was trying to convey through words alone. Thanks to the advent of computer graphics, it became possible for me to render images that depict both nature's patterns and the implicit energy dynamics, the results of which are found throughout this book.

On the "scientist" side of the equation, I've always had a deep interest in understanding the concepts and principles of scientific knowledge, especially in physics, yet I admittedly have been less attentive to the technical aspects of the pursuit. Ironically, I was actually a terrible student when it came to learning geometry in school, with all its theorems and hypotheses. Now I've written a book filled with geometric images and patterns! Fortunately, coming upon Fuller's writings when I was 19 and opening to new ways of seeing beyond obvious visible appearances set me on a path of exploration that engaged my scientific mind in a creative manner more suitable to my temperament. I've also been fortunate to be exposed over these years to the far-reaching ideas of innovative explorers like physicist David Bohm, artist-scientist polymath Walter Russell, and a host of contemporary visionary scientists and consciousness explorers, including Nassim Haramein, Foster and Kimberly Gamble, Alex and Allyson Grey, Jude Currivan, Robert Grant and others.

My two greatest teachers, though, have been deep immersion for over 55 years in the nature magic of the Adirondack High Peaks Wilderness, and an equally long immersion into the magical nature of Music. It feels to me at this point that we humans are an interface between these two fundamental realms (which, as is true with everything explored in this book, are actually one and the same thing). Musical harmonic dynamics literally in→form nature's patterns, structures, processes and systems simply because nature is a universally present vibratory phenomenon that is subject to the same harmonic dynamics found in music (i.e. the acoustic aspect of the cosmos). And we humans, with our self-reflective awareness, have the intellectual capacity to come to understand this and begin now to apply it to all of our sciences. The Art of music becomes the music of Science, informing our investigations with a universal harmonic code and establishing Harmonic Theory as an essential basis of inquiry within the full spectrum of scientific disciplines.

This field of knowledge is as vast as the cosmos, and I am the first to admit that the contents of this book are a mere skimming of the surface of what's already available "out there", let alone what's to come. This presentation is my synthesis of a core set of principles and concepts that when combined appear to form a unified model of wholeness that correlates to conceptual and literal observation across the full spectrum of cosmic phenomena. While I'm certain that much of it is "correct", I'm also quite certain that some of the ideas I propose are "incorrect" and in need of further investigation, understanding, reflection and refinement. My aim is to start a conversation, not to try to complete one.

I offer Cosmometry as an imperfect yet important step in the process of aligning our intellectual and spiritual insight with the nature of nature in which we are an equally imperfect yet important part.

ACKNOWLEDGEMENTS

My deep gratitude goes to all who have taught me, inspired me, guided me, questioned me, corrected me, and especially those who were willing to listen to me even as I was coming to understand what I was trying to say. I am especially grateful for the many conversations and experiences I've had with Teresa Collins that illuminated and confirmed essential aspects of what it means to both intellectually understand this knowledge and directly embody what it describes. And as well, my thanks to a few among many over the years who offered insightful reflections (and a few perplexed ones!) — my parents, brothers and family, Adam Apollo, Elijah Parker, Richard Rudd, Veena Devi, Kelly Lynn Ford.

To those who read the manuscript and provided valuable feedback, thank you!... Hal Lefferts, Randy Langel, William Brown, Amira Val Baker, Nassim Haramein, Foster and Kimberly Gamble, Jude Currivan, Meredith Sands Keator.

Big thanks to Andy Day for his expertise in modeling and rendering all of the 3D graphics, and to Daniel VanTassell for his extra care in creating the cover design.

My great appreciation to those who graciously permitted use of their proprietary images and text, including:

- Images and excerpts from *Synergetics*, Synergetics Dictionary, and picture of Buckminster Fuller courtesy of The Estate of R. Buckminster Fuller, with thanks to John Ferry and Robert Gray for their generous assistance.

- Richard Merrick for images and extensive excerpts from *INTERFERENCE – A Grand Scientific Musical Theory.*

- Alex and Allyson Grey for permission to use *Universal Mind Lattice* image and text excerpt.

- Thrive Movement for numerous images from the movie *Thrive: What On Earth Will It Take?*

- Erik Larson for cymatic images.

- Clay Taylor for his truly cosmometric inquiry and visual artistry.

Special thanks to Claudia Welss/NextNow Collaboratory, Jim Fournier and Elizabeth Thompson/Planetwork, Joshua Arnow, Adam Furgatch and Wendy Grace for their support in the "early days" (and still to today). And to Rosy Aronson for caring guidance.

And a deep bow of loving gratitude to Irina Dubin for being such a clearly reflecting sacred mirror in mind, heart and spirit… thank you for your pure presence and insatiable inquiry to know what lies beyond the veil.

Lastly, a special appreciation to Barbara Marx Hubbard, a dear friend, colleague and mentor, who made her Great Passage at the time of this book's completion. Her clarity of vision inspired me deeply, and the years we worked together informed my understanding of what humanity's imperative for Conscious Evolution truly means, both personally and collectively as the most powerful species on this planet. Your radiance shines evermore brightly throughout the cosmos, Barbara!

There is only one Light in the Universe.

There is only one Sound in the Universe.

There is only one Magnetism in the Universe.

There is only one Electricity in the Universe.

There is only one Gravity in the Universe.

There is only one Matter in the Universe.

There is only one Hologram in the Universe.

There is only one Intelligence in the Universe.

There is only one Consciousness in the Universe.

There is only one Love in the Universe.

There is only One Song in the Uni-Verse.

There is only One Thing going on in the Universe.

This book is dedicated to that One Thing.

INTRODUCTION

Our perception of reality is, first and foremost, very personal and subjective. Each of us has our own point of view within the shared experience of life on Earth. While we inherit viewpoints from others as well, especially during childhood in our families and schools, and culturally in more general ways, we each inevitably must come to our own conclusions about the nature of reality through our personal perceptions. How we perceive the world around us informs how we perceive ourselves (and vice versa). It also informs our behavior and the values upon which we base our relationship to other people, animals, nature and the Earth as a whole. Ultimately it informs even our sense of place within the vastness of the Universe itself.

This is our worldview.

While our worldview is very personal, it is also very much founded in a greater field of perception, interpretation, agreement and behavior that is collectively present in our cultures and societies — our shared worldview. This greater field of perception lays a strong foundation upon which our personal worldviews are based and is therefore highly influential in the formation of who we are, how we perceive and relate to the world, how we behave and the actions we take. This shared worldview is presented to us through the primary arenas of societal engagement — academia, science, technology, religion, economics, media, governance, art etc. A society's shared worldview is made evident through these expressions, providing us a mirror within which we can see ourselves, each other, and the whole of our cultural perceptions, and in so doing we are given the opportunity for self-reflection and evaluation of both our personal and shared perceptions. In this way there is a constant feedback loop between us and the world around us. Whether we are conscious of it or not, this feedback loop is at play in our lives, affecting how we perceive and respond to the events of life.

At this time in our shared human journey on this small planet, the feedback we are getting is all but screaming at us that our perceptions and actions — our worldviews — are in dire need of self-reflection and evaluation. Environmental, social and economic collapse is increasingly imminent, even while scientific and technological innovation is growing at an unprecedentedly rapid pace. We are certainly not lacking in the potential for innovation and change, and yet we continue to be faced with crises of great magnitude that appear insurmountable. Perhaps it's not the doing that is causing this fundamental conflict in our experience, but rather the place from which the doing is being generated — the worldview that is driving the doing and the consequences that fall out from it — that have become critical to all life on Earth.

We are truly at a make-or-break moment in history. We will either "pass the final exam" as Buckminster Fuller called it, or tip over the edge of no return through a rapid cascade of environmental systems collapse, economic and social collapse, or the ultimate "mistake" of destroying ourselves through nuclear war or reactor meltdowns (which is still all-too-real a possibility in our current circumstances).

The fundamental question underlying our predicament is: How can we create circumstances that support the thriving of life for all — human, plant, animal and planet alike? Upon what worldview would we base the pursuit of such circumstances? Could it be that there's a greater field of perception, even beyond our cultural worldviews, that can provide us the necessary feedback to inform our path towards balance, wholeness and healthy relationship with each other, the Earth and the boundless cosmos?

The answer to this last question is, fortunately… "Of course there is!" How foolhardy it would be if the grand cosmic scheme didn't include a clear basis upon which we could achieve such vital goals (even if just in the nick of time).

The cosmos as we know it has existed for billions of years. The Earth, Sun, Solar System and beyond have moved in continuous harmonic relationship through to this very moment, and from what's indicated by past experience, will likely continue to do so tomorrow and the next day for a long time to come. The cosmos is thriving! We are literally living in a greater field of healthy, balanced and self-sustaining systems that provide us with a constant feedback loop of how it's done. The critical challenges we face are not a consequence of the collapse of the cosmos. They are much smaller and more local than that. They are a consequence of the human field of perception, belief and action being based upon a limited view of reality that has become at odds with cosmic wholeness, balance and harmony. Thriving is inherent in the way of the cosmos, not an illusion of wishful thinking. It is achievable because it is inherent. Our role is to recognize the patterns, processes and principles upon which the greater field of reality we are in achieves it, and base our perceptions, beliefs and actions upon them so as to come into alignment and harmony with the inherent dynamics of life thriving in the cosmos.

The key word here is Harmony. Our great opportunity, and even requirement, we might say, is to come into harmony with the cosmos. While this may sound lofty and attainable only by enlightened spiritual masters, it is in fact a very pragmatic option, at this time. What has generally been held as a remote spiritual ideal, cosmic consciousness is in the process of becoming normalized in our human perceptual framework — our worldview. The "conscious awareness of cosmic phenomena" is emerging in the general field of human awareness. Whether it's through scientific and technological advancement (Hubble Telescope images, for example), through meditation or psychedelic experiences, or through immersive contemplation of nature's patterns and processes, we (as in the collective field of human consciousness) are rapidly awakening to a much greater understanding of the fundamental nature of the cosmos than ever before. And with this understanding comes the opportunity to harmonize our technologies, social systems, health modalities, education, governance, environment — all aspects of our life on Earth and beyond — with the same cosmic dynamics that have succeeded in getting us to this point over the course of billions of years.

By all reckoning, it appears that pursuing the path of harmonization with the cosmos is THE most important choice humanity can make at this time, for not doing so almost certainly leads us towards a cliff we're not prepared to jump off of with much hope of surviving. Fortunately for us, the cosmos has actually made it pretty obvious how to do this and given us all the clues, signs and instructions we need to enact this choice. By doing so, it is clear that we can quite readily achieve a state of harmony that will provide a solid foundation for many generations to come to create and live in a healthy, balanced and thriving world (and ultimately establish our place in the greater galactic community to whom we are perhaps already intimately related).

Thriving is inherent in the way of the cosmos, not an illusion of wishful thinking. It is achievable because it is inherent. Our role is to recognize the patterns, processes and principles upon which the greater field of reality we are in achieves it, and base our perceptions, beliefs and actions upon them so as to come into alignment and harmony with the inherent dynamics of life thriving in the cosmos.

The purpose of this book is to present an integrated picture of many threads of understanding that are converging into a unified model of cosmic wholeness and integrity. This is offered as a working blueprint upon which an ongoing dialogue of inquiry, articulation, clarification and agreement can be pursued. Its purpose is to serve the process of harmonization through informing the design of technologies and socio-economic systems that are based upon cosmic principles of wholeness and integrity — the fundamental basis for thriving. It is intended as a contribution into a process of re-orienting our perceptions and worldview that is vital to making it through the critical transition period we are in at this time as successfully and sustainably as possible and on behalf of all life.

The information presented is naturally limited in scope, having an emphasis on bringing to light the fundamental patterns, processes and principles found in cosmic dynamics. Its purpose is to provide a foundation of perception and understanding that can inform the process of harmonization through its application in the design of technological and social systems, as well as the development of scientific and spiritual worldviews, based upon an intelligent comprehension of this information.

My personal path to this understanding has been primarily through the exploration of fundamental patterns and theoretical frameworks found in three fields of inquiry — Cosmic Geometry, Unified Physics and Music. These will serve as the basis for how I present this picture, though by no means do they represent the entire spectrum of how it can be explored or presented. There are numerous other very important areas of research, theoretical analyses and application development that also contribute to this body of knowledge, some of which I will include on the companion website to this book at www.cosmometry.com.

INTRODUCTION

From my exploration of the three areas I'm viewing this picture through, I have come to what appears to be an integrated model of wholeness wherein these three are simply lenses through which to view one unified whole. My quest is to convey that model to you as simply and basically as possible with the intention that you will come to your own comprehension of it and discover how it informs your personal perceptions and overall worldview. I am not a professional scientist or academician, but rather a long-time investigator of things generally not often discussed in traditional scientific or academic institutions. I am grateful to have been exposed to and closely associated with other such outside-the-box explorers, some of whose ideas and research are represented in what I am presenting. I will provide clear acknowledgement of them as I go, as well as identify where my own original insights contribute to this emerging picture.

By all reckoning, it appears that pursuing the path of harmonization with the cosmos is THE most important choice humanity can make at this time, for not doing so almost certainly leads us towards a cliff we're not prepared to jump off of with much hope of surviving.

This presentation is offered as a starting place for a much larger dialogue involving many more people, rather than as a final conclusion to my or anyone's inquiry. It is intended to serve the process of awakening cosmic consciousness in the most practical sense, and that this awakening, in turn, serves the harmonization of humanity with the cosmos. The information and knowledge presented is ultimately very simple and will be readily embraced by younger generations as they're taught this perspective in schools to come. This is what makes the evolutionary leap possible — each successive generation being more innately aware of the cosmic nature of reality than the ones preceding it, and putting this awareness into application in the most pragmatic and aesthetically beautiful ways possible.

By seeing fundamental patterns in nature and understanding their correlations in physics and the workings of the cosmos, we experience an intellectual realization and spiritual revelation that there is a profound unity and wholeness present throughout the cosmos, and that we're integrally united and whole with it. To every degree that this book inspires this realization, its purpose will have been fulfilled.

> *"What I am proposing here is that man's general way of thinking of the totality, i.e. his general world view, is crucial for overall order of the human mind itself. If he thinks of the totality as constituted of independent fragments, then that is how his mind will tend to operate, but if he can include everything coherently and harmoniously in an overall whole that is undivided, unbroken, and without a border (for every border is a division or break) then his mind will tend to move in a similar way, and from this will flow an orderly action within the whole."*
> – David Bohm [1]

A MODEL OF WHOLENESS

Renowned physicist, David Bohm (1917-1992), proposed that the true nature of the cosmos is "undivided wholeness in flowing movement." Using the analogy of vortices in a stream of water, he said that all manifest phenomena that we call matter and energy are temporarily stable abstractions similar to what we perceive as individual whirlpools in what is fundamentally a unified, flowing movement of water. The vortices in the water are each unique and appear independent from the others, yet they are all connected simultaneously throughout the entire stream in a state of undivided wholeness. This is the same for the entire cosmos, according to Bohm's worldview.

Undivided wholeness in flowing movement… Not exactly our day-to-day experience of life here on Earth! It can be challenging to experience such a state when we're surrounded by what appears to be a very physical reality made up of seemingly separate objects, very often *not* in flowing movement (imagine an L.A. traffic jam crawling around a rear-end collision). It's not surprising that Bohm's ideas were not readily embraced by the physics community of his day, given the dominant worldview of reductionism and the analysis of parts in ever-smaller degree in search of "fundamental particles." That model seems to reflect our outer experience of life more than one of undivided wholeness in flowing movement.

Bohm also proposed that underlying the world we're familiar with — the physical reality that comprises our bodies, family, home, nature, planet, solar system, galaxy and universe — is a non-observable level of order from which all manifest things arise. He calls this the Implicate Order, and what we experience and study through our scientific instruments is the Explicate Order. The Implicate Order is the cosmic state of undivided wholeness in flowing movement, and all that emerges into physical manifestation (both as matter and energy) is continuously and intimately connected through this Implicate Order just as vortices of water are in a stream. For Bohm, this includes consciousness as well, which cannot be held as somehow separate from physical reality when considered in a model of undivided wholeness.

A conscious, unified, flowing, cosmic field that is the basis for all energy-matter phenomena, at all scales, which manifests as discrete yet intimately connected entities and events that we experience as everyday reality. Is this really an accurate description upon which to form a scientific worldview? Is there a practical model we can use to illustrate and even study such a proposal?

The answer to both of these questions is Yes. A quarter of a century after Bohm's passing, there is now a theoretical framework of physics complemented by a model of cosmic geometry that clearly shows that, in fact, Bohm was correct.

This theory and model are fundamentally very simple, yet the complexity that arises from this simple foundation can often make it challenging to see the simplicity as we study it. It is because of this apparent complexity that we are faced with highly complex and abstract theories in contemporary physics and mathematics, which in turn typically lead to confusion and "mind fry" when those other than the few elite researchers who derive these theories try to understand them. When we shift our perspective to seeking the simplicity of wholeness rather than focusing on the complexity of apparent fragmentation, the journey to understanding becomes much easier and more accessible to anyone.

In order to comprehend the underlying simplicity, though, we must be able to describe it, which is the purpose of this presentation. As with all such pursuits, this requires conveying concepts, principles and models that, when combined together, form the basis of our comprehension. While doing so can itself appear to be an exploration in complexity, it is helpful to keep in mind that there is indeed an inherent simplicity that is present throughout.

To describe the simplicity of the whole we need to understand the characteristics and relationships of enough "parts" that comprise the whole. In the case of this presentation, there are three such "parts" we are exploring (parts in quotes simply to highlight the fact that they're merely lenses through which to look at one unified and simple model). As previously mentioned, these are:

- **Cosmic Geometry** – a fractal-holographic model of energy-matter dynamics

- **Unified Physics** – a complementary theory of physics that unifies the fundamental forces

- **Music** – a system of harmonic relationships that is integral to form and structure in the cosmos

While each of these is a rich arena for extensive exploration, it is the fundamental simplicity and commonality within them that is the key to our comprehension and the quest of this presentation to convey.

Our journey begins by introducing these three components at a high level.

COSMIC GEOMETRY

The first fundamental component in our exploration (and central theme of this book) is cosmic geometry, or more appropriately termed, cosmometry (a word that was first coined a few hundred years ago but has not been in popular use, which I am reintroducing in a more expanded context than its defined meaning — "The art of measuring the world or universe."). It is *cosmic* geometry because it provides us a model upon which to study, measure and map the dynamic interactions and manifest structures of energy-matter-information at all scales, from Planck (the smallest that is theoretically possible to measure or otherwise experience from our scale) to Universal. While it incorporates classical geometry (geo = earth), it also includes the pioneering research of R. Buckminster Fuller that he called *Synergetics* (which lies at the foundation of Unified Physics), discoveries by other contemporary researchers, as well as original insights that I have gleaned in my study of cosmometry, music and unified physics, and through the study of patterns in nature.

Cosmometry is the study of the fundamental patterns, structures, processes and systems that are inherent in manifestation at all scales within the cosmos. All of these are ways of looking at one thing — energy-matter interactions, or what I call energetic articulation. It is essentially a visual language of form and flow that we can use to discern and describe how energy articulates in both rigid and fluid forms. As mentioned above, it has a basic set of components that are utilized for this study:

Patterns – the 2-dimensional abstractions we can use to illustrate basic forms of energetic articulation.

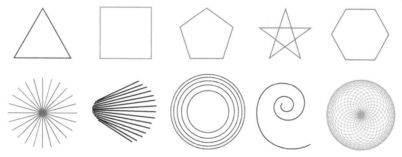

Structures – the 3-dimensional forms that make up our physical world, most basically represented by the simple Platonic forms and increasing in complexity from there. This is the tensegrity (tensional integrity) of atomic, molecular, crystalline, cellular, etc., forms.

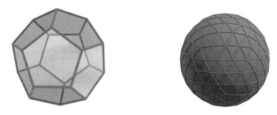

Processes – the dynamic flow of energy that is in its greatest state of coherence when in the form of a Torus — the flow form that allows for seamless fractal embedding of energy from micro to macro scales.

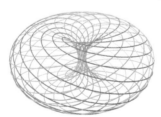

Systems – the ways we can map energetic relationships, such as with the 12-tone music system, as is illustrated here.

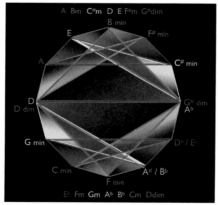

As with Unified Physics and Music, we'll explore Cosmometry in the context of a fractal-holographic model of the cosmos to see how it offers insights into and illustrations of how this model works.

UNIFIED PHYSICS

Although David Bohm did not label his theory as unified physics, it's obvious from his simple description of it — undivided wholeness in flowing movement — that this is an apt name for his model and scientific worldview. As mentioned, his ideas were received with much resistance by most of his colleagues, even though he was greatly respected as a leading physicist in his more familiar areas of research, specifically plasma physics. He was (as were his colleagues, including Albert Einstein) perplexed by the contradictory theories of Quantum Mechanics and Relativity — the realms of the very small scale (quantum) and the large scale (relativistic) — and he was seeking resolution by considering that perhaps there is an underlying level of order that was not understood (or even observable and measurable) that could provide a bridge between these two realms. He felt there must be an underlying wholeness that unifies the very small with the very large, which when understood could provide answers to the questions that arise due to the apparent theoretical contradictions between these realms. In Bohm's words:

> *"…relativity theory requires continuity, strict causality (or determinism) and locality. On the other hand, quantum theory requires non-continuity, non-causality and non-locality. So the basic concepts of relativity and quantum theory directly contradict each other… The basic notions of this new theory evidently cannot be found by beginning with those features in which relativity and quantum theory stand in direct contradiction. The best place to begin is with what they have basically in common. This is undivided wholeness. Though each comes to such wholeness in a different way, it is clear that it is this to which they are both fundamentally pointing."* [2]

Bohm's research into this idea is thoroughly presented in his books, articles and interviews. While he did present intellectually rigorous proposals to support his wholeness theory, a mathematical basis for it was elusive within the context of the Standard Model of Quantum Mechanics and Relativity.

In recent years, though, a mathematical basis has been established, and no doubt Bohm would be very pleased by the findings that indeed describe the very nature of the cosmos as undivided wholeness in flowing movement.

Independent physicist and Director of Research at the Resonance Science Foundation, Nassim Haramein, has been pursuing a theoretical framework and model of physics outside of (and often at odds with) the contemporary mainstream physics community for more than three decades. The fruits of his quest have resulted in a mathematically and geometrically based theory that offers a long-sought resolution to the fundamental discrepancies between quantum mechanics and general relativity — a theory of unified physics. In fact, it unifies these theories in a framework and model that also offers a practical understanding of the source of energy, mass, gravity and the speed of light, none of which have been accurately described in prior theories. Additionally, unified physics offers a broader context of physics as it applies to all sciences.

While it is not the purpose of this presentation to describe Haramein's unified physics theory in depth (see resonancescience.org for an online course that does this), there are fundamental aspects of unified physics that provide a basis of understanding as a component of our model of wholeness. These will be "unpacked" as we go, but as a starting place, here are a few of the key ideas:

- The cosmos (more specifically, the vacuum of space) is Quantized, and there is a primary "ground state" of quantization at the Planck scale. As such, spacetime is granular as "pixels" on the structure of space. (This quantization is obviously the basis for mainstream Quantum Theory, though the Planck-scale ground state is not explicitly incorporated in large-scale relativistic physics as it is in unified physics.)

- The cosmos is Holographic — the inherent wholeness is present at every point. (The Holographic Principle is also explored in mainstream theory, though the model for it is based upon the concept of a 2D hologram, whereas in unified physics it is generalized into the 3D (and 4D) structure of space itself.)

- The cosmos is Fractal — there is a repetition of fundamental patterns (cosmic geometry) at all scales from Planck to Universal.

- Matter (mass), Energy and Information are three ways of describing one phenomenon — electromagnetic wave interaction originating at the Planck scale.

- There is an intrinsic feedback/feedforward loop (toroidal geometry) of cosmic "intelligence" (as information) informing both the universal wholeness and all manifest entities within it simultaneously. (This is akin to Bohm's Implicate and Explicate Orders.)

- Gravity, confinement and the nuclear Strong Force are one and the same — they are the result of electromagnetic interactions from Planck to Universal scales.

- The information about all protons is present in every proton as a generalized holographic principle.

To put the above into a single statement:

There is a universal field of quantized electromagnetic wave interaction creating a generalized holographic interference pattern that manifests as discrete fractal boundaries of energy-matter (mass)-information across a gravitational density gradient from Universal to Planck scales (and beyond) in which the information of the whole is present in every point and the information of each point is shared throughout the whole.

A lot of concepts to take in at once, some of which may not as yet be familiar enough to comprehend their role within this statement. Yet in its essence, this is a rather simple statement. Electromagnetism permeates the cosmos at all scales and distributes the information content of each local entity throughout the whole.

These ideas will be further explored as we progress in our journey. For now, this provides an overview of some of the key concepts in the theory of unified physics.

MUSIC

The third fundamental component to introduce is music. Of course, music needs no introduction as to what it is in our daily lives. Music is really a most remarkable phenomenon, though, and even if we may somewhat take it for granted as "just a part of life on this planet," it is in fact entirely essential to our understanding of how the cosmos defines the fractal proportioning of energy-matter-information as it manifests in form and flow.

While the study of music theory is vast and varied across cultures around the world, there is again a set of fundamental concepts that are pertinent to our exploration of a model of wholeness. As a high-level introduction, these are:

- Harmonic Structure – the resonance and damping of waveform interactions that define a primary set of ratios found in music systems that are also inherent in the manifestation of physical form, as well as in the cosmic "ground state" field itself.

- Rhythmic Structure – cycles of time and the quantization of pressure impulses (sound) within the generalized spacetime field. (This applies to electromagnetic impulses as well, being they are quantized in the same manner as sound and as such are interchangeable in their information content, e.g. a microphone picks up acoustic pressure waves from a sound source, converts them to electromagnetic waveforms of the same frequency that transfer the information about the sound through an amplifier into loudspeakers that then convert back to sound waves at a stronger amplitude.)

- 12-Tone System – Music has an intrinsic 12-tone *system* of relationships that is fundamental to cosmic geometry. *System* is italicized to emphasize what is being stated here; that there is a way of studying the relationships of waveform interactions as a *system* independent of the actual frequency structures at play, and this system is based upon a 12-tone relationship at its most fundamental level of equilibrium and wholeness.

In our model of wholeness, music presents us with a structure for harmonic and rhythmic proportions that are inherent in the quantized nature of the cosmos. Harmonic and rhythmic proportions are characteristics of quantization itself and are the primary basis for the fractal aspect of manifestation — that which accommodates matter-energy formation seamlessly across all scales.

As mentioned above, the system of music that is based upon a 12-tone scale is relevant to our model, having a specific correlation to the most primary aspect of cosmic geometry when it is in perfect equilibrium. While the 12-tone system is by no means the only musical system, we will see that in fact it is intrinsic to the cosmometry itself and the harmonic interference patterns that comprise the cosmic hologram. For this we will incorporate the pioneering research of Richard Merrick, who has deeply studied the resonance and damping characteristics of sound wave interference patterns and the harmonic structures inherent in them, and applied these findings to harmonic and rhythmic proportion found in form and flow throughout nature — what he calls Harmonic Interference Theory.

THREE COMPONENTS, ONE THING

It may seem to be complex already, just introducing these three components. They are, once again, simply lenses through which we can view, analyze and map one thing: energy-matter-information interactions that comprise the observable universe as well as the conceptual foundations (the (presently) non-observable aspects) upon which it is manifest.

In a similar vein, you've likely noticed the repeated use of the term, **energy-matter-information**, all strung together. In the fundamental simplicity of the model we're exploring, these are words that all describe one phenomenon. We know from Einstein's famous equation, $E=mc^2$, that energy and matter are interchangeable when factored by the speed of light squared; therefore they can be understood as apparently different states of the same thing ("apparently" because it's simply a consideration of a mass density gradient in the spacetime field that makes for the distinction). Electromagnetic and acoustic energy waves are carriers of information. With this understanding, we view the three universal attributes of energy, matter and information as one phenomenon.

As we commence this journey, it's important to also emphasize the correlation to that which we call consciousness. We can say that information is the aspect of the cosmos that is directly related to the concept of consciousness, or an intrinsic systemic intelligence, and that with information being present at every point in the cosmos, perhaps there is intelligent awareness throughout that discerns specific relevance to the information at any given point. This will be explored in depth in Section 7.

I wish you a fun and insightful journey through *Cosmometry – Exploring the HoloFractal Nature of the Cosmos.*

Introduction Endnotes

1   Bohm, David (2012-12-06). *Wholeness and the Implicate Order* (Routledge Classics).

2   IBID (p. 223).

SECTION 1
WHOLENESS

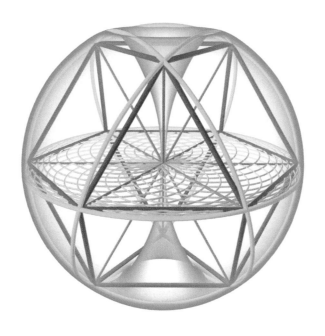

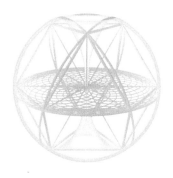

SECTION 1
WHOLENESS

Our exploration of the holofractal nature of the cosmos is based upon three components that combine to describe one phenomenon: universal dynamics of energy and matter manifesting in physical form and flow. As described at a high level in the Introduction, these components are Cosmometry (patterns, structures, processes and systems found at all scales), Unified Physics (a theoretical framework that unifies quantum and relativistic forces and scientific disciplines), and Music (a universal system of harmonic relationships of resonance) — three lenses through which we can look at one whole system.

Perhaps the most overarching theme and fundamental principle of this exploration is that of wholeness. While it's an easy word to use, almost casually as if we understand its meaning, it is also one that is highly ambiguous without some consideration and context within our exploration. Dictionary definitions include words to define wholeness (or whole) such as complete, total, entire, full, undivided, intact. As a noun, a whole is "an assemblage of parts associated or viewed together as one thing; a unitary system." Wholeness is commonly defined in terms that describe "parts" combining together, and the integrity of such an assemblage in their combined totality. While the cosmos is indeed whole in this way, it is also whole in ways not included in standard definitions that lie at the very foundation of our conceptual map of cosmometry and, when fully understood, provide us a more fundamental framework upon which to describe the nature of reality in its wholeness. These are the concepts of **Holographic, Fractal** and **Synergetic** wholeness.

As we venture into these concepts of wholeness, we need an understanding of what they are pertaining to, especially within the context of our exploration of cosmometry, unified physics and music. While the following may sound simplistic given the enormous variety and dynamic complexity of the human experience, **it appears that the entire cosmic phenomenon and our experience of it is composed of three fundamental attributes — Electromagnetic Radiation-Gravitation, Acoustic Compression, and Information.**

Electromagnetic Radiation-Gravitation encompasses the full spectrum of what we call Light, spanning a wavelength range from Universal to Atomic and Sub-Atomic scales, with visible light being a tiny fraction of this range (one octave, in fact). It is the source of the electrical and magnetic effects we are so familiar with, the universal presence of which makes possible our modern technologies for

3

power generation, telecommunication, celestial observation, medical imaging, as well as the very sight, hearing, taste, smell and touch of our everyday sensorial experience. As described in unified physics theory, gravity and the nuclear strong and weak forces are not different forces but rather they are specific behaviors of the ubiquitous electromagnetic field, with a prime ground state at the Planck scale (more on this in Section 2).

Acoustic Compression encompasses what we call Sound, and yet in a similar manner as with Light, the phenomenon of acoustic pressure waves goes far beyond the very small range of human hearing. Not only does it span infra- and ultra-sonic ranges, in the context of our exploration it encompasses all phenomena of pressure waves and all forms of compression. In fact, all "form" in the cosmos is a consequence of compression within the unified field of electromagnetic radiation-gravitation, and as such it can be said that all form is a manifestation of the acoustic attribute of the cosmos. This is why Music is an integral component in our inquiry, being that it is the system that defines the inherent harmonic and rhythmic dynamics of acoustic pressure waves, and therefore by extension all phenomena of form as compression dynamics.

Information encompasses Intelligence and Consciousness.* Just as the Electromagnetic and Acoustic attributes are universal in their spectral potential, so too is Information. In fact, given that electromagnetic and acoustic waves are fundamental information carriers in the cosmos, it is safe to say that information, and therefore intelligence and consciousness, is present everywhere throughout the entire cosmic phenomenon.† In the same way that our visible and auditory senses perceive only a small fraction of the spectra of Light and Sound, so too is our direct perception of information typically confined to these same spectral ranges in our day-to-day experience. Yet we can also extend this range with instruments that can observe above and below these ranges, and when we do we access information that is otherwise invisible and inaudible to us. We're able to do so across a scale spanning outward to the expanse of the known cosmos and inward to the structure of atoms, and at every point there is information. In the words of Jude Currivan from her highly "informative" book, *The Cosmic Hologram,*

> *"Everything at all scales of existence is being progressively discovered to be inherently related by in-formational content, flows, and processes… this isn't just basic data but all-pervasive in-formational patterns and relationships."*

This last sentence provides a key to understanding the meaning of information in this context: it is the patterns and relationships found within energy-matter (e.g. light and sound) dynamics. Similarly, Beth Macy writes in an April 2014 blog post:

> *"Once into the implicate domain, [David] Bohm would likely say that there is no such thing as "location," but rather, there is only information that sets relationships of parts into patterns of movement or flow."*

---

* This is where it gets tricky for the purely materialistic sciences.

† Why intelligence and consciousness are universally equated with information will be explored in Section 7.

In their September 2017 physics paper entitled *Consciousness in the Universe is Scale Invariant and Implies an Event Horizon of the Human Brain*,[3] authors Dirk K.F. Meijer and Hans J.H. Geesink write:

> *"Another major finding is that physical information should be seen as a modality of energy and that information and energy can be mutually converted to each other (Bérut et al, 2012; Toyabe, 2010; Peterson et al 2016), confirming previous ideas on three fundamental building blocks for the fabric of reality (Meijer, 2012): matter, energy and information. A recent study of Aharonov et al, 2013, even indicates that information can be physically separated from the matter it describes."*

Rupert Sheldrake attributes information as playing a role of formative cause:

> *"To inform literally means to put into form or shape. Information is now generally taken to be the source of form or order in the world; information is informative and plays the role of a formative cause, as for example in the concept of 'genetic information.'"*[4]

As we'll also explore further, Nassim Haramein's theory of unified physics proposes that "space is actually granular at the very fine scale and can be conceptualized in terms of information bits on the structure of the vacuum..."[5]

All of the above researchers place information as primary to the emergence of energy, mass and matter, informing these physical dynamics from a plane of existence beyond the constraints of the classical laws of space and time.

The three attributes of Electromagnetism (Light), Acoustic Pressure (Sound), and Information (Consciousness) are what comprise Energy-Matter-Information, the "three components, one thing" described in the Introduction. There's only one thing going on in the cosmos, and it's this one thing manifesting as electromagnetism, acoustic pressure and information that we're exploring as Wholeness. In what may seem paradoxical, though, in order to explore the wholeness of this one thing we must break it down into its constituent components, all the while inviting ourselves to continually consider them from a unified perspective.

It is from this perspective that we begin by exploring the Holographic, Fractal and Synergetic concepts of Wholeness.

WHOLENESS

CHAPTER 1
HOLOGRAPHIC WHOLENESS

When I was a young child in the late 1960's, my brother, Seth, became interested in the relatively new science and technology of holography. This was my initial exposure to the concept of holography and the first time for seeing the remarkable characteristic of holographic images. How could a flat glass plate display an image of an object such that one could see above, below, side-to-side and partially behind the object? This was obviously very different from a regular photograph. While a photograph is clearly a flat, 2-dimensional image of a scene, a holographic image is able to represent a scene as a 3-dimensional image that is much more similar to the actual reality we experience. This phenomenon has intrigued me ever since seeing those early holographic images (as it has many others, especially through the simulation of spatial holographic projections in Star Wars and other sci-fi films).

While the science and technology of holography is both fascinating and informative, for our exploration the most essential thing to know about a holographic image is this:

The image of the whole is present at every point.

Whereas with a photograph the image being captured is whole only at one scale — the full size of the photograph — in a hologram the entire image is captured at all scales from the entire holographic plate down to the smallest point on the plate. In fact, if you break the plate into pieces, the entire image will still be present on every piece. The whole image of the object that is facing the plate is captured at every point. It is because of this difference that a holographic image is more closely representative of our 3D experience of reality than is a photograph. **This is a huge clue about the actual nature of our every-day reality — it is, in fact, fully holographic.** And as it turns out, our visual perceptual experience of reality wouldn't work the way it does if it were not holographic.

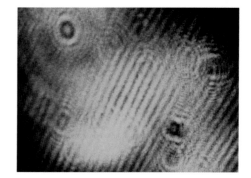

Before going into that, though, there is an important aspect of this principle of wholeness to consider. The word "holo-*graphic*" specifically refers to a visual representation of an object or scene. It is an appropriate description of capturing the whole *image* of an object. A holographic image isn't like a photograph, though. When you look at a hologram made using laser light, you don't actually see the image of the object. What you see is an abstract pattern of overlapping circles, much like the rings in water when you throw a bunch of pebbles into a pond (an important correlation as we extend this concept into reality as a whole — take note). What you're seeing is an interference pattern of the light field that is illuminating the holographic plate. It's actually the waveform *information* about the whole object that's being captured, rather than the image itself. As such, we can use the term "hologram" to describe this concept, with the suffix "gram" meaning information. **This is key to understanding this principle of wholeness as it pertains to the deeper nature of reality — the *information* of the whole is present at every point. The cosmos is holo*gramic*.**

To date, scientists are debating whether the universe is one big hologram. Numerous magazine articles and scientific theories have explored this idea, and yet there is typically an assumed limitation imposed upon the concept that makes the quest for an answer more abstract than it needs to be. Quite simply, the model they use for the inquiry is that of a holographic image on a glass plate — a 2-dimensional surface that encodes information and displays a holographic "projection" of 3-dimensional reality. It is conjectured that the universe is just such an illusory projection that resides on a 2-dimensional surface.[6] Finding a 2-dimensional surface anywhere in the universe would be the first step to validating such a theory, if such a thing exists. (As Nassim Haramein points out, even a holographic plate has a light-sensitive chemical emulsion that is 3-dimensional in its molecular structure, making it possible to capture the standing wave patterns of the laser light.)

While there is a lot to learn about the holographic principle by studying a so-called 2-dimensional holographic image and how it's created, it is in itself not a sufficient model upon which to base an inquiry into whether reality is holographic. Doing so is akin to analyzing a photograph to describe the nature of reality; we can come to some accurate conclusions, but only in a very limited scope. Applying those conclusions to describe reality will yield equally limited theories. This is why the debate as to whether the universe is a hologram is struggling to find an answer — it's based upon too limited a model.

The appropriate description of the holographic nature of the cosmos is one that is generalized, wherein *the entire field of universal reality is the hologram*, rather than only the surfaces.

A simple way of understanding what this means can be illustrated like this: **when we make a holographic image, we're simply capturing a "slice" of the generalized holographic information field that is present at the location of the holographic plate.** The holographic image is already present in space, not solely a phenomenon of the laser light that is illuminating the object and photosensitive plate. A photograph is doing the same thing; capturing a slice of the generalized image field we call reality, albeit with a more limited amount of information than the holographic image. Holography and photography are only possible because of the generalized nature of the holographic information field that is present everywhere. Whereas a hologram is specifically made with laser light (which is coherent in its frequency and phase waveform), we perceive the generalized hologram of light every day through our eyes, brain and consciousness.

This next statement is one of the most important points to understand as it informs our entire perspective on the hologramic nature of the universe being explored in this book:

Perception only works because reality is hologramic.

My understanding of this began one balmy evening as I was driving to my home that was high up a mountain overlooking Santa Barbara, California. I stopped to take in the expansive beauty of the night sky — the stars and planets scintillating in the clarity of the moment. As I quietly gazed at them, marveling in the cosmic wonder of it all, I came to the realization that the image of every one of those pinpoint light sources was present at every point in space around me. Wherever I put my eye, the image of the whole night sky was there. This would be true a foot away, a mile away or 100,000 miles off the surface of the planet. The image of the whole is present at every point; therefore, the entire field of light around us and throughout the cosmos must be holographic. We are inseparably living in a cosmic hologram!

Light from the stars of Orion is present at every point in space.
(Sky image: Bob King / Astro Bob)

This fundamental quality of wholeness is essential to the function of our visual and auditory perception. In fact, our perceptual framework is entirely dependent upon there being a generalized hologramic information field. Let's explore how this is so…

In the case of vision, the light field we're immersed in is completely holographic. By definition, then, the image of the whole is present at every point within the light field, as in the night sky example. To understand this in relation to your personal experience, visualize that **the light that is reflecting off of every object around you and emanating from every light source in sight is ALL converging at EVERY point in the field of space surrounding you.** As such, the image of the whole is present at each point. There is nowhere that this phenomenon of optical physics is not occurring. The entire field of light is holographic. **It is because of this that we can see our surrounding reality as a seamless whole, without gaps or voids in the image field.** It is, by necessity, a relative image, being unique to our angle of perception based upon where we place our eyes in the field (otherwise there would be no relative reality),

Pinwheel In A Pinpoint

A stellar example of just how detailed the holographic information is within the universal field of light is seen in this image of Spiral Galaxy M83, the Southern Pinwheel, captured by the Hubble Space Telescope (HST). Located in the Hydra constellation, it is 15 million light years distance from us, yet the image of the galaxy is whole and extremely detailed, and the totality of information is present in what would be a veritable pinpoint in space (relative to its source) where HST's light-receiving optics are located outside the atmosphere of Earth. As with sight, the HST can only capture this information because it is holographically present where it's located and at every point in the universal light field.

Image: NASA, ESA, and the Hubble Heritage Team (STScI/AURA); Acknowledgement: W. Blair (STScI/Johns Hopkins University) and R. O'Connell (University of Virginia)

but it is an image of the whole nonetheless. Because of this, I propose a new postulate of holographic physics: ***The angle of incidence equals the angle of perception.*** The relative holographic image of the whole is entirely predicated upon your unique perspective!

"YOU" ARE EVERYWHERE

Here's another way of seeing this relative to your own presence in the cosmos. Wherever you are reading this, take a look around yourself and notice the environment surrounding you. All objects — be they walls, ceiling, chairs, computer, people, trees, sky — are reflecting photons of light that are reaching your eye. As in the night sky example, every point in space contains an image of the whole environment. This means that at every point on the surface of your skin and clothes, the light that is illuminating you is doing so with an image of all that is surrounding you. Imagine a picture of your present environment imprinted into your skin at every point. This is literally what's happening.

Conversely, your image is also present at every point in space. Photons of light reflect off of each point on your body in all outward directions. Imagine this: I can take a mirror and place it anywhere in the space around you and you will see your image reflected back. This means your image is everywhere. (See photograph on next page.) People around you can see you wherever they are in a line of sight. Even if they're 50 miles away and have a strong enough telescope, they can see your whole image. When you step outside on a clear day, your image is literally filling all space around you, even out to the moon and beyond. Just as you are illuminated by photons reflected from all points in your environment, your environment is illuminated by photons reflected off of you. "You" are everywhere.

So, in each point in space surrounding you there is both an image of your total environment and an image of you; a complete image converging into every localized point in space, no matter how small a point you can conceive of.

Mirrors also only work the way they do because the light field is holographic. If it weren't, when you looked in a mirror you would see gaps in the image where light information was missing. A mirror is not fully holographic, of course. It is more photographic, reflecting what appears as a 2D image. This is simply a "stepping down" of the

10

perceptual framework into a more primary duality of actual and reflected objects. The actual object is the full holographic manifestation while the reflected object is a "slice" out of the holographic field into which the actual object's image is projected (as photons of light reflecting off of the object in all directions). This photograph of Coco Chanel by Robert Doisneau shows how her image is holographically surrounding her as each mirror reflects a slightly different angle of view.

So our visual perception works the way it does because the light field is holographic. It simply would not work if it weren't. Wherever we place our eyes, the generalized field of light is converging to a point at that location, providing us the holographic information of visual reality.

The same "image of the whole in every point" phenomenon also holds true for sound and our experience of acoustic reality. Sound waves converge from direct and reflected sources at every point within the generalized sound field. **The information of the whole soundscape is present at every point — reality is also holosonic.** If it were not this way there would be gaps in the field where we could not hear certain sounds.

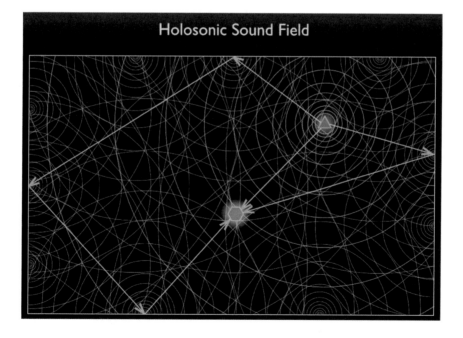

Together, the generalized field of light and sound that makes up the primary experience of our reality is what I call the **Sonoluminous Holofield**. Sono is sound, lumen is light, holo is whole, and field is generalized presence. The sonoluminous holofield is our everyday experience of reality. The information of the whole is present at every point. If it weren't, you would experience places where the visual and acoustic fields would not be there, leaving visual and auditory gaps in your perceptual experience of reality.

Suffice it to say that shifting from a 2-D surface model to a 3-D (and even 4-D) generalized model offers a more accurate and whole concept of the hologramic nature of the cosmos. This principle of wholeness will be discussed further as we explore the rest of our model of cosmometry, especially as it relates to the hologramic nature of physical reality described in unified physics. For now, as we close this introduction to it, consider this question, especially in light of the current scientific debate as to whether or not the cosmos is holographic:

Is it possible to make a holographic image in a non-holographic universe?

"The value of the hologram in this context is that it may help to bring this new notion of order to our attention in a sensibly perceptible way; but of course, the hologram is only an instrument whose function is to make a static record (or 'snapshot') of this order. The actual order itself which has thus been recorded is in the complex movement of electromagnetic fields, in the form of light waves. Such movement of light waves is present everywhere and in principle enfolds the entire universe of space (and time) in each region (as can be demonstrated in any such region by placing one's eye or a telescope there, which will 'unfold' this content)."
— David Bohm, *Wholeness and the Implicate Order*

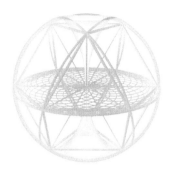

CHAPTER 2
FRACTAL WHOLENESS

When we look around at our world, we see a vast variety of shapes, forms, patterns, sizes, relationships; a diversity of life and substance that is incomprehensible in magnitude. Trees, plants and flowers of all shapes and sizes. Animals, insects, birds, fish, clouds, lightning, water, fire, metal, earth, crystal… humans… all co-existing on a small planet revolving around a star in a galaxy within our ultimate home we call Universe.

Universe — the sum of all-that-is in its totality. Our most encompassing concept of wholeness, a concept that is perhaps beyond our rational mind to fully comprehend, given its scale. Thinking in terms of billions of light-years of distance is simply without logical reference in our day-to-day lives. And yet, that's how big the observable universe is estimated to be, approximately 93 billion light-years across (8.8×10^{26} meters). (A light-year is the distance light travels in a year at ~300 million meters (186,000 miles) per second. Imagine that!)

On the other end of the scale spectrum is the very small. So small, in fact, that it is equally out of the realm of daily logic to comprehend. Vastly smaller than the size of an atom is the Planck scale, named after renowned physicist, Max Planck. At the end of the 19th Century, Planck proposed a set of units of measurement that are derived from properties of nature, rather than from human contrivance (such as degrees of temperature). These "natural units" (based solely upon known physical constants) are at the foundation of physics theories, including Quantum, Relativistic and Unified Physics. The Planck Length is a mere $1.616199(97) \times 10^{-35}$ meters,[7] some 61 orders of magnitude smaller than the scale of the observable universe.

Between these two extremes is a lot of scale potential! From Planck units to atoms to molecules to cells to organisms to planets, stars, galaxies and universe, there is a remarkably cohesive spectrum of form across an incomprehensibly vast scale. How does the universe accommodate this great a scale difference while operating as a unified whole?

Enter the fractal.

Mathematician Benoît Mandelbrot coined the word fractal in 1975 to describe a mathematical model that defines a (potentially infinite) repeating scaling pattern. While the science and study of fractals is very deep and rich with mathematical precision and aesthetic beauty, it is this simple definition that is pertinent to our exploration:

The same pattern repeats at all scales.

We can see this exhibited in nature in a variety of ways, such as with the repeating patterns of plant parts, coastal and mountain contours, river branching, lightning, clouds, wave patterns, etc. Even our skeletal structure is fractal, with the smaller bones of the fingers and toes scaling to the larger bones of the arms and legs in a similar manner.

 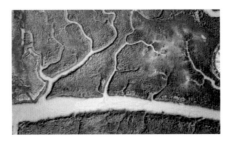 

A common phrase to describe the fractal principle is self-similarity, and this concept is key to understanding how the cosmos accommodates a seamlessly unified "division" of matter across such a vast range of scale from Universal to Planck. There are fundamental patterns and natural harmonic ratios that are found at all scales, and it is this harmonious repetition of self-similarity that provides for an integrated wholeness and diversity of form and flow. **Similar to the hologramic principle of the whole being present at every point, we can say that the whole pattern is found at every scale.** It is the intimate relationship between these two fundamental aspects of wholeness that is described by the term holofractal universe. These co-exist as one phenomenon. We can see this when we break a holographic image into fragments; we fracture it and see smaller fractal images of the original whole image. The information of the whole is not only present holographically, it's also present fractally.

In our exploration of cosmometry, we're bringing attention to fundamental aspects of how energy-matter-information creates form and flow across scales. Are there patterns in this form and flow that are fundamental to the fractal nature of the cosmos? What ratios of scale are present in the fractal aspect of wholeness that provide for a harmonious division of this wholeness?

It turns out that there are quite simple answers to these seemingly complex questions. A simplicity of pattern underlies the complexity of manifestation in the universe, and it is due to this simplicity that the scaling from small to large occurs with seamless integrity.

"A formula can be very simple and create a universe of bottomless complexity."
– Benoît Mandelbrot

In our quest to discern the cosmometry of this fractal simplicity we have a basic set of components we can use for deriving a fractal model. As described briefly in the Introduction, these are the Patterns, Structures, Processes and Systems that comprise the "parts kit" with which we can construct a model. These will be explored in greater depth as we go, but for the purpose of this introduction of fractal wholeness, let's start with the simplest patterns — **Radials, Rings and Spirals**.

As we do, remember that we're talking about patterns of energy, since all matter is a form of energy dynamics — what I call energetic articulation. The entire phenomenon of the observable universe is energy and therefore cosmometry is entirely about energetic articulation.

Every dynamic manifestation — be it an atom, a sound, a sunflower, a hurricane, a planet, a galaxy — is an energy event, an energy process. Underlying the myriad ways in which energy manifests itself lies an "idealized" energetic patterning that is foundational to cosmometry. Yet "out there" in the world, in nature, in the cosmos, the forms of energy get "messy", i.e. distorted, chaotic, random, changing. It's not always obvious that there is an under-

A simplicity of pattern underlies the complexity of manifestation in the universe, and it is due to this simplicity that the scaling from small to large occurs with seamless integrity.

lying coherent pattern given the natural dynamics at play. Yet, it's all energy and it's all following the same fundamental patterning when it articulates into a given form. The more coherent and organized the energy pattern is, the more obvious will be the underlying patterning upon which it is based.

In the simplest way of illustrating energetic articulation, we have these three basic patterns:

Radial vectors,   **Rings or waves,**   **and Spirals.**

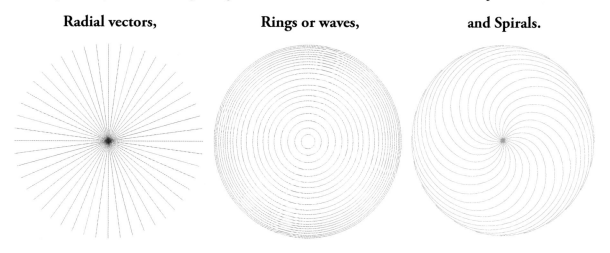

When all three are combined we see these basic components unified in an integrated pattern:

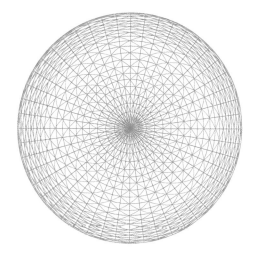

We can see from this integrated pattern that these three components are symmetrically compatible and can therefore consider them as co-existing. By this I mean that when we see a vortex in water, for example, it is the spiral component that is most obvious, and yet both the radial and ring patterns are inherently present as well. Similarly, when we see rings of waves rippling on a pond surface, we can surmise that the radial and spiral components are at play as well. These three are the fundamental guidelines, so to speak, upon which energy creates all form and flow.

These patterns are, of course, 2-dimensional illustrations. In cosmometry, **the component of a "pattern" generally refers to a conceptual 2-dimensional illustration**, rather than an actual 3-dimensional representation. It is conceptual because, as far as we can tell, the cosmos does not demonstrate the existence of any actual 2-dimensional things. There is usefulness to this conceptual 2-dimensional patterning, though, as we can utilize simplified pattern illustrations to represent specific attributes of how energy articulates and how the fractal structure of the cosmos comes into form.

For example, the integrated double spiral pattern shown on the previous page is a 2-dimensional illustration of what is actually a 3-dimensional form that itself is perhaps the most fundamental component of the dynamic fractal structure of the cosmos — the Torus.

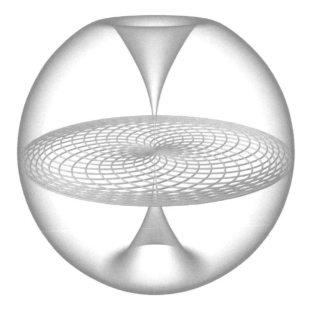

As can be seen in this simple illustration, the 2-D pattern is depicting the cross-section of a 3-dimensional form of dynamic flow process. A torus is a doughnut-shaped form that energy takes when in a coherent and stable state. A magnetic field exhibits this behavior, as can be seen in the classic arrangement of iron filings surrounding it. A contemporary method of making magnetic field lines visible is through the use of a ferrocell, as seen on the next page. When viewing a circular magnet with the ferrocell on top of it, it's easy to see the double spiral pattern as depicted in the illustration above.

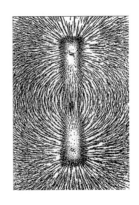

16

 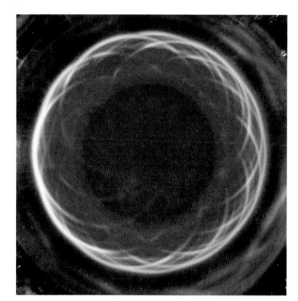

Ferrocell magnetic field, images courtesy of Destino Stellavem, Vimanika, LLC

The torus is a fundamental form of energetic articulation that accommodates a dynamic fractal embedding of energy flow within a unified structure. As described in the Introduction, David Bohm's concept of "undivided wholeness in flowing movement" is illustrated by vortex structures within a flowing stream of water. The vortexes are localized forms that are seamlessly connected by the water that makes up the stream, which of course also makes up the vortexes. The same is true for the torus form within the cosmic stream of energy flow. In fact, a vortex in a stream is actually a torus structure. We're only seeing one end of the torus flow dynamic as a vortex in the water.

This same dynamic flow process is found at all scales in the cosmos, from galaxies to stellar and planetary magnetic fields, to hurricanes and tornados, trees and plants, on down to cells, atoms, and even at the extremes of the Planck and Universal scales. The same pattern repeats at all scales — the definition of fractal in our model. The water vortex is literally a fractal expression of cosmic energy dynamics.

The torus flow process will be explored further in Section 3. For the sake of this introduction of the fractal aspect of wholeness, in the simplest terms we can say that the torus is a basic model of wholeness as a dynamic fractal energy process ocurring at all scales in the universe.

WHOLENESS

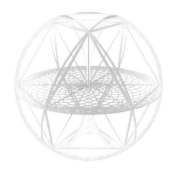

CHAPTER 3
FRACTALIZATION IS THE HARMONIC EXPRESSION OF QUANTIZATION

37.2 Trillion. (37,200,000,000,000)

That's the estimated number of cells that make up an average adult human body.[8]

100 Trillion. (100,000,000,000,000)

That's the estimated number of atoms that make up each one of those cells.[9]

37.2 Octillion. (37,200,000,000,000,000,000,000,000,000)

That's an estimated total number of atoms that make up our human body.

These are all fantastically large numbers! And that's just for one human body!

Our bodies are a remarkable example of unified wholeness composed of a vast quantity of cells and atoms. And, as we well know, everything in the physical universe is made up of atoms, with a total estimate of 10^{80} atoms that make up the visible universe. (For comparison, the above 37.2 Octillion equals 3.72×10^{27} atoms.)

This is an example of the quantized nature of the cosmos; whole systems composed of large numbers of unit parts, or quanta. While this kind of quantization is integral to our exploration of the fractal nature of wholeness, there is another kind of quantization that is much more fundamental to the physical nature of the cosmos — the scientific fact that all electromagnetic radiation, such as the visible light you are reading this by, is quantized.

Along with the Planck Units mentioned earlier, Max Planck made another essential contribution to physics when in 1900 he proposed that the energy emitted from every kind of electromagnetic radiation (visible light, x-rays, infrared, radio waves, etc.) comes in discrete packets, or quanta, of action. Though he did so as what he considered to be a mathematical work-around to the problem he was trying to solve, Albert Einstein validated Planck's proposal in his 1905 explanation of the photoelectric effect. This phenomenon was experimentally confirmed by Millikan in 1914 and became the foundation of Quantum Theory. The science of Quantum Mechanics has dominated the theoretical landscape ever since.

From the smallest electromagnetic wavelength at the Planck scale to those at the atomic scale, on up in size to visible light, microwaves, radio waves and beyond, the entire cosmic phenomenon of electromagnetic radiation is quantized.

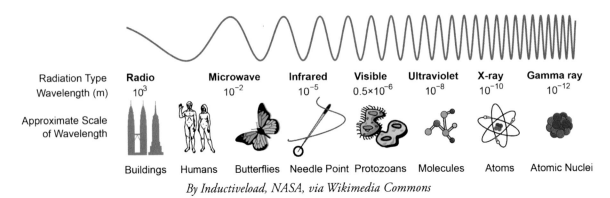

Radiation Type	Radio	Microwave	Infrared	Visible	Ultraviolet	X-ray	Gamma ray
Wavelength (m)	10^3	10^{-2}	10^{-5}	0.5×10^{-6}	10^{-8}	10^{-10}	10^{-12}
Approximate Scale of Wavelength	Buildings	Humans	Butterflies	Needle Point	Protozoans	Molecules	Atoms	Atomic Nuclei

By Inductiveload, NASA, via Wikimedia Commons

The same holds true for sound waves, which are simply pressure waves within the electromagnetic medium of atoms that make up air, water, earth, gases etc. As mentioned in the Introduction, acoustic and electromagnetic waves are convertible, as evidenced by our ability to capture a sound using the magnetic field of a microphone, convert it to an electromagnetic waveform at the same frequency, then convert it back to a sound wave amplified through a loudspeaker.

This universal attribute of quantization is a fundamental point to keep in mind in our exploration of cosmometry, unified physics and music. The quantized nature of energy-matter is the source of all number, proportion, ratio, mathematics and dimensional scale of every kind. While the Planck Units are fundamental natural units of this quantization, we humans have otherwise devised units of measure for every aspect of the physical universe, be it temperature, pressure, density, size, distance, weight, angle, luminosity, time, frequency, etc.

In our exploration, the concept of quantization pertains both to the "quantum of action" found in electromagnetic and acoustic waves (and the physics of quantum mechanics), as well as to the discrete quantization of the material world manifest as atoms, molecules, cells, sand particles, people, trees, etc.

All of this leads to a working premise for our exploration:

The fractal aspect of wholeness is the harmonic expression of quantization.

Fractality is an intrinsic property that emerges from harmonic relationships (i.e. resonance and interference patterns) within the quantized cosmos.

One of the best ways to both illustrate and study the phenomenon of quantization and the fractal systems that arise from it is through music. At a most basic level of description, music is a system of harmonic relationships inherent in the energetic expression of sound. In terms of both sound frequencies and rhythmic impulses, music demonstrates fundamental fractal relationships and ratios that underlie the dynamics of energy, form and cyclic flow in the cosmos. This is, again, a natural consequence of quantization, with the harmonic structure of music being a fractal manifestation of the harmonic structure of the universe. It is because of this that music is included as a fundamental component of this model, which will be explored in Section 6.

In closing this introduction to the fractal aspect of wholeness, I'd like to highlight two basic ratios that are fundamental to the harmonic structure of both music and the very foundation of the cosmos itself — Octave Doubling (binary) and Golden Ratio (phinary) scaling.

"It was Planck's epoch-making discovery that action comes in wholes, a discovery which in retrospect we can see to be true of human actions. We cannot have 1½ or 1.42 actions. We cannot decide to get up, vote, jump out the window, call a friend, speak, or do anything one-and-a-half times. Wholeness is inherent in the nature of action, of decision, of purposive activity. Planck's discovery about light touches home: it is true of our own actions. But we didn't really know this until the physicists had made this a principle."

– Arthur Young [10]

WHOLENESS

CHAPTER 4
OCTAVE DOUBLING AND GOLDEN RATIO SCALING

Two of the greatest passions that have driven my life's journey are music and cosmometry. I'm blessed to have been born into a musical family, with my mom singing classical opera and musicals throughout our early years and my three brothers and I being musically activated children of the '60s. Even my dad let out his musical self in his later years, composing lovely tone poems on his computer. I had the good fortune of studying piano and classical music theory from 8-13 years of age… then my brother Pieter brought home a Fender Telecaster guitar, Twin Reverb amp, and the just-released Allman Brothers *Live at the Fillmore* double album, and well… listening to Duane Allman play guitar says it all about why I became a guitar player.

I am grateful for my study of music theory over the years, and especially appreciative of the opportunity when I was 22 to learn from Allaudin Matthieu, then Director of the Sufi Choir, who gave me some essential insights that inspire me musically and cosmometrically to this day.

While playing and writing music can be done "by ear" (an indication that the harmonic structure of music is innate in our physiology), the study of music theory offers a rich and fascinating understanding of sound as a system of harmonic relationships. This system is actually quite vast in scope and potential for complexity, as is evidenced by the wide range of musical styles around the world, and yet it is all founded upon some simple sets of harmonic relationships. A few of these will be explored later as we correlate the cosmometry of the cosmos to that of music. We'll begin here with what is perhaps the simplest harmonic relationship, the interval of an octave.

OCTAVE DOUBLING – BINARY SCALING

Every musical tone is a frequency of sound vibration, measured in cycles-per-second, or Hertz (Hz). The contemporary standard for tuning is the note A at 440 Hz (for all you 432 Hz folks, this will be addressed later, so don't close the book at this point). This means there are 440 cycles of a sound wave in 1 second of time. To the right is an illustration showing both 4 and 14 cycles per second:

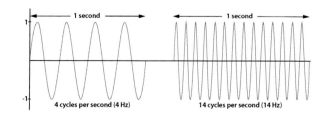

23

Using 440 Hz as a reference, the interval of an octave is achieved simply by doubling the frequency to 880 Hz. This new pitch of the note A is higher by one octave. In music, it is the same "note" (called A), and to our ears it sounds the same within the harmonic structure of music, just at a higher pitch. We can also use a frequency that's half of 440 Hz and we'll hear another note A at 220 Hz that is one octave below the first note. This octave ratio of doubling/halving is the most basic aspect of fractal scaling within the structure of music, and generally speaking within the structure of sound itself, whether heard in a musical context or not.

The word octave comes from the Latin octavus, meaning eighth. In the basic western music system, an octave is eight notes above or below the reference note. This is the familiar do-re-mi-fa-so-la-ti-do scale. The second "do" is eight steps in the scale above the first one, or one octave.

As previously mentioned, octave doubling is one of the basic ratios found in both music and the fundamental structure of the universe itself, not surprisingly, given that what we call music is actually a system of harmonic relationships inherent in the universal cosmometry, rather than one contrived by us merely for the sake of our pleasure. We are more "discoverers" of the music system than we are "inventors" of it. This is why music holds a primary role in our exploration.

It is this octave ratio of 2:1, doubling and halving, that is the basis for the Binary system of quantization. Most anyone who has been around computers and digital information systems is generally familiar with the concept of a binary system. While computers use a binary code composed of only zeros and ones (0 and 1), for our purpose we'll refer to the Binary system of quantization as a simple number system, writing it out as:

1   2   4   8   16   32   64   128   256   512   1024   etc.

Obviously, each number in the sequence is double the previous one. If these numbers are sound frequencies in Hertz, they're all octave intervals from their neighbors. They can, of course, be applied to any scale of measurement, effectively giving us a potential correlation of the octave doubling found in music with a similar ratio found in other aspects of the cosmos, such as with electromagnetic frequencies, atomic vibration, size scaling, etc. (It is interesting to note here that a factor of 2 is very common in physics equations.[11])

The doubling ratio is also found in the rhythmic aspect of music. Musical notation is based upon this ratio to convey the rhythm of a piece of music, utilizing a Whole note, Half note, Quarter note, Eighth, Sixteenth, Thirty-second, Sixty-fourth and One-hundred-twenty-eighth notes. Beyond the One-hundred-twenty-eighth, the notes tend to blur into more of a tone than a distinct rhythm, if they can even be played at all!

As we'll see in Section 2: Starting from Zero, the octave ratio Binary system is inherent in the most fundamental aspect of the quantized structure of the cosmos, with a specific correlation to both 8 (as octave) and 64 (8 octaves). First, let's also have a look at the other basic fractal ratio that is ubiquitous in the dynamics of the cosmos as it comes into form and flow at every scale.

GOLDEN RATIO – PHINARY SCALING

The Golden Ratio is likely the most well-known ratio of all time, other than Pi (π). There are many books written solely about this ratio and its remarkable qualities of self-similarity. We might even say it is the ratio of self-similarity most commonly found in natural forms throughout the cosmos, from the smallest to the largest of scales. It is not only a ratio of size, though. It can be applied to any and every dimensional scale, be it weight, distance, temperature, frequency, etc.

In mathematics, the name of this ratio is Phi (often pronounced with a long "i" as in "pie" but originating from the Greek letter Φ, pronounced "fee", that is used as its mathematical symbol). It is what's called an irrational mathematical constant, one of those never-ending numbers like Pi.

The value for Phi is 1.6180339887... on into infinity. For simplicity's sake it's commonly stated as just 1.618. For those who are mathematically inclined, here are algebraic and mathematical formulas for Phi:

$$\frac{a + b}{a} = \frac{a}{b} = \phi \qquad \phi = \frac{1 + \sqrt{5}}{2} = 1.6180339887...$$

Just as with the octave ratio being 2:1, when something is in the Phi ratio it has a proportion of 1.618:1. One part is equivalent to a value of 1, and the other part is 1.618 larger. Here's a simple illustration of this:

$$a \qquad b$$
$$a+b$$

$a+b$ is to a as a is to b

Line segment *b* in red is equivalent to 1, and *a* in blue is 1.618 longer than it. The remarkable self-similarity quality of Phi is illustrated here as well, wherein the length of *a* is in the same Phi proportion relative to the whole line segment, *a+b*. If *a* is given a value of 1, *a+b* is equal to Phi, or 1.618 larger than *a*.

While this process shows Phi scaling growing larger, the opposite holds true for getting smaller by the inverse ratio. In this case, when *a+b* is equal to 1, *a* is equal to .618, and then *b* is .618 smaller than *a*. So, the ratio of 1.618 can be seen as a scaling up in magnitude and .618 can be seen as a scaling down in magnitude — macro and micro.

The bones in our hands and arms scale in the Golden Ratio, for example. Take a look at your hand and arm now, and marvel in the remarkable phenomenon that nature has used this proportion to optimize the functioning of your body!

While this is all well and good, what does it have to do with the quantized nature of the cosmos? It's an irrational number, after all. Our quantized model

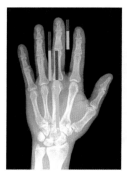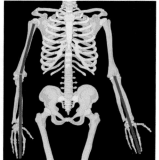

is based upon single units of quanta, therefore it needs to be related to a whole number system. Well there is one, and it's what can be called the Phinary system (complementary to the Binary system).

For those familiar with the Golden Ratio of Phi, you no doubt are also familiar with a set of numbers called the Fibonacci Sequence. This sequence was first published in 1202 by Leonardo of Pisa, also known as Fibonacci, in his book *Liber Abaci* (though it was discovered much earlier). It is derived in a very simple manner.

Starting with 0 and 1 (note correlation to binary code system), the Fibonacci sequence adds pairs of numbers to derive the next number in the sequence, like this:

0+1=1, 1+1=2, 1+2=3, 2+3=5, etc., …deriving this sequence:

0 1 1 2 3 5 8 13 21 34 55 89 144 233 377 610 987 …

This is a sequence of whole numbers that, as it turns out, is directly related to the Golden Ratio. When you divide any pair of adjacent numbers in the sequence the result achieves an increasing accuracy to Phi the farther out the sequence you go.

For example (remembering that mathematical Phi = 1.6180339887…):

8/5 = 1.6

55/34 = 1.617647…

144/89 = 1.617977…

987/610 = 1.618032…

This creates a wave-like pattern that always approximates Phi, never achieving the irrational value of mathematical Phi. Our quantized model now has a whole number system that directly correlates to Phi. It is a system of quantitative proportion that is a fundamental harmonic structure inherent in the cosmos, just as is the octave ratio.

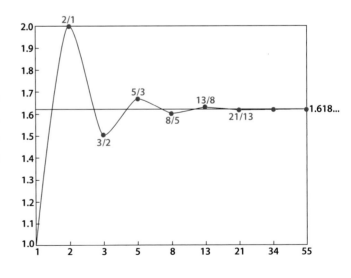

So, we now have two basic number systems of quantized harmonic structure in our cosmometric toolkit:

Binary

1   2   4   8   16   32   64   128   256   512   1024 ...

and Phinary

0   1   1   2   3   5   8   13   21   34   55   89   144   233   377   610   987 ...

It is important to note that both the Binary and Phinary systems include the number 8 — the octave. They begin the same (1 and 2), deviate (4 in Binary, 3 and 5 in Phinary), and then converge on 8 before deviating again into their respective sequences.

And there's another interesting observation to make about these two systems of quantized harmonic relationships: It could be said that they are perhaps two intimately related expressions of one basic phenomenon. Here's why…

The Binary system has these numbers:

1   2   4   8   16   32   64   128   256   512   1024 ...

And the Phinary system resolves to the Phi ratio of **1.618**.

In the Binary we have **16**, and in the Phinary we have **1.6** when we resolve to one decimal. These are a factor of 10 of each other (note correlation to base 10 counting system). When we apply the Binary system to the Phinary, we then get a set of numbers that is very similar, suggesting an intimate association between these two number systems:

	Phinary	**=**	**Binary**
Phi/16 =	.10112	=	1
Phi /8 =	.20225	=	2
Phi /4 =	.40450	=	4
Phi /2 =	.80901	=	8
Phi =	**1.61803**	=	16
2x Phi =	**3.23606**	=	32
4x Phi =	**6.47213**	=	64

These basic number systems will inform our exploration as we go, so expect to see them regularly.

WHOLENESS

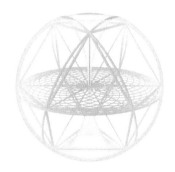

CHAPTER 5
SYNERGETIC WHOLENESS

In 1978 I had the happy fortune of coming upon the writings of R. Buckminster Fuller[12] and subsequently meeting him the following year when he came to speak in the small chapel at Lewis and Clark College in Portland, Oregon, where I was a sophomore. I've been a devoted student in the school of Bucky ever since.

"That each individual is a complete integrity is one of the reasons I don't have to make any effort in loving my fellow human."
– Buckminster Fuller

While not an easy task to read his books, it is for those who commit to doing so a highly rewarding one. Fuller was a deeply wise, caring, informed and pragmatic man while simultaneously being a wildly broad-thinking cosmic fisherman and philosophical idealist, and his writings encompass all of that at once. *Utopia or Oblivion* is the title of one of his books, and you could say that his life was unflinchingly a stand for utopia. Not a far-fetched sci-fi utopia, but rather a practically realizable end goal based upon the conscious application of humanity's innate ability to innovate new systems and technologies towards the singular objective of bettering life for all people and inhabitants of Earth. His idea of a revolution was through what he called Comprehensive Anticipatory Design Science. His motto: "To make the world work for 100% of humanity through spontaneous cooperation and without ecological offense or the disadvantage of anyone."

One of the core principles that Fuller expounded upon was Integrity. "Only integrity counts," he often stated. For him, the universe was a constantly shining example of integrity. He devoted himself to the study of cosmic patterns through which he could discern the integrity of "eternally regenerative universe." Through this study, Fuller came to discover what he referred to as nature's coordinate system, a universal system of cosmic accounting that he called *Synergetics*. He documented his discoveries in a two-volume book by the same name, with the insightful sub-title, *Explorations in the Geometry of Thinking*. Fuller's synergetic geometry is one of the core pillars of our comprehensive model of cosmometry, as will be further explored.

Example of Synergy in Metal Alloys

"In chrome-nickel-steel, the primary constituents are iron, chromium, and nickel. There are minor constituents of carbon, manganese, and others. It is a very popular way of thinking to say that a chain is no stronger than its weakest link... If I were to say that a chain is stronger than the sum of the strengths of all of its links, you might say that that is preposterous. Yet that is exactly what happens with chrome-nickel-steel... So we put down the tensile strength of the commercially available iron — the highest that we can possibly accredit is about 60,000 pounds per square inch (p.s.i.); of the chromium it is about 70,000 p.s.i.; of the nickel it is about 80,000 p.s.i. The tensile strengths of the carbon and the other minor constituents come to another 50,000 p.s.i. Adding up all the strengths of all the links we get 260,000 p.s.i. But in fact the tensile strength of chrome-nickel-steel runs to about 350,000 p.s.i. just as a casting. Here we have the behavior of the whole completely unpredicted by the behavior of the parts."

– Synergetics, section 109.02, R. Buckminster Fuller (http://synergetics.info/s01/p0100.html)

For Fuller, the human mind is one of the most essential qualities of the manifest universe. Our ability to apprehend abstract concepts such as mathematics, color, love and integrity, indicates that we hold a unique role in the evolving cosmic play. We are metaphysical beings in equal measure as we are physical beings. When studying the "parts" that make up the "whole" that we call the physical universe (as we do in traditional materialist and reductionist science), there is nothing in that analysis that predicts our metaphysical capabilities of mind. As such, we are a synergetic phenomenon.

Synergy means:

The behavior of whole systems that is unpredictable from the behavior of the parts when taken separately.

One could look at all of the atomic elements that make up the universe, studying their unique characteristics and behaviors, and find nothing in them that would predict a human being with the ability to think in abstract concepts. Nor could you predict a Universe.

According to Fuller, *"The words synergy (syn-ergy) and energy (en-ergy) are companions. Energy studies are familiar. Energy relates to differentiating out sub-functions of nature, studying objects isolated out of the whole complex of Universe — for instance, studying soil minerals without consideration of hydraulics or of plant genetics. But synergy represents the integrated behaviors instead of all the differentiated behaviors of nature's galaxy systems and galaxy of galaxies."* [13]

It is by studying the integrated behaviors of systems that we can come to understand their true wholeness, and these whole system behaviors are often synergetic. The dominant scientific proclivity towards reductionism is counterintuitive to this approach; hence synergy is, as yet, mostly overlooked in academia. As such, the majority of our education is oriented away from thinking in whole systems and our minds are therefore not trained to think synergetically. For many, it is often through mystical experiences, whether induced through psychedelics or intense breathwork, or through deep meditation, that we first catch a glimpse of something bigger and beyond the scope of our daily lives. We may see beautiful geometric patterns in our inner vision, or experience a sense of unity with the cosmos that is outside the realm of words to describe, or have an epiphany of insight that answers deeply fundamental questions about who we are and the nature of reality in the blink of an eye. We might say that these kinds of experiences are the awakening of synergetic awareness.

The ability to consider wholeness is, at some point, an intuitive sense rather than a logical one, for it's the combined behavior of integrated parts that is being discerned, rather than just the behavior of the parts themselves. This is actually where the simplicity of the model of wholeness we're exploring resides. For once you comprehend the nature of the parts that we're exploring, you may then come to see their integrated behavior with new eyes as a simplicity of wholeness arising from a seeming complexity of parts.

Arthur Young expresses this idea in a manner that brings great insight into the role of synergy in cosmic manifestation of wholeness:

> *The ability to consider wholeness is, at some point, an intuitive sense rather than a logical one, for it's the combined behavior of integrated parts that is being discerned, rather than just the behavior of the parts themselves.*

> *"Only when the device is put together can it express its function and its purpose, something its parts alone could never do… Since purpose is in the whole and not in the parts, the whole must be greater than the parts. How can we account for this? Because the whole cannot function when divided. It follows that function is that aspect or "cause" which is not in the parts and which science cannot deal with, because science deals with mass, length, and time, which are parts. This leads to a basic cosmological postulate: the parts are derived from the whole, and not the whole from the parts. In other words, the whole exists before the parts."* [14]

By definition synergy is unpredictable, which means that the mystery of the universe is alive and well! There will always be a new whole that is greater than and unpredictable from the parts ready to be made manifest. There is much as yet to discover, understand, and put into application on behalf of making the world work for all life. Fortunately, we are assured that by bringing our attention to establishing wholeness where fragmentation has occurred, the process will yield results that are greater than, and unpredictable from, the sum of the parts. By restoring wholeness to humanity through harmonizing our technical and social systems based upon cosmic patterns and principles, a synergetic effect is most certainly guaranteed.

Fractal Hologramic Synergetic Universe

Four words, one phenomenon — wholeness.

These words represent so much about the nature of wholeness, which I hope has been conveyed simply enough to provide a foundation of understanding that will carry through the rest of this exploration. Each one expresses a key concept that is important to keep in mind as you continue in the journey.

Put simply again, these are:

Fractal – the same patterns repeat at all scales.

Hologramic – the information of the whole is present at every point.

Synergetic – the behavior of a whole system that is unpredictable from the behavior of the parts taken separately.

Universe – the sum total of all fractal-hologramic-synergetic phenomena, both physical and metaphysical.

We began this section by saying that the most fundamental theme of this exploration is that of wholeness. Ultimately, all of the information presented in this exploration is talking about one thing — the integrated nature of wholeness as it manifests form and flow throughout the cosmos at all scales. From a most basic perspective, comprehending what these four words mean, and more importantly how they are intimately combined as one phenomenon, is a valuable take-away if it were to be all that you receive from this book. Bringing a sense of wholeness back into our perspective on life — our worldview — and applying the pursuit of re-establishing a harmony of wholeness to our relationship with Earth's ecosystems, with each other, and in our societies is of paramount importance at this time in our history. Why is this idea of re-establishing wholeness important? Well, just imagine boarding a jet airplane that is not in a condition of integrated wholeness. A scary thought! No doubt you wouldn't board it if you knew its dangerous condition. Now apply that same idea to the operating integrity of the planet we're flying on. In terms of safety and a sense of smooth travels in our journey, an airplane and a planet are fundamentally one and the same thing.

While we'll continue our exploration of wholeness here within the context of cosmometry, music and unified physics, take time to contemplate how wholeness is and isn't present in your life, in your world, in our world, and consider how any and all of these basic concepts of wholeness can inform ways in which you may be able to bring about wholeness where it appears of value to do so.

Let's now head into a deeper exploration of the fundamental patterns, structures, processes and principles of cosmometry, starting at the place where it all begins — and ends — Zero.

Section 1 Endnotes

3   Meijer, Dirk, and Geesink, Hans, *Consciousness in the Universe is Scale Invariant and Implies an Event Horizon of the Human Brain*, Neuroquantology, September 2017.
     https://neuroquantology.com/index.php/journal/article/view/1079/852

4   http://www.sheldrake.org/research/glossary#information

5   Nassim Haramein, quote excerpted from Laszlo, Ervin. *What is Reality?: The New Map of Cosmos, Consciousness, and Existence.* (A New Paradigm Book)

6   "Substantial evidence of holographic universe", Science Daily.
     https://www.sciencedaily.com/releases/2017/01/170130083231.htm

7   *The Planck scale: relativity meets quantum mechanics meets gravity*, The University New South Wales.
     https://newt.phys.unsw.edu.au/einsteinlight/jw/module6_Planck.htm

8   Bianconi, E. et al, "An estimation of the number of cells in the human body", PubMed.
     http://www.ncbi.nlm.nih.gov/pubmed/23829164

9   "How Many Atoms Are There in a Human Cell?", ThoughtCo.
     https://www.thoughtco.com/how-many-atoms-in-human-cell-603882

10   Young, Arthur M. *The Reflexive Universe: Evolution of Consciousness* (Page 51). Anodos Foundation.

11   Rowlands, Peter, *The factor 2 in fundamental physics.*
     https://arxiv.org/abs/physics/0110069

12   About Buckminster Fuller, Buckminster Fuller Institute.
     https://www.bfi.org/about-fuller/biography

13   http://synergetics.info/s01/p0100.html

14   Young, Arthur M. *The Reflexive Universe: Evolution of Consciousness* (Page 51). Anodos Foundation.

SECTION 2
STARTING FROM ZERO

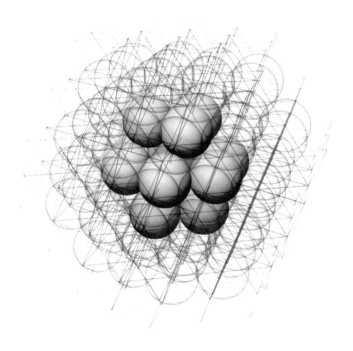

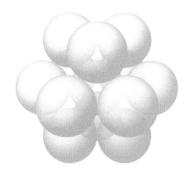

SECTION 2
STARTING FROM ZERO

Breathing.

We do it all day, every day. The most vital activity of our existence that activates the moment we're born, providing us the atomic ingredients of air that fuel the processes of our bodies day and night. This rhythmic exchange between our self and our environment is as profound as it is simple. In concert with the rhythm of our heart, it is the pulse of life that is so innate to our experience that we nearly always go through our days unaware of it.

Take a moment to sit quietly where you are, close your eyes, and put your attention on your breathing, even if just for one minute. When you're ready, come back to this page and read on.

Becoming conscious of our breathing is one of the best ways to become conscious in our lives — conscious in a way that opens us up to the beauty and subtlety of the present moment. We hear and see things differently when we're more fully present to our awareness of the environment we're in and the people and other living beings we're with. Taking a few minutes to become present through following the flow of breath is a simple practice that has been at the heart of meditation traditions for millennia, and which can be done anywhere at any moment.

The cyclical rhythm of our breath is our most consistent experience of a fundamental quality of the cosmos that, from what we can discern, is common to all things — a dynamic pulsation of energy. Given that every atom in the universe vibrates, it is safe to say that everything in the universe has some quality of dynamic pulsation. Even within the hardest crystalline structures there is this dynamic vibratory pulsation at the atomic level.

We can, of course, see and hear other more obvious kinds of cyclic pulsation and oscillation in our lives, such as the cycles of day and night, waves lapping on a shoreline, the flapping of a bird's wings, the gait of animals as they walk, the rhythm of drums and the sound of voices and musical instruments, the beating of our heart and pulsing of blood through our veins, to name a few. Even the electrical energy that runs our modern world oscillates in an alternating current as it's transmitted through cables.

At the most fundamental level of energy dynamics, both electromagnetic and acoustic waveforms are oscillating movements that pulse in a spectrum of cycles or frequencies of energy. The waveforms are typically represented as having a sinusoidal shape, with a peak and trough that are above and below (plus and minus) a zero-value point of reference.

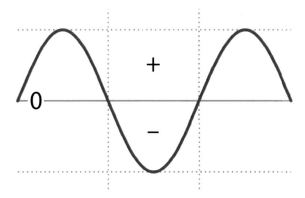

Simple_sine_wave.svg by Omegatron [modified]

The relationship between this zero-reference and the peaks, troughs and number of cycles of this oscillation per second is how the wavelength, frequency and amplitude of sound and light waves are measured.

In every system of measuring there is a frame of reference upon which the units of measurement are established — seconds, minutes and hours of Time; degrees of Temperature and Angle; Imperial and Metric units of length and spatial distance. While each is unique in its special-case application, they all share one common point of reference — Zero.

Even our breathing comes to a point of stillness for a brief moment as it cycles between inhalation and exhalation. It is in this momentary pause, this point of stillness between in and out breaths, that many spiritual teachings say we can access unity with the cosmos. This stillness — of the mind, of the emotions, of the body — is the portal through which we can experience our spiritual nature beyond our personality selves. It is central to many mystical traditions in the pursuit of realizing our whole Self as unified with all that is.

It is at this point of stillness, this zero-reference, where we begin our exploration of cosmic geometry.

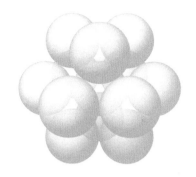

CHAPTER 6
THE EMPTY CIRCUS

VECTOR EQUILIBRIUM

Vector Equilibrium:

"The vector equilibrium is the zero starting point for happenings or nonhappenings: it is the empty theater and empty circus and empty Universe ready to accommodate any act and any audience."

- Cite SYNERGETICS, (2nd. Ed.) at Sec. 503.03; 11 Dec'75

39

The image on the previous page is of one of the many thousands of index cards that comprise Buckminster Fuller's *Synergetics Dictionary*.[15] Compiled with the dedicated assistance of his collaborator, E. J. Applewhite, it is a remarkable record of the vast and varied ideas that Fuller spoke and wrote about over many decades, gathered together as a research aid and organized alphabetically by topic. It is an education in the finer points of Fuller's geometry of thinking just to browse through the collection.

The quote on the card, cited as being from his book *Synergetics*, describes the essential cosmic role played by a unique geometric form that Fuller named the Vector Equilibrium. It is the zero starting point for happenings and non-happenings. The empty theater and empty circus and empty universe ready to accommodate any act and any audience. It is the blank page to the left, ready to accommodate any imaginable idea. (Feel free to write or draw in it!)

Every time we look at a blank page, a blank canvas, an empty stage, we are experiencing as close as we ever will the presence of the Vector Equilibrium as the zero starting point for all experiential reality.

Every time we look at a blank page, a blank canvas, an empty stage, we are experiencing as close as we ever will the presence of the Vector Equilibrium as the zero starting point for all experiential reality. It is the presence of pure potential before it becomes realized. It is what Fuller describes as the *"zerophase of conceptual integrity inherent in the positive and negative asymmetries that propagate the differentials of consciousness."* [16] A somewhat heady statement, and yet actually quite simple in meaning: The "positive and negative asymmetries" are the fluctuating energetic waveforms (electromagnetic and acoustic) that we perceive through our senses, which, through their oscillation, create the "differentials of consciousness" — our experiences.

Fuller begins this statement in *Synergetics* by saying:

> **"Equilibrium between positive and negative is zero. The vector equilibrium is the true zero reference of the energetic mathematics."**

From the perspective of energy dynamics, he is saying that the Vector Equilibrium (VE for short) is the geometric form that is the mathematical zero reference for our 3-dimensional experience of reality (called "spacetime" in physics) wherein all positive and negative differentials are in perfect equilibrium equal to zero.

He goes on to say, *"Zero pulsation in the vector equilibrium is the nearest approach we will ever know to eternity and god."* A statement worthy of considerable contemplation, once we come to truly understand what the VE conceptually represents. While being pragmatically grounded in the purpose of his reasearch, Fuller was profoundly spiritual as well, regularly integrating practical thinking and spiritual insight into a single unified idea.

41

If this is your first time hearing about the Vector Equilibrium, you may by this point be wanting to know, "Just what the heck is this VE thing?" Here's an illustration of it:

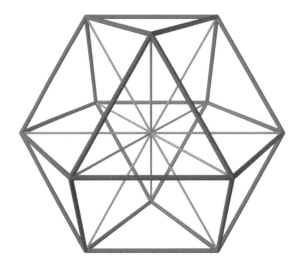

This simple geometric form is the origin of all dynamic activity in the cosmos; origin meaning it is the zero reference of equilibrium around which exists all oscillating vibration and movement, and within that movement emerge the resonant structures of atomic, molecular, crystalline, fluid, gaseous, biological, planetary, solar and galactic forms of matter. With a bit of tongue-in-cheek, we could say it's what puts the "mom" in cosmometry, for as we'll see, all of the most fundamental geometric structures — the Platonic "solids" — are inherently "born" from the dynamic symmetry of the VE.

What Fuller is saying above is that the VE is the zero starting place for any and every physical and conceptual phenomenon, and that this zero state is the phase of undifferentiated potential prior to and following the manifestation of all such physical and metaphysical phenomena. It is the geometry of the ground-state of the cosmos when in perfect zerophase equilibrium.

Let's take a deeper look into this unique zerophase of cosmometry.

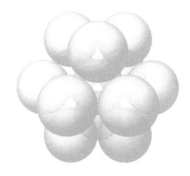

CHAPTER 7
VECTOR EQUILIBRIUM

There are those precious and wonderful times in our lives when everything appears to be in a natural state of harmonious balance. Our health is good, our relationships are happy and inspired, our creative work in the world is on purpose, our environment is comfortable and nurturing; all is in a state of dynamic equilibrium, both relaxed and active simultaneously. It is in these times when we could say we are in close proximity to the experience of the cosmic and eternal equilibrium that resides at the center of everything. This cosmic equilibrium is always present, even in the midst of the wildest and most chaotic of times, as it is the prime stillness around which everything we experience is oriented.

In the Introduction of this book I shared that the quest, and even imperative, to harmonize our human-contrived systems with the natural state of the cosmos is of the greatest importance in these wild and chaotic times on Earth. It is through understanding and application of the principles of **equilibrium** and **wholeness** that we have the opportunity to consciously engender the conditions for attaining a state of harmonious balance for humanity and all life. The experience in our lives of such a state seems rare and fleeting and appears to be an idealist's fantasy that it could be achieved on a global scale. However, when we understand how it is achieved in nature and the cosmos, we have only to choose to apply that knowledge with the conviction that it will inevitably evolve us towards that outcome. Engendering wholeness produces synergetic effects, so it's almost guaranteed we'll be pleasantly surprised by the outcome!

We can call this pursuit "cosmomimicry" — a term coined by David McConville, former Chairman of the Board of the Buckminster Fuller Institute — similar to the term biomimicry that is used to describe the application of principles and functions of biological systems to the design and development of technological and social systems.

One of the principles of cosmomimicry is Equilibrium. By definition, equilibrium means:

1. ***a:*** a state of intellectual or emotional balance: poise

   b: a state of adjustment between opposing or divergent influences or elements

2. a state of balance between opposing forces or actions that is either static (as in a body acted on by forces whose resultant is zero) or dynamic (as in a reversible chemical reaction when the rates of reaction in both directions are equal)[17]

43

Your car keys sitting on a table is an example of static equilibrium — the gravitational movement of the key inward towards the center of the Earth is met in equal and opposite force by the dense matter and rigid structure of the table. If the force were greater it would lift the keys away from the ground. If it were lesser the keys would continue moving towards the ground.

An example of dynamic equilibrium in our daily lives is the process of maintaining a comfortable temperature in our homes. In the summer when it's hot outside we may run an air conditioner to cool the air inside. Meanwhile the hot air outside is constantly emitting heat into the house through the windows, doors and walls, so there's a continuous back and forth between heating and cooling. A dynamic equilibrium is achieved when the right amount of cooling balances out the incoming heating and the house maintains a comfortable temperature. There's a point of balance, a zero reference, on either side of which the positive (heat) and negative (cooling) dynamics fluctuate as the temperature settles ever closer to equilibrium.

All dynamic energy events — light, sound, a person walking, wind — have a fluctuation of positive and negative values. Light and sound waves have their frequency and amplitude, a person walking oscillates between left and right feet, wind is a result of high and low atmospheric pressure differences. Imagine as we make those differences smaller, we come to a point of perfect equilibrium wherein all energy fluctuations achieve a state of absolute balance and the dynamic activity gets cancelled out altogether. In Fuller's synergetic geometry and our exploration of cosmometry, the Vector Equilibrium is the model of such a state of absolute zerophase equilibrium. Here's why…

The VE is the only energetic form wherein all of the vectors that radiate from its center and all of the vectors surrounding its circumference are of the same length.

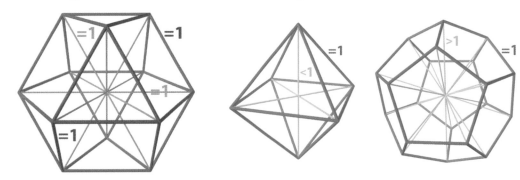

This is unique from all other geometric structures, such as the Platonic Forms (note: I choose not to call them "solids" as that is not representative of their true nature as energy event structures, which we'll explore later). The Platonic Forms all have equal length circumferential vectors, but their central radial vectors are of longer or shorter length compared to them. As such, there's a differential in the force values associated with those vectors.

While the outer shape of a VE is traditionally known as a cuboctahedron (having symmetries with both the cube and octahedron), it was its unique characteristic of equal length vectors that Fuller discovered in 1917 and named the Vector Equilibrium in 1940.

In the VE, all of the vectors are the same length, which means they all have the same force value. As Fuller describes it, the inner radial vectors are radiating energy outward (explosively, as radiation) and the circumferential vectors are containing this radiation with an equal value of force (implosively, as gravitation). (Note that this condition describes the event horizon of a black hole.[18]) As such, all of the energy vectors are in perfect zerophase equilibrium and get cancelled out. Fluctuation as energy we can observe and measure ceases. Absolute equilibrium is conceptually modeled by the VE because of this.

Of this zerophase model Fuller writes,

> *"Being the zerophase of energy the vector equilibrium is inherently invisible and non-empirically-discoverable, which accounts for its having been for so long unrecognized as the spontaneous equilibrious model. As specialists, scientists seek only the somethings."*

```
RBF DEFINITIONS

    Vector Equilibrium:
    "The vector equilibrium is absolutely dead center of
    Universe and will never be seen by man in any physical
    experience-- yet it is the frame of reference.  And it is not
    ▪ in rotation and it is sizeless and timeless. . . "

    - Cite tape transcript RBF to BO'R, Carbondale Dome,
            p. 39, 1 May '71
```

The VE is not and never will be observable because observation through our senses and scientific instruments requires fluctuation — disequilibrium.

He goes on to say,

> *"The vector equilibrium is the only model of nonbeing zero inflection at the nonmoment of omniintertransformabilities, where anything can happen and must happen single-atomically within and multi-atomically without. Specializing science, seeking only somethings, inherently overlooked the nonthing vector equilibrium. Vector equilibria in isotropic vector matrixes produce the discontinuity of particles, while the vector-weaving around the VE nuclei produce the continuity of wave phenomena."* [19]

Here you get a glimpse of how dense Bucky's writings can be! To summarize, what he's saying is that the VE is a model of energy prior to becoming manifest *(nonbeing zero inflection)*, beyond the concept of time *(at the nonmoment)*, and is the origin of the particle *(discontinuity of particles)* and wave *(continuity of wave phenomena)* duality we find in modern physics. It is the pure potential and origin of all manifest phenomena of matter, light and sound.

> *"The vector equilibrium itself is only a referential pattern of conceptual relationships at which nature never pauses."* – Synergetics, 205.01

Fuller mentions "isotropic vector matrixes" as well, and that's where we're going next, but before we do there's another aspect of the VE to highlight at this point in our journey.

12-AROUND-1 EQUILIBRIUM

Buckminster Fuller was supremely interested in the modelability of fundamental concepts such as the VE. He felt that if something could be modeled it was then made both practical and teachable; otherwise it remains too abstract. In his quest to discover nature's coordinate system, he created many models to demonstrate the generalized principles that he found at play in the way cosmic dynamics behaved. For modeling, he commonly used sticks (representing vectors of energy) and spheres (representing fields of energy). Seeing how ocean waves could spontaneously make billions of perfect little spherical

bubbles with every crashing upon the shore, Fuller felt that the spherical energy dynamic was of primary importance to understanding nature's efficiency (the sphere possessing the quality of encompassing the greatest amount of volume within the least amount of surface area).

Inevitably, Fuller experimented with close-packing of spheres, wherein equal-sized spheres are arranged in a manner such that they are touching each of their closest neighbors (tangential). As is well known, this arrangement creates the familiar pattern we see when oranges are stacked in a food market.

When packing spheres in this way, we find there's a basic arrangement that consists of 12 spheres around one central sphere, as in this image:

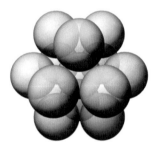 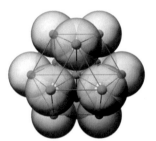 

The centers of all adjacent spheres are equidistant from each other; therefore when we connect them together we get the Vector Equilibrium.

So the Vector Equilibrium as the minimum system of cosmic equilibrium is a 12-around-1 geometry.

This gives us a clue in our consideration of how we can engender equilibrium in the world in pursuit of harmonization with cosmic wholeness. Perhaps if we utilize a system in which this wholeness is represented by a set of twelve interrelated areas (or spheres) of human activity as a means to ensure a minimum-sufficient state of equilibrium in our communities, we may engender a new level of synergetic harmony and balance, both in our individual and societal lives. By putting the idea of cosmomimicry into action in this way, there may well be a simple design inherent in universal dynamics that virtually assures this kind of strategic success when we so choose to apply it. We may, in fact, be able to consciously create a state of harmonious balance (as described at the beginning of this chapter) that could bring the vital stability and wholeness so needed in our chaotic and fragile world.

Just such a whole-system model has been created over many years by a dedicated group of people, and it's ready to be put into comprehensive action. As seen in this illustration, the 12 Sectors model provides a framework for assuring that a minimum-sufficient set of areas of human

Perhaps if we utilize a system in which this wholeness is represented by a set of twelve interrelated areas (or spheres) of human activity as a means to ensure a minimum-sufficient state of equilibrium in our communities, we may engender a new level of synergetic harmony and balance, both in our individual and societal lives.

activity are considered holistically when pursuing solutions to challenges in our local communities, regional societies, and global systems. It is, in fact, a fractal-hologramic-synergetic model.

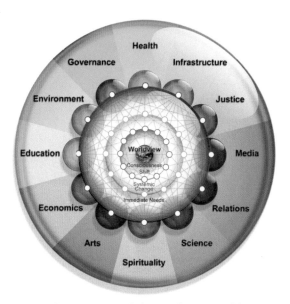

Image courtesy of Thrive Solutions Model
www.ThriveOn.com

From 1999 to 2004 I had the honor of serving with Teresa Collins as Co-Directors of Barbara Marx Hubbard's Foundation for Conscious Evolution. Barbara had been working with an eight-sector version of this model for many years, inspired in part from early conceptual development work by Jahn Ballard. With my familiarity of Fuller's 12-around-1 equilibrium geometry, I recommended expanding the model to encompass twelve sectors as a system of minimum sufficient wholeness. In the later 2000's, a group representing a number of organizations and initiatives who wished to incorporate this model into their organizing frameworks came to consensus on labeling the twelve sectors as represented in the illustration included here. This version comes from Thrive Movement, which I helped develop with

Foster Gamble as a central component of our Solutions Strategy. This is an example of putting the principles and concepts of cosmometry into application, in this case within the context of social organization and whole-system problem solving. I have complete confidence that widespread adoption and utilization of this sector model and solutions strategy will engender coherence within and across all sectors while restoring integral wholeness in our communities, both locally and globally.

STARTING FROM ZERO

CHAPTER 8
ISOTROPIC VECTOR MATRIX

Cosmometry is the study of fundamental patterns, structures and processes that we can discern in nature and in energy dynamics throughout the cosmos. As we've just seen, central to all such dynamics is a primary system of equilibrium that is represented by the 12-around-1 Vector Equilibrium model. It is the zerophase reference found at the origin of every manifest phenomenon — the zero starting point.

At the center of the VE is a single sphere or central point around which the other twelve are equally distributed, what Fuller called a nucleus. Being that the outer twelve are distributed equally around it, we can extend this idea such that every one of those twelve can become the nucleus of another VE, thus creating a larger matrix of equal-length vectors in the same relationship of equilibrium. This matrix can be extended in all directions in what is then referred to as an Isotropic Vector Matrix.

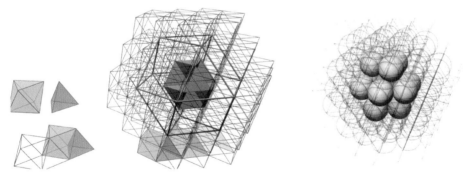

Isotropic means "the same everywhere."
Vector means "energy dynamic."
Matrix means "a pattern of lines and spaces."

So we have a pattern of energy dynamics that is the same everywhere — an Isotropic Vector Matrix (IVM for short). It is the *universal field* of energy in zerophase equilibrium. Every point in this universal matrix is a potential nucleus of a Vector Equilibrium, so every point is potentially a localized zero-point upon which the fluctuating energy dynamics of manifesting events is centered. As such, **the IVM is the geometry of the fundamental zero-point unified field at the center of all phenomena**, be it a galaxy, a star, a planet, a human, a heart, a cell, or an atom. The VE is the "local" version of the universal IVM state of equilibrium.

"Such a universal system of identically dimensioned lines, growing outwardly from any one nuclear vertex, constitutes a universal vector system in dynamic equilibrium, for all the force lines are of equal magnitude." [20] – Buckminster Fuller

As we explore cosmometry and how it relates to unified physics, we can consider the VE and IVM as describing the same fundamental principle of zerophase equilibrium in the energy dynamics of the cosmos. In essence, the VE and IVM *are* the same thing. The VE refers to a single unit and the IVM is used for the field of such units. So, as these terms are used in our exploration, know that they're always referencing this zero-point state. This is, of course, directly related to the idea of zero-point energy, as we'll see.

First, let's explore some of the important characteristics of the cosmometry of the IVM. While this next excerpt from Fuller's *Synergetics* may seem hard to comprehend in his style of writing, it does a great job of introducing these characteristics.

"The isotropic vector matrix is four-dimensional and 60-degree coordinated. It provides an omnirational accounting system that, if arbitrarily accounted on a three-dimensional, 90-degree basis, becomes inherently irrational. The isotropic vector matrix demonstrates the ability of the symmetrically and asymmetrically terminaled, high-frequency energy vectors to accommodate the structuring of any shape." [21]

Let's unpack this a bit.

The IVM is four-dimensional and 60-degree coordinated...

Everyone is familiar with the concept that we live in a 3-dimensional world — "3D reality" we like to call it. We are taught this in school from an early age, and base all of our scientific and engineering specifications upon the Cartesian XYZ coordinate system of space, seen to the right, that is the 90-degree, cubic system used to measure and map our 3D world. While it is very useful for this purpose, it turns out that as the basis for all of our primary spatial measuring systems, this coordinate system has introduced unanticipated complexities in our mathematics.

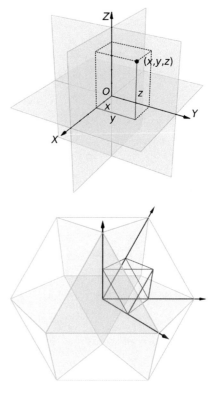

What Fuller is describing is a different coordinate system that is based upon a 4-dimensional, 60-degree spatial model, which is the IVM. It is four-dimensional because the VE (and by extension the entire IVM) has the characteristic of having four planes that intersect a common zero-point center, as seen in the image to the right.

The four hexagonal planes play the same role in the VE/IVM as do the three square planes of the Cartesian dimensional system. The VE/IVM is therefore a four-dimensional coordinate system. These planes are at 60-degrees from each other, as are all of the vector angles in the IVM, therefore it is 60-degree coordinated in the same manner that the Cartesian system is 90–degree coordinated. The use of this coordinate system is significant because…

It provides an omnirational accounting system that, if arbitrarily accounted on a three-dimensional, 90-degree basis, becomes inherently irrational…

Without going too deeply into Fuller's comprehensive analysis of this (which *Synergetics* thoroughly presents), he's saying that using a prime spatial unit based upon the IVM's four-dimensional, 60-degree coordinate system produces rational values (whole numbers and rational fractions — omnirational) rather than irrational values that arise as a consequence of using the three-dimensional, 90-degree cubic system.

Here's a simple version of his analysis of this to help illustrate the point.

Our current 90-degree system uses the Cube as the basic unit of measure, such as in the Centimeter-Gram-Second units of measuring. The cubic centimeter (cm^3) is the standard unit of measuring the spatial dimension of volume. When a cube is used as the fundamental unit of volume (cube value = 1), the other basic Platonic Forms end up having volumes that are not rational number values, as is the volume of the unit cube. To the right is a chart illustrating those values, wherein you can see that every volume except the cube is approximated (≈).

Polyhedron (a = 2)	Volume (unit edges)
Tetrahedron	≈ 0.117851
Cube	1
Octahedron	≈ 0.471404
Dodecahedron	≈ 7.663119
Icosahedron	≈ 2.181695

"To begin with undivided wholeness means, however, that we must drop the mechanistic order. But this order has been, for many centuries, basic to all thinking on physics… the mechanistic order is most naturally and directly expressed through the Cartesian grid. Though physics has changed radically in many ways, the Cartesian grid (with minor modifications, such as the use of curvilinear coordinates) has remained the one key feature that has not changed. Evidently, it is not easy to change this, because our notions of order are pervasive, for not only do they involve our thinking but also our senses, our feelings, our intuitions, our physical movement, our relationships with other people and with society as a whole and, indeed, every phase of our lives. It is thus difficult to 'step back' from our old notions of order sufficiently to be able seriously to consider new notions of order." – David Bohm

This has been taken for granted in science as just the way things are because there's been no other coordinate system to consider using, until Synergetics came along.

In synergetic geometry, the fundamental unit of volume is the tetrahedron, which is the most basic structure in the universe with its four faces, four vertexes, and six edges. When this is used as the fundamental unit of volume (tetrahedron value = 1), the volume of the other Platonic forms then equate to rational number values.

Here's a chart from *Synergetics* showing equivalent values of volume based upon the tetrahedron (tetravolumes):

Locally Symmet-rical Omni-triangu-lated	Locally Mixed Sym-Asym. Omni-triangu-lated	Locally Asym-metrical Omni-triangu-lated		1 Rational Quanta Module Volumes	2 Rational Regular Tetra-hedral Volume or Comple-mentary Rational Tetra-volumes
△			Vector – Edged Tetrahedron	24	1
◇			Vector – Edged Octahedron	96	4
		◈	Vector – Diagonaled Cube	72	3
	◈		Vector Equilibrium	480	20
◉			Vector – Edged Icosahedron	444.24 ⎤ 648	18.510 ⎤ 27
		◈	Vector – Edged Cube	203.76 ⎦	8.490 ⎦
		◈	Vector – Diagonaled Rhombic Dodecahedron	144	6
		◈	Vector – Edged Rhombic Dodecahedron	623.664 ⎤ 2,184.096	25.986 ⎤ 91.004
		◈	Vector – Edged Dodecahedron	1,506.432 ⎦	65.018 ⎦

It's important to remember at this point that we're exploring a *quantized* model of energy and matter. As such we are working with rational number quanta and ratios within the quantized structure, rather than mathematical abstractions of irrational numbers. Realizing that the tetrahedron is a more fundamental unit of quanta than is the cube is highly informative of our process of harmonizing with the balanced wholeness of the universe. According to Fuller, switching to a tetrahedron-based system simplifies much of our mathematical calculation of spatial relationships, as we'd no longer need to accommodate the irrational consequences of the currently predominant cubic system. (As we'll see later, though, the 90° coordinate system is an essential attribute of spatial organization when the IVM's zerophase geometry goes out of equilibrium to produce the Platonic Forms and 3D reality as we perceive and measure it.)

As for the last sentence in the *Synergetics* excerpt:

The isotropic vector matrix demonstrates the ability of the symmetrically and asymmetrically terminaled, high-frequency energy vectors to accommodate the structuring of any shape.

The IVM's universal field of ultra-high-frequency vectors (i.e. extremely small wavelength at the Planck scale, as we'll see in the next chapter) is so fine in its triangulated structure that it can accommodate any shape, be it a rock, a tree, an elephant, a building, a tornado, a star, a galaxy, etc. In the same way that a 3D modeling program uses triangulation to create forms of all kinds, including spheres and fluid surfaces, the extremely fine triangulation of the IVM allows for every imaginable shape to arise from its equilibrious structure. 3D models are, indeed, crude fractal representations of the highly refined structure of manifest forms in the cosmos.

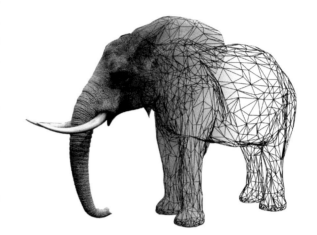

This brings us to the next level of considering the nature and structure of the IVM. While it has been so far described as a vector matrix and illustrated with a pattern of straight lines that form tetrahedrons and octahedrons, the IVM is actually more appropriately described as a superfluid medium composed of dynamic spherical (toroidal) oscillations in a state of balanced equilibrium. This is the foundational concept of the theory of unified physics that is central to our exploration of cosmic wholeness and the holofractal structure of space itself.

"It is highly probable that universal comprehension of synergetics is strategically critical to humanity's exodus from the womb of originally permitted absolute helplessness and ignorance at birth and entry into the realization that planetary society can spontaneously co-ordinate in universally successful life support, that is, achieve freedom from fundamental fear and political bias inherent in the ignorant assumption of life-support inadequacy."
– Buckminster Fuller, *Synergetics* [22]

STARTING FROM ZERO

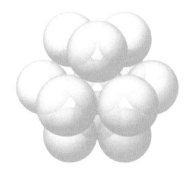

CHAPTER 9
PLANCK SPHERICAL UNITS

My study of Buckminster Fuller's ideas began in 1978 when I spontaneously chose to read a book by him called *Intuition* that was in my parents' home library. I have no idea how it got there as neither of them was "into" Bucky then. In hindsight it was one of those cosmic joke events where we realize we've been set up and we're the last one to know it! (Update 2016: turns out it was my brother Hal's book, he informed me upon reading this, which makes perfect sense now.)

Though I had the pleasure of befriending Bucky's grandchildren, Jaime and Alexandra, in the late 80's, and later his daughter, Allegra Fuller Snyder, there were many years where those with a similarly dedicated obsession for the deeper technical aspects of Bucky's research were few and far between in my life. That changed in a profound way when at the beginning of this century I had the good fortune of meeting two men who had not only been deeply immersed for many decades but were applying the foundational concepts of synergetics and the VE/IVM to various arenas of science, most specifically to physics and atomic geometry. These two are Foster Gamble and Nassim Haramein, and they have been my dear friends, primary mentors, and trusted allies in the journey ever since.

With Foster Gamble and Nassim Haramein at Saqqara Pyramid in Egypt — 2017 Resonance Academy Delegate Gathering

Foster and Nassim had met and collaborated on research prior to my meeting them, and through many in-depth discussions they came to conclude that the two most fundamental patterns of energy dynamics are the VE as the model of zerophase equilibrium and the Torus as the model of balanced flow process in the universe. I had through my own more experiential and non-academic path of discovery come to the same conclusion. So I was very delighted to hear their more scientific analysis confirming my more intuitive understanding at that time. For all of us (and many others, including Fuller… hence his book title), it was intuition that had led us down a different path than is presented in mainstream academia long enough to piece together this emerging model of cosmic wholeness.

In continuing our exploration of the IVM, we're going to focus a bit on Haramein's theory of unified physics as we expand our perspective on the nature and structure of the IVM, and as a consequence, space itself. Let's begin first with some simple cosmometry.

IVM AS 2-DIMENSIONAL PATTERN

The simplest way to illustrate an isotropic vector matrix is as a 2-dimensional grid of triangles, like this:

This is a 60-degree matrix.

We can then add circles that are close-packed in alignment with this grid, with their centers located at the vertexes of the triangles. This makes a hexagonal grid pattern, as illustrated here with the orange line highlighting a hexagon:

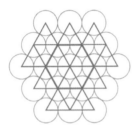

Imagine this matrix extending out indefinitely and you'll have a 2D isotropic vector matrix pattern.

Each one of those circles can, of course, be a sphere, just as in the case of the 12-around-1 packing of spheres to create the VE as Fuller did. (Note in the illustration to the right that Fuller refers to the "frequency" of the triangulation in the top three diagrams. Imagining this being correlated to waveform frequencies begins to provide insight into the superfluid model of space that we're leading towards.)

So, we have a triangulated grid of vectors and a hexagonal array of circles/spheres that are the basis for our model of the IVM. *At this juncture, we need to make an important leap in how we perceive this model, though.* While it is useful to illustrate

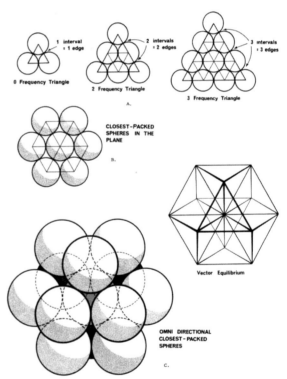

Fig. 413.01 *Vector Equilibrium: Omnidirectional Closest Packing Around a Nucleus:* Triangles can be subdivided into greater and greater numbers of similar units. The number of modular subdivisions along any edge can be referred to as the *frequency* of a given triangle. In triangular grids each vertex may be expanded to become a circle or sphere showing the inherent relationship between closest packed spheres and triangulation. The frequency of triangular arrays of spheres in the plane is determined by counting the number of intervals (A) rather than the number of spheres on a given edge. In the case of concentric packings or spheres around a nucleus the frequency of a given system can either be the edge subdivision or the number of concentric shells or layers. Concentric packings in the plane give rise to hexagonal arrays (B) and omnidirectional closest packing of equal spheres around a nucleus (C) gives rise to the vector equilibrium (D).

this IVM pattern showing the vectors in triangular and tetrahedral arrays, **the actual structure of the IVM of space isn't to be conceived as having any sort of rigid structural vectors**, as it may look like in these illustrations. These vectors represent, quite simply, *invisible lines of dynamic tension* between the energy events that are represented by the spheres. The lines show us the pattern, but they're not actually there in any visible sense. What is there are spherical fields of energy events that are *arrayed* in the triangulated/tetrahedral matrix.

In Fuller's eyes, the spheres represent the protons and neutrons of atomic nuclei and the atoms of molecular structures. These "particles" are dynamic energy events, not Ping-Pong ball-like spheres. Atomic structures are symmetrically arranged in harmonic alignment with the IVM, this being due to the fact that the zerophase reference is the underlying equilibrium state that the atomic elements seek to resolve to in their structural integrity. The electron scan image to the right, of the atoms comprising a nanographene molecule, clearly shows the tendency towards hexagonal equilibrium.

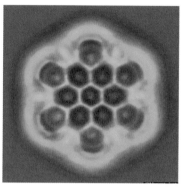

Image of Nanographene Molecule. Notice the hexagonal sphere packing symmetry. (IBM Research Zurich)

While Fuller considered these energy dynamics in the atomic realm, Haramein took the idea of sphere packing to a whole other scale… literally!

Welcome to the realm of the **Planck Spherical Unit**.

We're now getting down to the very base of our universe, as we know it — the zerophase ground state of dynamic equilibrium at a scale vastly smaller than that of atoms, let alone our scale of perceptual reality.

As briefly described in Section 1, the Planck Units are a set of natural units that are at a scale that is so small it's quite impossible to fully imagine it. The Planck Length, for example, is a tiny $1.616199(97) \times 10^{-35}$ meters. If we use the size of a grain of salt as a comparative reference of scale for the Planck Length, the relative size of a grain of salt would increase to be larger than the entire observable universe!

If Planck Length = size of Grain of Salt, then Grain of Salt > size of Universe.

NASA/WMAP Science Team

You start to get the idea of just how difficult it is to imagine. Suffice it to say, the Planck scale is the tiniest scale of reference used in scientific analysis.

What Haramein did was to imagine that at the Planck scale there are "eeentsy-weensty" little spherical energy units that are packed together in an isotropic vector matrix. In doing so, though, he made a fundamental shift in the arrangement of the little spheres. Instead of having them just touching each other tangentially (therefore leaving small gaps between them), he realized that they could be overlapping each other in a coherent standing wave pattern of dynamic energy in equilibrium, thus becoming all-space-filling with no gaps between them. (Another clue here… remember that a holographic image is made up of a standing wave pattern of coherent laser light.) This is because these little spheres are not solid balls, but rather they are *spherical oscillators of electromagnetic energy*. They are the same as Light energy, just at a wavelength that is extremely small. It is these little quanta of electromagnetic energy that he calls Planck Spherical Units.

Tangential Packing with gaps   *Overlapping Packing without gaps*

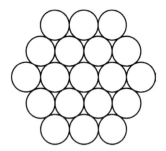 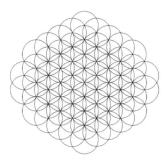

Both tangential and overlapping arrangements of sphere packing produce the same triangulated and hexagonal pattern that creates an isotropic vector matrix.

We now have an IVM of overlapping spherical oscillators of electromagnetic energy at the Planck scale, in a pattern popularly known as the Flower of Life. This, according to Haramein's theory, is the ground state of the universe. It is essentially the **pixel** size of the structure of space and all matter that manifests in space, the pixel that is *the prime quantum unit relative to our size universe*. Being a sphere, though, it is more correctly called a **voxel** since it has volume, rather than considered as a flat square pixel as in the case of a computer screen.

So, **a Planck Spherical Unit (PSU) is the prime quanta of our dynamic electromagnetic universe, and this unit at this extremely small scale is seen as the origin of quantized energy-matter-information dynamics found at all scales.** As such, we now know what the "resolution" is for our universe (in the same way that a computer screen has a specific size pixel that determines the resolution of the screen's image data). It is such a high resolution (meaning tiny wavelength and high frequency) that it is vastly beyond the reach of our contemporary scientific technology's smallest scale of direct observation, which, as of this writing, is achieving molecular and atomic scale imaging ($\sim 10^{-10}$ meters; for comparison, the visible light spectrum falls in the 10^{-6} m range).[23] The Planck scale being 25 orders of magnitude smaller than that (10^{-35} m), it becomes obvious why this field of energy at the zero-point ground state has not been directly observed, and why space is considered to be an empty vacuum devoid of energy. It's simply well beyond the reach of our experimental capacities to observe it; therefore, we must at present go the route of conceptualizing it as we are in this exploration.

It is this Planck-scale field of electromagnetic equilibrium that was historically referred to as the **Aether** in the early days of both ancient and modern physics prior to the mid-20th century when, due to a lack of experimental evidence for its existence, the idea was generally dismissed. As we'll see next, the concept of aether was indeed correct.

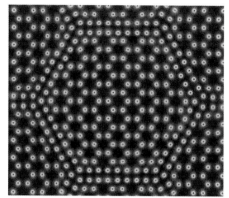

Illustration of electron scan image of molybdenum disulfide, also showing hexagonal equilibrium symmetry.
(by Clay Taylor – artofclaytaylor.com)

This painting by visionary artist, Alex Grey, provides an evocative glimpse into what the dynamic PSU energy field may look like. Entitled *Universal Mind Lattice*, it also offers us a point of contemplation regarding the relationship of consciousness to this universal field. In Alex's own words:

"In 1976, Allyson and I had an experience which changed our lives and our art. We sacramentally ingested a large dose of LSD and lay in bed. Eventually, a heightened state of consciousness emerged where I was no longer aware of physical reality or my body in any conventional sense. I felt and saw my interconnectedness with all beings and things in a vast and brilliant Universal Mind Lattice. Every being and thing in the universe was a toroidal fountain and drain of self-illuminating love energy, a cellular node or jewel in a network, which linked omnidirectionally without end. All duality of self and other was overcome in this infinite dimension of spiritual light. I felt I had been there before, or perhaps in some way was always there. This was the state beyond birth and death, beyond time, our true nature, which seemed more real than any physical surrounding and more real even than my physical body. The clear light matrix arose out of a field of pure emptiness. As utterly convincing as it was, when the light receded, I opened my eyes to behold Allyson and our bedroom once again. I was somewhat shocked to learn that she had experienced the exact same transpersonal dimension at the same time, which we determined by our descriptive drawings and discussion of the awesome beauty of the state. This experience of the infinite net of spirit transformed our lives and gave us a subject which became the focus of our art and our mission."

Baryonic Acoustic Oscillations

In January of 2014, the Baryon Oscillation Spectroscopic Survey (BOSS) collaboration announced that they had measured the scale of the universe to an accuracy of one percent. They did so by calibrating cosmological-scale measurements to the "standard ruler" of baryon acoustic oscillations (seen as white circles in the illustration below). "Periodic ripples of density in visible matter ("baryons," for short) pervade the universe like raindrops on the surface of a pond. Regular galaxy clustering is the direct descendant of pressure waves that moved through the hot plasma of the early universe, which was so hot and dense that particles of light (photons) and particles of matter, including protons and electrons, were tightly coupled together."[41] Biophysicist, William Brown, posits that these spherical oscillations form a universal "flower of life" pattern at the large scale in a manner very similar to the Planck scale PSU Isotropic Vector Matrix.

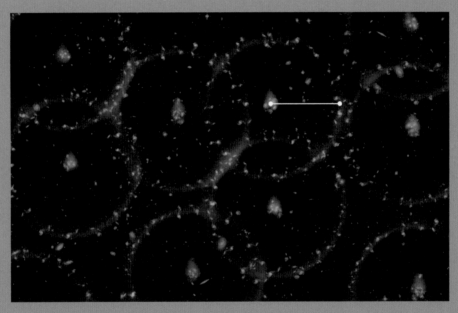

Illustration by Zosia Rostomian, Creative Services, Berkeley Lab
Lawrence Berkeley National Laboratory

CHAPTER 10
INFINITE ENERGY AND THE AETHER

"What we perceive as empty space, and what our eyes would see if they could see much smaller distances and resolve much faster times, is actually a medium that is full of spontaneous activity… We are ethereal beings. We're children of the ether."
– Frank Wilczek, Nobel Laureate Physicist, January 2017

When you switch on a lamp in a room it immediately fills the space with an illuminated field of light energy. In our modern age of electricity, we are so accustomed to this that we pretty much take it for granted. It's really quite a phenomenal occurrence, though, when we fully come to understand what's happening.

Firstly, the light fills the room at the incredible speed of 186,282 miles (299,792 kilometers) per second. *Per second!* To our perception, that is instantaneous. We'd have to go off the planet 186,000 miles in order to perceive the 1-second delay between switching it on and seeing the light. And what's even more remarkable is that the light doesn't need to ramp up to achieve this velocity; it already is at this speed the moment the lamp gets switched on! This suggests that perhaps this speed of light phenomenon is already present, even when there is no visible light that we can see.

Secondly, even a tiny source of light (such as a small LED or a candle flame) will fill the entire room in all directions without gaps. The light radiation is omnidirectional and all-space-filling. Sound familiar?

The radiant energy we call Light is most commonly associated with the visible aspect of our perception of reality — the visible light spectrum; that beautiful palette of colors we see in a rainbow that creates our visible experience of life.

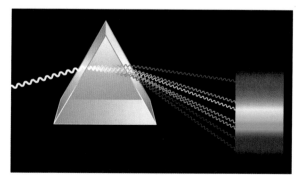

This visible light is made of waves of electromagnetic energy at different frequencies, and while it encompasses such a large portion of our experience of life, the visible light spectrum represents a very tiny fraction of the total spectrum of electromagnetic (EM) energy frequencies present in the universe. In theory, EM energy wavelengths could span from the size of the universe to the Planck scale.

All of this EM radiation carries a specific amount of energy dependent upon the frequency. As a rule, higher frequencies of light equate to higher levels of energy. Violet light has a higher energy value than red light, for example. A beam of light is composed of tiny packets of energy, which Einstein called photons (quanta of light), and it is due to this quantized nature of light that we can determine the energy value.

When we apply this to the highest frequency of EM energy at the wavelength of a Planck distance (i.e. a PSU, ~1.6 x 10^{-35} meters), we determine that **within one cubic centimeter of so-called "empty space" is actually a density of energy that is *vastly greater than the sum of all the energy in the entire observable universe*!** In other words, the EM energy fluctuation of the PSU-IVM field that is present in a cubic centimeter of space represents a mass-energy potential that is far greater in magnitude than the estimated mass of all the matter in the whole universe, by 39 orders of magnitude in fact. (The PSU-IVM "vacuum" energy or Planck density = 10^{93} grams/cm³, while the mass of the Universe = 10^{55} grams.)[24]

So, based upon this hypothesis, the energy available in the very structure of space (EM oscillations at the Planck scale in Isotropic Vector Matrix) is, for all intents and purposes, infinite!

If this is the case, then why don't we see it "out there"? Quite simply because: A) it is at too small a wavelength to be even close to detecting, and B) it is in a state of zerophase equilibrium and therefore undetectable by any instrument that requires non-zero fluctuation for detecting energy waves (which means every experimental apparatus in existence).

```
RBF DEFINITIONS

    Isotropic-vector-matrix Field:

    "Nature always starts every ever freshly with the equilibrious
    isotropic-vector-matric field.  Energy is not lost; it is just
    not yet realized.  It can be realized only disequilibriously.




    - Cite RBF rewrite of SYNERGETICS galley at Sec. 955.50, 20 Dec'73
```

This is the "zero-point energy" that many emerging technologies are designed to access. The usual argument against zero-point technology theories is first-and-foremost as contradicting the Conservation Law — we can't pull energy from nothing (an empty vacuum) or get out more energy than we put into a system. We can clearly see why this is not the case, and in fact these technologies actually adhere to this fundamental principle of physics. We'll explore more about this in the next Section.

Let's summarize things a bit here…

According to unified physics theory, the PSU-IVM field is the smallest voxel resolution relevant to our size universe. Composed of a vast potential of electromagnetic energy in triangulated zerophase equilibrium, it behaves as a superconducting, superfluid medium in which all manifest (disequilibrious) Electromagnetic (tension) and Acoustic (compression) forces create form and flow at all scales (wavelengths) in what we know as the observable universe. When the PSU-IVM goes out of equilibrium (creating a spin density gradient) there arise local instances of size, shape, time, rotation, temperature, etc., centered on a zero reference Vector Equilibrium.

Whew!

Might be a good time to pause and put your attention on breathing again for a minute or two and let that settle in (especially when you realize it's what we're all made of!).

WELCOME BACK THE AETHER

The concept of a ubiquitous Aether field was considered an important component of theories of light propagation and gravity in scientific theory during the 17th and 18th centuries. Isaac Newton referred to it in his first published theories of gravity in the *Principia*,[25] originally published in 1687. Johann Bernoulli (1667-1748) described the aether as "excessively small whirlpools" that permeate all space.[26] A remarkably accurate description of the PSU-IVM field!

In ancient and medieval times the aether was thought of as a "fifth element" — along with air, fire, water and earth — that filled all space and was the source of movement in the celestial sphere. While the idea of aether has been present in scientific thought and theory for centuries, it was generally dismissed from scientific discourse in modern times after the initial experiments of Albert A. Michelson and Edward W. Morley in 1887, and subsequent experiments throughout the 20th century, which found no evidence for such a field of energy. These experiments were predicated on a model of aether as producing an "aetheric wind" which, if present, would influence the path and speed of light when measured at different angles within a given region of space.

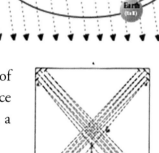

While it would make logical sense to consider that a medium such as aether would exhibit a directional current as do the familiar elements of water and air, perhaps these experiments showed no evidence for it because the aether is actually in a state of zerophase equilibrium (as the PSU-IVM field*) and is therefore undetectable through any experimental means (as well as our inability to directly measure anything

---

* According to Haramein, the PSU matrix, which curves in the presence of mass to produce gravity, would show no measurable curvature close to the surface of the Earth.

close to the Planck scale thus far). So, even though Michelson, Morley and many other researchers have found no evidence for it, it stands to reason from this perspective that the aether may indeed be present after all.

At this point there's something very important to note here about the PSU-IVM field. Even though it's in equilibrium, since each PSU is oscillating *it still has a current of electromagnetic energy flowing through it at the speed of light*. So, it is both zerophase stillness and speed-of-light motion simultaneously! As such, it has the ability to transfer photons of light throughout its matrix (the original proposal for the presence of aether) while remaining undetectable by scientific experimentation. Just because we can't "see it" does not necessarily mean it's not there. (As an analogy, think about observing waves in the ocean without knowing it's actually the water molecules moving up and down that's transferring the wave energy.)

According to Haramein's model of unified physics, what was called the aether is the PSU-IVM field that acts as a fundamental superconducting, superfluid medium with a vast energy potential from which properties of light propagation, mass and gravitation originate.[27] David Bohm held a similar view, stating:

> *"What is implied by this proposal is that what we call empty space contains an immense background of energy, and that matter as we know it is a small, "quantized" wavelike excitation on top of this background, rather like a tiny ripple on a vast sea."*[28]

Let's go back to our lamp in the room for a second…

To round out this picture in more familiar realms we need to apply this idea in the context of the seemingly instantaneous and omnidirectional radiance of light filling the room described at the beginning of this chapter. Flip a switch and POOF, it happens. Magic! Generally speaking, that's all we need to know to be content. For those who are more curious to understand what's going on…

In regard to the instantly-moving-at-the-speed-of-light phenomenon, this is because at the underlying level of the PSU-IVM aether field, everything is already and always moving at the speed of light! The light we see radiating from the lamp is simply a *harmonic* fluctuation at a much larger wavelength and lower frequency that is visible to our eyes, riding upon the eternally present speed-of-light aether field. It's an excitation of this field

> *The light we see radiating from the lamp is simply a harmonic fluctuation at a much larger wavelength and lower frequency that is visible to our eyes, riding upon the eternally present speed-of-light aether field.*

in quantized packets of photons at a fractal scale of frequency we call visible reality (*"a small, "quantized" wavelike excitation on top of this background…"*). It may well be that photons are massless because they are simply harmonic waves moving through the zerophase aether field.

As for the omnidirectional quality of radiant light that's all-space-filling with no gaps, that's the omnidirectional structure of the underlying PSU-IVM aether field. Whatever portion of this field is harmonically excited (i.e. illuminated) will "light up" in our eyes. Whereas a flashlight or laser constrains this excitation in a specific direction, a candle or light bulb excites the whole field surrounding it (less the more dense portion of it that is the matter that comprises the candle or bulb itself, of course).

The world as we know it is fundamentally a standing-wave fluctuation within the underlying aetheric superfluid medium of the PSU-IVM field.

Think about *that* the next time you flip a light switch!

STARTING FROM ZERO

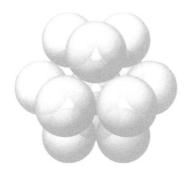

CHAPTER 11
ABSOLUTE AND RELATIVE HOLOGRAM

In Section 1 we took our first foray into the hologramic wholeness of the cosmos, stating that "the information of the whole is present in every point" — one of the fundamental principles of this exploration. As such, we ought to be able to associate it within this journey of Starting From Zero. To be a hologramic universe it must be so all the way to its very foundation. How, then, does the hologramic principle relate to the IVM zero-point field?

It begins with understanding the relationship of *information* to what has so far been explored through the dynamics of energy and matter. As discussed in the section of the Introduction called **Three Components, One Thing**, in our unified model of wholeness, Energy, Matter and Information are considered three attributes of one phenomenon. Nassim Haramein describes this in his theory of unified physics, saying that the electromagnetic voxel "bits" of the PSU-IVM energy act as an information storage and distribution network that is fractally connected at all scales throughout the material cosmos.

Information is another potentially ambiguous term if not appropriately defined in the context of this exploration. Of the various definitions found in the *Merriam-Webster Dictionary*, these ones are the most relevant:

1. the communication or reception of knowledge or intelligence

2. *(1)* a signal or character (as in a communication system or computer) representing data

    (2) something (as a message, experimental data, or a picture) which justifies change in a construct (as a plan or theory) that represents physical or mental experience or another construct[29]

Information is a signal or character of data, which justifies change in a physical or mental construct through the communication or reception of knowledge or intelligence.

In his book, *Science and the Akashic Field*, Ervin Laszlo offers another definition, making a distinction between information as data in localized systems as traditionally defined, and "in-formation" (an active form of information) that is the non-local interconnection of all things, saying:

> *"In-formation is a subtle, quasi-instant, non-evanescent and non-energetic connection between things at different locations in space and events at different points in time. Such connections are termed "nonlocal" in the natural sciences and "transpersonal" in consciousness research. In-formation links things (particles, atoms, molecules, organisms, ecologies, solar systems, entire galaxies, as well as the mind and consciousness associated with some of these things) regardless of how far they are from each other and how much time has passed since connections were created between them."* [30]

Accordingly, the zerophase PSU-IVM field is just such an information network wherein the "signal" of every energy event in the cosmos (i.e. every EM fluctuation at the atomic scale) is instantly shared throughout the entire field such that every point receives and responds to the knowledge and intelligence of the whole. It is shared "instantly" because the zerophase "nonmoment" is the center of *all* dynamic activity (i.e. singularity), therefore at this universal center all things are one, transcendent of time and space.* As such, the sum-total Universe of information is what we might call the Absolute Hologram that is instantaneously present everywhere in the omnipresent zerophase PSU-IVM state. **The entire cosmos knows about itself in every moment.**

Ervin Laszlo offers additional perspective on the nature of this cosmic hologram:

> *"We should note that the information carried in the vacuum is not localized, confined to a single location only. As in a hologram, the vacuum carries information in distributed form, present at all points where the wavefields have propagated. The interfering wave-fields in the vacuum are natural holograms. They propagate quasi-instantly, and nothing can attenuate or cancel them. Thus nature's holograms are cosmic holograms: they link—"in-form"—all things with all other things."*

While this may all sound like a fantastical abstract theory, Haramein has shown that at fractal scales from protons to galaxies, we can mathematically demonstrate that just such a universal information network exists. Here's a very simplistic explanation of his theory. (See his *Quantum Gravity and the Holographic Mass* and other physics papers for the full theory, found at www.resonancescience.org).

All matter is composed of atoms, with the proton being the primary "particle" that comprises 99.99% of the mass of the observable universe (the mass of every atom is 99.99% attributed to the protons in the nucleus of the atom). And as is well known in physics, all atoms are composed of 99.99% empty space, with the size of the nucleus being exceedingly small relative to the diameter of the atom's electron shells. As Haramein says, perhaps it's the space itself (i.e. the PSU-IVM field) that defines matter, rather than matter defining space, as is typically viewed in physics.

---

*In physical terms, this would be described as a wormhole. The universal center is the inside nexus of the multiply-connected spacetime, where information is shared instantaneously, completely in accordance with general relativity.

With this in mind, Haramein realized that a proton is a spherical energy event that's spinning at near the speed of light within the cosmic PSU-IVM sea (a.k.a the "vacuum of space") and is itself composed of PSUs co-rotating in the volume defined by the proton diameter (in a similar way as water molecules co-rotate in a bathtub whirlpool, except contained in a spherical space). The size difference between the PSU and the proton is vast (~20 orders of magnitude), therefore contained within the volume of a proton is a very large number of PSUs — approximately 10^{60}. In the same manner that a cubic centimeter of "vacuum energy" results in a mass-energy density of 10^{93} grams/cm^3, the energy density within the volume of a proton comes out to be 10^{55} grams/proton volume (10^{60} PSUs x 10^{-5} grams per PSU = 10^{55}). This value of 10^{55} immediately

> *The sum-total Universe of information is what we might call the Absolute Hologram that is instantaneously present everywhere in the omnipresent zerophase PSU-IVM state.*

jumped out at Haramein because it is, in fact, equivalent to *the total mass of the observable universe!*[31] The mass-energy density *inside* every proton is equivalent to the mass of all the protons *outside* each one of them. The mass density inside each proton (10^{55} grams) he calls the **holographic mass**, and the external mass of all the protons (also 10^{55} grams) is the local or **relative mass**.

OK, that was a bit heady. Here's another way of saying all this...

The fundamental voxel of our size universe is a Planck Spherical Unit — the ground state fractal scale. The next fractal scale most directly relevant to matter formation is the proton that makes up the mass of the observable universe. Every proton is made up of a spinning spherical volume that's filled with PSUs. The energy-matter-information (EMI) *within each proton* (holographic mass) is equivalent to the EMI of the entire universe of all protons (relative mass). The information of the whole (universe) is present in every point (proton) — our definition of the holographic principle. Connected through a ubiquitous "micro-wormhole" system, the proton network is a fundamental fractal level of the cosmic holographic information system, and the PSUs are the electromagnetic quantum "bits" that "receive the knowledge of the signals of data communicated throughout the network which justifies change in the physical construct."

There is a built-in information feedback loop so that every single entity is informed about every other entity simultaneously (an essential characteristic of the dynamic flow process we'll explore in the next Section). It is this hologramic information feedback loop that allows for the fractal complexity of the cosmos to operate with seamless integrity at all scales — what Haramein calls the holofractographic principle.

Where things get even more interesting is on the surface of the proton. It is the surface, after all, that is the interface between the holographic mass within each proton and the universal mass surrounding each proton. The proton surface is the balance point of equilibrium between the internal and external mass-energy densities, with the internal 10^{55} being highly compacted PSU mass and the external 10^{55} being highly distributed proton mass. Equilibrium is inherent in the cosmos.

Substituting information for mass-energy (EMI), the proton surface is therefore the data interface between the Absolute Hologram within the PSU-IVM zerophase field and the Relative Hologram of the manifest universe (i.e. all atomic/molecular matter). Manifesting anything requires a relative relationship to any and all other manifest things; otherwise there would be no localized distinction of objects within an environment. The proton surface is the localized hologramic information "hard drive" that is relative to the total information of the universal hologram within and without it — the "event horizon" of the Relative Hologram within the Absolute Hologram.

What is the surface of a proton made of? PSUs of course, the same as its interior volume. The proton surface can be thought of as a sphere made up of overlapping PSUs in a triangulated pattern that is just like a geodesic dome. The overlapping PSUs create a "bumpy" surface arranged in a pattern similar to the familiar Flower of Life pattern found in many ancient cultures, and the same as we saw in Chapter 9 when first describing sphere packing.

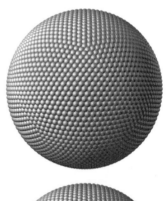

Haramein discovered that there is a relationship between the holographic mass (information) inside a proton (the 10^{60} PSUs that fill the proton volume) and the relative mass (information) of the approximately 10^{40} PSUs on its surface.* Through the application of a simple ratio relationship between the two, he was able to produce the exact mass of a proton as previously determined by standard methods of analysis (see diagram below). He then went on to predict the charge radius of a proton,[32] which was subsequently verified through experimental data to be within one standard deviation of accuracy, indicating it is likely to

be the correct value for the proton radius. By comparison, the Standard Model radius is 4% larger (or seven orders of deviation), which is causing a crisis in modern physics theory that is presently unable to explain this large and perplexing discrepancy of size.

Using the same holographic mass solution, Haramein and colleagues have also successfully solved for the mass of the electron, extending the solution to derive the correct atomic number for the entire periodic table of elements.[33]

Haramein's very simple geometric solutions, based upon PSUs as the fundamental "granularity" of space

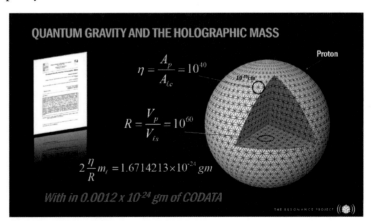

QUANTUM GRAVITY AND THE HOLOGRAPHIC MASS

$$\eta = \frac{A_p}{A_{\ell c}} = 10^{40}$$

$$R = \frac{V_p}{V_{\ell s}} = 10^{60}$$

$$2\frac{\eta}{R} m_\ell = 1.6714213 \times 10^{-24}\ gm$$

With in 0.0012 x 10^{-24} gm of CODATA

Proton

THE RESONANCE PROJECT

*Correlated to the music aspect of our exploration, it is noteworthy that the ratio of the proton's volume to surface is 3:2, which is a Perfect 5th interval.

70

and matter, can be applied to objects at macro scales, such as stellar or galactic black holes, to derive the exact gravitational mass of such objects. **Gravity is, in fact, an effect of the Planck field co-moving at the cosmological scale, defining the mass of an object and the gravitational "tensegrity" between objects, which are all centered by a singularity.**

Additionally, his theory has shown that the so-called Strong Force that binds protons together in the nucleus of an atom is actually an effect of quantum gravity. The quantized gravitational influence of the PSUs holographic mass within a proton relative to its surface diameter spinning at close to the speed of light (which introduces mass dilation) adds up to a value exactly equivalent to the Strong Force. In other words, **there is no Strong Force; it is a behavior of gravity at the atomic scale.**

"Omnitriangulated geodesic spheres consisting exclusively of three-way interacting great circles are realizations of gravitational field patterns. The gravitational field will ultimately be disclosed as ultra high-frequency tensegrity geodesic spheres. Nothing else." – Buckminster Fuller

This level of physics is beyond the purpose of this presentation, yet it's important to highlight these findings here as they mathematically confirm the accuracy of this model of quantized space at the Planck scale and the hologramic wholeness it describes. You can dive more deeply into the physics via the Resonance Academy's online course, *Exploring the Connected Universe*, found at www.resonancescience.org.

For our purposes here, the most important characteristic to consider is that it appears that the protons that make up all matter in the cosmos act as a universal information network that hologramically stores both the information of the entire universe (the holographic mass within each proton) and the relative information of each proton (the surface mass of the proton) via the PSU quantum bits that they are composed of.

We're beginning to see fundamental ratio relationships within the cosmic model of wholeness based upon the PSU-IVM field as the ground state resolution of the universe in equilibrium. As we explored in Section 1, the fractal quantization of the cosmos inherently leads to fundamental scaling ratios, one of which is Octave Doubling. Let's see how this fits into our zerophase model of equilibrium.

CHAPTER 12
VE OCTAVE SCALING

Music — that wondrous experience of sound in melodic, harmonic and rhythmic play, so vast in its variety of song and style. One of the best examples of "free energy", for there's never a lack of a new song ready to emerge from the creative potential of the cosmos. And as all songs must come to their end, music inevitably returns to this source as the last notes fade into silence, leaving us with a lingering memory of its moving presence. Indeed, it is the silence that makes music even possible. As Claude Debussy said, "Music is the space between the notes."

As mentioned before, the phenomenon we call music is really more of a discovery of a harmonic system that already exists in the cosmos than it is an invention on our part. Certainly we have applied this discovery to musical invention of all kinds, and yet we do so only with the inventor's "toolkit" of acoustic vibration and the relationships of sounds it provides us and the silence from which they arise.

The most basic relationship in music is that of an Octave. As initially described in Chapter 4, the octave is the doubling and halving of a given frequency to produce the same musical tone at a higher and lower pitch respectively, a ratio of 2:1. While cultures around the world divide the musical space between octaves in different ways, the octave itself remains fundamental to most systems of music "theory", whether academic or intuitive.

As we round the bend on this exploration of Starting From Zero, let's see how the octave itself is intrinsic to the geometry of the Vector Equilibrium and Isotropic Vector Matrix (VE-IVM).

In its basic state, the VE-IVM is composed of alternating tetrahedron (orange) and octahedron (blue).

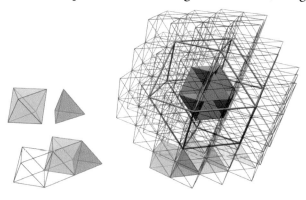

In his quest to find the most basic structure of equilibrium that consists of tetrahedrons only in balanced polarity, Nassim Haramein spent many days and nights, long before the benefit of 3D computer modeling, imagining just what this structure would look like. While you can watch him describe his process of discovery in the informative DVD, *Black Whole*, Haramein eventually came upon a solution in what he then named the 64 Tetrahedron Matrix, which looks like this:

As is evident by the name, it consists of 64 tetrahedrons, all arranged in such a way that there is a tetrahedral symmetry in balanced polarity, meaning upward- and downward-pointing tetrahedrons.

The 64 Tetrahedron Matrix is actually a *polarized* version of the VE-IVM system, and in that polarized state we find an inherent octave doubling is present in the fractal division of the VE-IVM system. Here's what that looks like…

Buckminster Fuller's synergetic geometry was based upon what he called "multiplication by division." Universe is the prime unity of wholeness, and all that is in it is the division of this wholeness into an increasing multiplicity of form and structure. Imagine, then, that we start with a Vector Equilibrium at the size of the universe, composed of eight tetrahedrons all pointing inward towards the center:

This is a non-polarized state of equilibrium, representing the dynamic of energy going towards the singularity at the center. Next we begin to polarize the VE by adding another tetrahedron, this time pointing outward, creating its "dual" or polar opposite:

Doing this for all eight tetrahedron results in the 64 Tetrahedron Matrix (64 Tet):

We've now created a tetrahedral array that is in balanced polarity, with 32 upward pointing and 32 downward pointing tetrahedrons. Additionally, we've created a balanced polarity of contracting (gravitational) and expanding (radiational) dynamics, represented by the orange VE (original tetrahedrons pointing inward) and the green Star Tetrahedron (new tetrahedrons pointing outward). These polar-balanced tetrahedra are twice the size of the 64 tetrahedra that make up the matrix, our first case of octave scaling.

In the middle of the 64 Tet there is another Vector Equilibrium at exactly half the size of the original, or one octave smaller. This new VE can then be polarized again to create another 64 Tet matrix that is half the size of the first one, or one octave smaller. And the same pattern repeats ad infinitum at octave intervals of fractal scaling from the size of the universe to the Planck scale.

The octave ratio in music as the doubling and halving of frequencies of sound is exactly replicated in the fractal scaling of the polarized IVM! The very ground state of the cosmos inherently includes the primary ratio relationship of music, our first clue that what we experience as music is directly correlated to the fundamental nature of form and flow throughout the universe.

And as well, it's worth noting here (which will be expanded on later) that the 12-tone music system can be relationally correlated to the 12-around-1 geometry of the Vector Equilibrium, as pictured here:

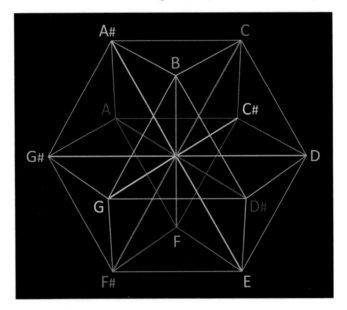

Finally in our octave scaling exploration, it's also noteworthy that the 64 Tet is itself composed of eight star tetrahedrons, each containing eight tetrahedra — 8 x 8 = 64. Our fundamental octave-scaling **Binary number system** is intrinsic to the quantized structure of the cosmos found within the geometry of silence — the zerophase IVM.

In collaboration with Dr. Amira Val Baker, Haramein has determined that this 64-fold geometry is a threshold at the Planck scale that creates the conditions for a black hole, wherein there are 64 Planck Spherical Units (PSUs) on the inside and 64 PSUs on the surface. As such, the 64 Tetrahedron Matrix represents the first fractal iteration of mass within the polarized structure of space.

The 64-fold cosmometry also has a direct correlation to the fundamental coding structure within biological systems, DNA, which is composed of a defined set of 64 codons. And as well, in cell division, it is at the 64-cell stage that the internal and external cells branch into separate developmental lineages.[34] It appears that the "64" fractal scale of the binary system may be intrinsic to the information of physical structures. Perhaps the 64-fold level represents a threshold at which the simplicity of the underlying cosmomctry is able to diversify into the vast complexity of form and function in the cosmos.

The ancient Chinese *Book of Changes*, the *I Ching*, suggests this to be so, with its 64 hexagrams in an 8-by-8 grid arising from the fundamental binary duality of Yin and Yang that describe the dynamic interplay of the elements in nature and human relationship. With both the *I Ching*'s hexagrams having six lines and tetrahedra having six edges, it is possible to map the hexagram system to the 64 Tetrahedron Matrix in a balanced symmetry of positive and negative, Yin-Yang, dynamics.

CHAPTER 13
FROM ELECTRONS TO ATOMS TO SNOWFLAKES TO SUPERCLUSTERS

The model of an Isotropic Vector Matrix as the zerophase cosmometry is, for all intents and purposes, purely conceptual, given that it is not directly observable or measurable. It is fair to wonder, then, whether we can find any indication of this basic cosmometry "out here" in the macro world of nature and the cosmos. Can the 4-dimensional, hexagonal geometry of the VE and the IVM's tetrahedral/octahedral matrix be seen to influence the dynamics of energy in the physical universe? To explore this possibility, here are a few examples of how we may, in fact, be observing the presence of the VE-IVM's energetic symmetry in the patterns of physical structures across vast scales.

ELECTRON SPIN IN A HONEYCOMB LATTICE

In a 2016 paper entitled *Spin and the Honeycomb Lattice: Lessons from Graphene*,[35] researchers Matthew Mecklenburg and B. C. Regan describe a triangular chessboard matrix that exactly maps the "up" (blue) and "down" (yellow) spin states of electrons in a sheet of graphene. This triangulated tile pattern and hexagonal lattice matches the 2-dimensional Isotropic Vector Matrix we saw in Chapter 9. Extending this polarized triangular matrix into a tetrahedral space results in the same isotropic arrangement as the 64 Tetrahedron Matrix. The caption from the paper's image suggests just such a discrete, chessboard-like structure to space:

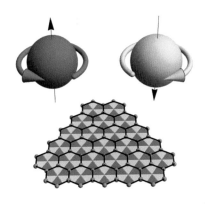

> *"Electrons are thought to spin, even though they are pure point particles with no surface that can possibly rotate. Recent work on graphene shows that the electron's spin might arise because space at very small distances is not smooth, but rather segmented like a chessboard. The standard cartoon of an electron shows a spinning sphere with positive or negative angular momentum, as illustrated in blue or gold above.*

However, such cartoons are fundamentally misleading: compelling experimental evidence indicates that electrons are ideal point particles, with no finite radius or internal structure that could possibly "spin". A quantum mechanical model of electron transport in graphene, a single layer of graphite (shown as a black honeycomb), presents a possible resolution to this puzzle. An electron in graphene hops from carbon atom to carbon atom as if moving on a chessboard with triangular tiles. At low energies the individual tiles are unresolved, but the electron acquires an "internal" spin quantum number which reflects whether it is on the blue or the gold tiles. Thus the electron's spin could arise not from rotational motion of its substructure, but rather from the discrete, chessboard-like structure of space."

A NEW STATE OF WATER

On April 22, 2016, a physics paper was published on the website of the American Physical Society entitled, *Quantum Tunneling of Water in Beryl: A New State of the Water Molecule.*[36] According to a review of the paper on the same site, the authors suggest that they have discovered a state of water molecules that is unique from the other states of water as liquid, gas or solid. These water molecules are confined inside an extremely small hexagonal channel within a beryl crystal (like an emerald), so small in fact that only one water molecule can fit in the channel. A water molecule is, of course, made up of two hydrogen atoms and one oxygen atom, H_2O. Within a hexagonal beryl channel, the H_2O molecule can potentially occupy six different symmetrical orientations in a triangular arrangement, like a V shape, with the two hydrogen atoms at the tips of the V on one of the channel's sides and the oxygen in the center of the channel.

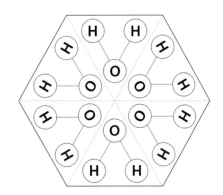

Between each orientation is an energy barrier that would typically inhibit the reorientation of the hydrogen atoms between the six positions, yet in the case of the water molecule inside this extremely confined space, they have found that the atoms do indeed pass through these barriers (quantum tunneling). Not only can they occupy each of the six positions, what they discovered is that they do so simultaneously! An excerpt from the review states:

"…they found the hydrogens' kinetic energy to be 30% lower in beryl than in water's normal liquid or solid state. The lower energy implies that the hydrogens are less confined, as the tunneling frees them to be at the six positions simultaneously. The resulting charge density of each hydrogen is smeared out into a corrugated ring… This smearing out, or "delocalization," of the hydrogen atoms has a dramatic effect on the shape of the water molecule."[37]

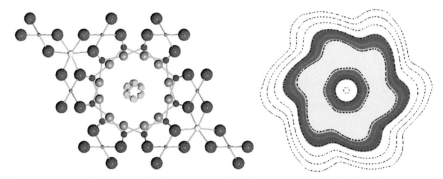

Water rings. A single water molecule can be confined inside a hexagonally shaped channel of the gemstone beryl (left). The light-blue spheres show the positions of one hydrogen atom in a water molecule as it takes on six different rotational orientations simultaneously. Tunneling among these orientations means the hydrogen atom is not located at one position, but smeared out in a ring shape. The right panel has an expanded spatial scale and shows the calculated hydrogen charge density, going from blue (lowest) to yellow (highest). [Credit: A. I. Kolesnikov et al., Phys. Rev. Lett. (2016)]

The structure of the water molecule is "delocalized" and the charge density of each of the two hydrogen atoms is "smeared out into a corrugated ring."

What is perhaps suggested here is that the atomic symmetry of the water molecule is approaching the VE's hexagonal zerophase state in resonance with the hexagonal channel of the beryl crystal, thus shifting from a localized molecular structure to a non-local, simultaneous positioning of the hydrogen atoms within the IVM matrix. Could it be that the atoms are in quantum superposition and they're beginning to exhibit a holographic image of the atoms at each possible location in the VE/beryl symmetry?

Given the characteristics of the VE-IVM as non-local holographic equilibrium, it makes sense that molecular structures such as the water molecules may begin to display these characteristics as they approach the zerophase state.

THE UNIFORMITY OF SNOWFLAKES

Probably the most familiar example of physical symmetry is the six-sided snowflake. Everyone is taught about this beautiful property of water when it freezes around a dust particle at high altitude in the cold air. While it is said that "no two snowflakes are alike," they are nonetheless all hexagonal in their crystalline structures. Obviously this symmetry is anything but random.

In the geometry of the cosmos, the only form in our basic parts kit that has a fundamental 6-fold symmetry is the cuboctahedron, otherwise known as the Vector Equilibrium. The tetrahedron is all triangles (3-fold), the octahedron has triangles and a mid-plane square (3- and 4-fold), the cube is squares (4-fold), and the icosahedron and dodecahedron are triangles and pentagons (3- and 5-fold). (Note that the cube, octahedron and dodecahedron all produce a plane of hexagonal symmetry when properly bisected.)

Could it be that the underlying hexagonal equilibrium within the quantized structure of space itself is harmonically coordinating the symmetry of the snowflakes at our visible fractal scale? Overlaying a few of the above images onto the octave-scaling VE model, the symmetry is quite accurate and suggests that perhaps this is so.

These two show the snowflakes with a distinct 3-octave doubling ratio in their structure:

This one shows a two-octave ratio in the inner structure and then a Phi ratio for the next layer, incorporating both the Binary and Phinary quantized number systems:

And this one displays a remarkable resonance with the 64 Tet structure's symmetry:

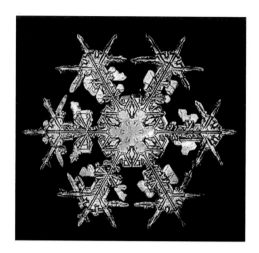 

It certainly appears that snowflakes may be forming their hexagonal crystalline structures in resonance with the underlying IVM symmetry of the cosmos. This may also be true for many crystals that exhibit hexagonal symmetry, as in the case of beryl in the previous example.

Rob Lavinsky, iRocks.com – CC-BY-SA-3.0

GALACTIC SUPERCLUSTERS

From the super-small size of an electron and atom to the visible scale of a snowflake, we now go to a scale beyond comprehension — that of superclusters of galaxies billions of light-years across.

In 1998, E. Battaner and E. Florido published a paper entitled *The egg-carton Universe.*[38] The authors describe an observable *supercluster* network of galaxies (not just individual clusters of galaxies but clusters of clusters!) that clearly defines a fractal octahedral structure on a massive scale. Here is the abstract and illustrations from the paper:

> *"The distribution of superclusters in the Local Supercluster neighbourhood presents such a remarkable periodicity that some kind of network must fit the observed large scale structure. A three dimension chessboard has been suggested. The existence of this network is really a challenge for currently-suggested theoretical models. For instance, CDM models of the formation of the large scale structure predict a random distribution of*

superclusters. If the filaments of matter that are now observed building up the network are fossil relics of over-dense regions of magnetic field energy before Recombination, then it has been shown that the simplest network compatible with magnetic field constraints is made up of octahedra contacting at their vertexes. This suggests a set of superimposed egg-carton structures. Our aim in this paper is to show that the real large-scale structure is actually fitted by the theoretical octahedron structure."

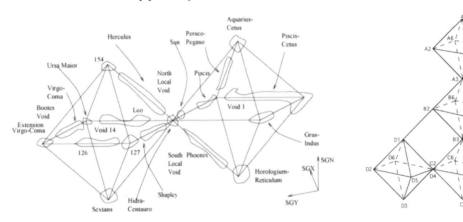

This fractal octahedral arrangement is exactly the same as the IVM's octahedral structure that we saw earlier. It seems the authors are unaware of the IVM cosmometry when they say, "*A three dimension chessboard has been suggested. The existence of this network is really a challenge for currently-suggested theoretical models.*" Seeing this direct correlation to the IVM, though, it seems evident that the structure of galactic superclusters is in symmetrical resonance with the zero-point structure of space at a truly massive scale.

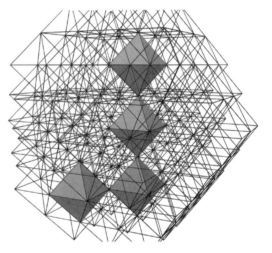

CHAPTER 14
AND SO BEGINS THE COSMIC DANCE

"At the still point of the turning world. Neither flesh nor fleshless;
Neither from nor towards; at the still point, there the dance is,
But neither arrest nor movement. And do not call it fixity,
Where past and future are gathered. Neither movement from nor towards,
Neither ascent nor decline. Except for the point, the still point,
There would be no dance, and there is only the dance."
– T.S Eliot

We might never have imagined that so much could be said about that which is essentially nothing! As the "zero starting point for all happenings and non-happenings," the zerophase equilibrium is so fundamental to our model of fractal-hologramic wholeness that it warrants a comprehensive exploration and is truly the starting place for our journey into cosmometry.

The Vector Equilibrium provides us with a model for the zero reference of all energy dynamics in the universe, the state of zero pulsation wherein all energetic forces are in balanced equilibrium. Remarkably enough, with all that we've explored about it in this Section, *we've so far only covered half the story*. While the VE is indeed the zero reference model, it turns out to be a model of dynamic pulsation as well!

Just as the dynamic pulsation of the universe is meaningless without a zero reference, so too is the zero reference meaningless without pulsation. In the wholeness of cosmic geometry, the VE accommodates both. Not only is it unique in being the only geometric form with equal-length vectors throughout, it is also unique in that the form is able to dynamically pulsate in an oscillating motion and, in so doing, it generates the basis for all form and flow in the cosmos. This pulsating characteristic of the VE was also discovered by Buckminster Fuller, and being as he did so in the era of the 1930's when the Jitterbug dance was popular, he named this dynamic motion after it. The VE is the origin of the cosmic dance of creation and it's called the Jitterbug. Now there's some good cosmic humor for you!

Let's have a look at how this is so…

When we view a model of the VE without its internal radial vectors, we see that it's made up of alternating triangular and square faces.

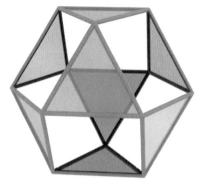

Triangles are inherently stable structures and are the basis for all truly structural form in the cosmos. As such, the eight triangular faces are structurally stable. This is not the case for the square faces, though. Being that squares have no triangulation they are inherently unstable and are therefore considered non-structural in Fuller's synergetic geometry. Due to this instability, the VE is able to collapse at each of these square faces, and as it does so all twelve of its vertices move inward simultaneously towards the center. Here's an illustration of this jitterbug movement from Fuller's *Synergetics*:[39]

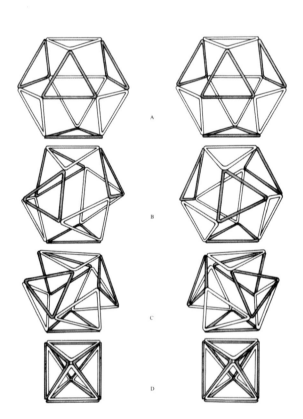

Symmetrical Contraction of Vector Equilibrium: Jitterbug System: If the vector equilibrium is constructed with circumferential vectors only and joined with flexible connections, it will contract symmetrically due to the instability of the square faces. This contraction is identical to the contraction of the concentric sphere packing when its nuclear sphere is removed. This system of transformation has been referred to as the "jitterbug." Its various phases are shown in both left- and right-hand contraction:

A. Vector equilibrium phase: the beginning of the transformation.

B. Icosahedron phase: When the short diagonal dimension of the quadrilateral face is equal to the vector equilibrium edge length, 20 equilateral triangular faces are formed.

C. Further contraction toward the octahedron phase.

D. Octahedron phase: Note the doubling of the edges.

As you can see in the jitterbug sequence, the square faces collapse until the edges come together as in the bottom image. At this point the VE has transformed itself into an Octahedron (right). It is important to note that the VE's form is also known as a cuboctahedron, this being because it has the symmetry of both a cube and octahedron in its outer form such that both of these forms can fit around it, as seen here:

It turns out that the ratio of size between the octahedron that surrounds the open VE and the octahedron that is created when the VE is contracted is 2:1, our familiar octave! Once again this fractal scaling relationship is seen, this time in the dynamic pulsation of the VE.

As is shown in the jitterbug illustration on the previous page, there are other points of symmetry that Fuller calls "phases" that arise as the VE contracts. The first is the **Icosahedron phase**, as seen to the right, which is when the span across the contracting squares is the same length as the VE's vectors.

Further along the transformation is another phase that was originally discovered by Robert Gray,[40] who worked with Fuller and whom we have to thank for transferring the complete text of Fuller's *Synergetics* to digital web pages. This is the **Dodecahedron phase**.

And as we've just seen, the VE has the symmetry of both the **Cube** and **Octahedron** and, as well, it is composed of eight **Tetrahedra**. So this one fundamental form, the VE, is the origin of ALL of the five Platonic Forms! As light-heartedly mentioned earlier, it's the "mom" of cosmometry.

The VE jitterbug motion contracts in both left- and right-handed spiral directions and can dynamically pulsate between the two. This is the basis for all vibratory action that ultimately manifests as the universe as we know it. The zerophase VE pulsates from equilibrium to disequilibrium and back again, passing through the zerophase "nonmoment" with each pulsation. Remember when considering all this that we're talking about *energy patterns* rather than models made of sticks (though quite remarkably, the stick model actually demonstrates this exact energetic dynamic).

So, **the Zerophase equilibrium is the starting-point reference for all form and flow, and the Jitterbug motion is the pulsating disequilibrium that generates all form and flow.** One model encompasses both as a unified dynamic — undivided wholeness in flowing movement. Within the aetheric sea emerge vibrating structures of protons, atoms, molecules, cells… combining in resonant geometric relationships of harmonic proportions throughout the cosmos as a fractal "music of the spheres." The cosmic dance goes on and on as a dynamic flow process at all scales in an eternally regenerative hologram of energy-matter-information in absolute unified integrity.

The cosmic dance goes on and on as a dynamic flow process at all scales in an eternally regenerative hologram of energy-matter-information in absolute unified integrity.

That is our launching point as we move from Starting From Zero to exploring the dynamic Flow Process that is, well… everything.

"Ere long science will give you ample grounds for saying that things are not material, as science will soon see that all things can be reduced to one primal element containing innumerable particles universally distributed, responding to vibratory influences, and all in perfect and absolute equilibrium and balance."
— Attributed to Jesus, from *Life and Teaching of the Masters of the Far East*

Section 2 Endnotes

15   http://www.rwgrayprojects.com/SynergeticsDictionary/SD.html

16   http://synergetics.info/s04/p4000.html#440.01

17   http://www.merriam-webster.com/dictionary/equilibrium

18   Rovelli, Carlo, Vidotto, Francesca, *Planck stars*.
https://arxiv.org/pdf/1401.6562.pdf

19   http://synergetics.info/s04/p4000.html#440.01 (see 440.09)

20   http://synergetics.info/s04/p2000.html#421.00 (see 421.01)

21   http://synergetics.info/s04/p2000.html (see 420.02)

22   http://synergetics.info/s02/p0000.html#216.03

23   Jiang, Yi et al, *Electron ptychography of 2D materials to deep sub-ångström resolution*, Nature International Journal of Science, July 2018.
https://www.nature.com/articles/s41586-018-0298-5

24   Wang, Qingdi, Zhu, Zhen and Unruh, William G., *How the huge energy of quantum vacuum gravitates to drive the slow accelerating expansion of the Universe*.
https://arxiv.org/pdf/1703.00543.pdf and https://arxiv.org/pdf/1401.6562.pdf

25   https://en.wikipedia.org/wiki/Aether_(classical_element)

26   IBID

27   Sinha, K.P. & Sudarshan, E.C.G., *The superfluid as a source of all interactions,* Found Phys (1978) 8: 823.
https://doi.org/10.1007/BF00715056

28   Bohm, David (2012-12-06). *Wholeness and the Implicate Order* (Routledge Classics) (p. 242)

29   http://www.merriam-webster.com/dictionary/information

30   Laszlo, Ervin. *Science and the Akashic Field: An Integral Theory of Everything* (pp. 68-69). Inner Traditions/Bear & Company.

31   "What is the mass of the Universe?", Ask an Astronomer at Cornell University.
http://curious.astro.cornell.edu/about-us/101-the-universe/cosmology-and-the-big-bang/general-questions/579-what-is-the-mass-of-the-universe-intermediate

32   Haramein, N. (2013), A*ddendum to "Quantum Gravity and the Holographic Mass" in view of the 2013 Muonic Proton Charge Radius Measurement*, Hawaii Institute for Unified Physics.
https://resonance.is/research-publications/

33   N Haramein, A K F Val Baker and O Alirol, *The electron and the holographic mass solution*, Hawaii Institute for Unified Physics.
https://resonance.is/research-publications/

34   Early Embryonic Development: The Morula and Blastula, Study.com.
https://study.com/academy/lesson/early-embryonic-development-the-morula-and-blastula.htmll

35   Mecklenburg, Matthew & Regan, B. (2011). *Spin and the Honeycomb Lattice: Lessons from Graphene*. Physical review letters. 106. 116803. 10.1103/PHYSREVLETT.106.116803.
https://journals.aps.org/prl/abstract/10.1103/PhysRevLett.106.116803

36   Kolesnikov, Alexander I. et al, *Quantum Tunneling of Water in Beryl: A New State of the Water Molecule*.
http://journals.aps.org/prl/abstract/10.1103/PhysRevLett.116.167802

37   IBID

38   Battaner, E., Florido, E, *The egg-carton Universe*, Cornell University, February 1998, arXiv.org.
      http://arxiv.org/abs/astro-ph/9802009

39   http://synergetics.info/s04/figs/f6008.html

40   http://www.rwgrayprojects.com/

41   "BOSS Measures the Universe to One-Percent Accuracy", Berkeley Lab, January 2014.
      http://newscenter.lbl.gov/2014/01/08/boss-one-percent/

SECTION 3
FLOW PROCESS

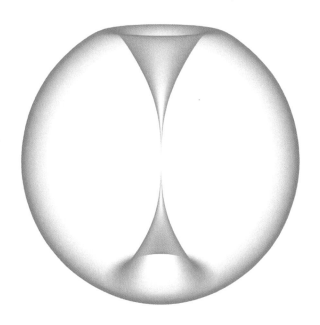

SECTION 3
FLOW PROCESS

When I was 19, I had the good fortune of taking a class in the martial art of Aikido during freshman year at Lewis & Clark College in Portland, Oregon. I had never heard of Aikido, but something about it attracted my interest. Just a couple of weeks before the semester started, I had experienced a spontaneous spiritual awakening that I liken to a "frying pan over the head" moment of realization. It was very simple really — in the midst of an intense emotional frenzy arising from an identity crisis in which I was blaming everyone and everything around me for my woes, a thought managed to surface that burst my victim bubble… "I'm creating the whole thing." Short and to the point, and very potent! In that moment I popped into a state of awareness in which I now knew that there was something bigger going on in life and I wanted to find out more about it. That state of awareness has remained present ever since, though I've also been through the very human experiences of bumbling in the dark along the path of discovery, as it seems we all must do to some degree.

In this state of newly expanded awareness I stepped onto the mat in Aikido class and proceeded to learn some of the most profound knowledge I've encountered even to this day. The instructors were from the Oregon Ki Society[42] (I see they're still teaching nearly 40 years later!), and their branch of the martial art included an emphasis on learning about Ki energy and how to coordinate one's mind and body through the practice of Aikido with Ki awareness. Ki is the Japanese word for the Life Force energy that flows through everything (same as qi or chi in Chinese). The word Aikido means "The way (do) of harmonizing (ai) with the universal life force (ki)." As described in the Introduction of this book, that is exactly the purpose and goal we humans must fulfill at this critical juncture in our evolutionary journey. The principles of Aikido, as both spiritual insight and grounded practice in our daily lives, offer some of the best techniques and methods for achieving this goal. It is, after all, why Morihei Ueshiba founded Aikido in the 1940's. It is often referred to as the Art of Peace.

"Aikido is the Way and Principle of Harmonizing Heaven, Earth and Man"
– Morihei Ueshiba

The first thing one encounters when studying Aikido is that it's a very fluid martial art. It is based upon the principle of non-dissention, meaning that rather than countering an attack with reciprocating conflict (such as punching or kicking), we instead receive the attacker's energy, blend with it, and redirect it into a neutral state that no longer can cause harm (harmonize it with the rest of the universe). The practice of this looks more like a dance than it does a fight, as it is based primarily upon a spiral movement rather than a stance of rigid resistance. At the center of this spiral movement, we were taught in our class, is a point of stillness called the One Point. It is at this still point where we begin our journey into the dynamic Flow Process of the cosmos.

CHAPTER 15
THE ONE POINT

The Cosmic Dance is alive and well! Whether expressed as Aikido, the flamboyant Jitterbug of the '30s, the whirling of Earth through space, the endless spin of a proton… the spiraling choreography of the cosmos is present in everything. As we've just seen in the previous Section, the cosmometric origin of this spiraling dynamic is the Vector Equilibrium as it "jitterbugs" in a pulsating dance of disequilibrium, thus causing the fluctuation of energies we call the observable universe. These "positive and negative asymmetries that propagate the differentials of consciousness" are always-and-only centered by one thing — zerophase stillness. Everything in the universe is manifest around the same still center, and though we might call it by many names, in Aikido class it was taught as the One Point.

The Vector Equilibrium represents a "local" zero reference within the "non-local" Isotropic Vector Matrix, or the universal PSU-IVM field. The VE is, of course, oriented around a single point, what's often called a singularity. In physics, this is the name for a point that has zero-volume in which the energy density (e.g. gravity) goes to infinity. Since every manifest entity has a localized zero reference at its center, we can infer that everything is centered by a singularity. This is, in fact, the premise of unified physics theory.

With this in mind, we can say that **everything, including ourselves, has a direct connection to the fundamental state of unified wholeness at the center of its being**, and as I learned in Aikido class, this is an extremely powerful and stabilizing resource.

The dance of Aikido, as with any dance, is obviously done with our whole body. The energetic center of our physical body is located at a point just below our belly button, midway between our belly and back. This is the One Point in Aikido, and the lower "tan t'ien" in Chinese energy systems. Although there are other such energetic center points in our body, this one is most oriented to our physical being. Take a moment to bring your awareness to this point. Sometimes it helps to put your hands on your belly just below the navel as a guide your mind can tune into.

When learning the art of Aikido, students are taught to "move from your One Point." When we bring our attention to this point in our body and hold it steady while we move about, something quite remarkable happens; we suddenly and effortlessly become phenomenally stable in our body, and therefore we become stable in the world. Simply by using our mind to center our self in this primary point of singularity within our body, it seems that we innately tap into a source of power far greater than we previously knew was available to us. There appears to be a synergetic effect at the ready just from this one extremely simple action — place your attention in the One Point and become physically stabilized. I truly believe that this and the other basic principles of Aikido ought to be taught to children starting at a young age, as it's remarkably empowering on many levels.

> *Simply by using our mind to center our self on this primary point of singularity within our body, it seems that we innately tap into a source of power far greater than we previously knew was available to us.*

Just as the zero-reference is meaningless without dynamic pulsation, so too is the One Point only relevant within the context of a dynamic flow process in which it resides at the center. That flow process is the spiraling motion of Aikido, and it is this combination of the dynamic spiral movement of the body centered by a stable point of singularity that makes the art so powerful and graceful at the same time. As it turns out, this is exactly the way all dynamically flowing processes in the universe attain stability and harmony, and in our quest to find a model that best illustrates this universal dynamic flow process, we find the Torus.

CHAPTER 16
THE TORUS

Hurricanes and tornadoes; whirlpools in water; magnetic fields around Earth, Sun, Saturn; smoke rings and bubble rings; red blood cells; trees, plants and flowers; pinecones, pineapples, apples and oranges; cloud>rain>evaporation>cloud cycles; galaxies… At all scales throughout nature and cosmos we can find the energetic signature of a dynamic flow process in the form of what's called a torus. The torus is for the manifest universe what the VE is for the pre-manifest universe — a form of energy that is fundamental to our overall model of fractal-hologramic cosmometry.

A dictionary defines the word torus as "a doughnut-shaped surface generated by a circle rotated about an axis in its plane that does not intersect the circle."[43]

In simple terms, it's a form that looks like a ring, like this:

What the dictionary definition doesn't indicate is that **a torus is actually a *dynamic flow process* rather than simply a topological surface**. Science has historically leaned towards the concept of "solids" when analyzing the physical universe, hence the description of the torus form based upon surface characteristics. The fact is, whenever we find the form of a torus present in nature, it is due to a dynamic movement of energy rather than a defined surface of a static solid form. A more accurate way of illustrating a torus, then, looks like this:

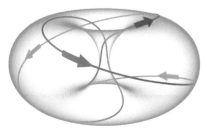

Compare those two images of a torus when you read the first sentence of this chapter again. Every one of the physical phenomena listed there is better illustrated by the dynamic energy movement in the second image than it is by the surface of a solid form as depicted in the first image. In fact, the only torus-shaped object that is appropriately described as being like a doughnut is, well, a doughnut!

From the fluid-dynamic perspective of energetic articulation, when we watch the movement of water, we're actually seeing the fundamental dynamics of space itself, because it's what the water is made of.

Everything that is manifest in the universe is in dynamic motion. Even an apparently motionless rock is made up of atoms that are dynamic in the spinning activity of electrons and nuclei. From Planck to Universal scales, the cosmos is one big ocean of spinning movement. David Bohm called this the Holomovement because, as has been stated numerous times, he describes the true nature of the cosmos as undivided wholeness in flowing movement. His model sees all manifest entities as "temporarily stable abstractions" within a unified sea of energy movement, just as vortices in a river of water can temporarily appear as independent forms while still being completely connected to the entire river of water. The water analogy is really very accurate to illustrate the fundamental dynamics of space at all scales, and this is because it's actually not an analogy at all. From the fluid-dynamic perspective of energetic articulation, when we watch the movement of water, we're *actually seeing the fundamental dynamics of space itself,* because it's what the water is made of.

As described in the previous Section, the so-called vacuum of space is actually filled with a Planck-scale matrix of electromagnetic (EM) energy fluctuations in balanced equilibrium — the PSU-IVM, which more appropriately ought to be called the plenum. This is the superfluid "aether" within which all observable EM energy dynamics (e.g. the observable universe) are "temporarily stable abstractions" of spiraling movement within a current of flow. The PSU-IVM is to the river as energy-matter manifestations at all scales are to the vortices in the river. Water is simply a manifestation of this universal dynamic at a specific density of molecular organization.

As can be seen in the second image on the previous page, the torus is a defined field of energy with two opposing vortexes that converge at the center point of this energy field — our now familiar One Point singularity. There is a dynamic flow process that moves throughout the whole toroidal system wherein the energy moves out one vortex, wraps around the outer boundary that defines the torus form, then moves back into the torus through the other vortex. This creates a reciprocating cycle from center point, outward expansion, generalized distribution throughout the toroidal field and boundary, to contraction back in to the center point. It is a feedback loop process that, as we'll see, is fundamental to the entire mechanism of universal energy-matter-information exchange at all scales.

The expansion/contraction dynamic first showed up in our exploration with the VE's jitterbug motion. It too is a dynamically reciprocating process occurring around a center point. Could it be that the VE jitterbug and torus dynamics are one and the same thing? When we think of the VE as a relationship of energy events (the vertex points of the VE) rather than a structural form (the vector edges of the VE) and imagine the twelve points dynamically moving inward toward the center and back outward to the circumference in rapid oscillation, we can see how this describes a reciprocating toroidal dynamic. The disequilibrious pulsation of the VE manifests into observable reality as a torus flow process in dynamic equilibrium. The VE is still the zerophase reference, and the torus is the manifestation in form of the VE's jitterbug motion as it contracts and expands in a spiraling motion around a localized center point.

It is precisely this relationship that makes the One Point of Aikido so amazingly powerful. The spiraling movement of one's body is the dynamic flow process of the torus expanding and contracting around a zero-reference center point of stillness in the belly that is directly tapped into the universal aetheric energy field.

When we consciously engage the One Point, we're literally harmonizing our personal energetic dynamics with the two primary fundamental patterns of the VE/IVM (as universal equilibrium) and the Torus (as local dynamic equilibrium), the combination of which creates a most powerful stability at the very core of our being. (The same thing happens in two more "one points" located in our heart and head, which we'll explore later in our journey.)

Note that the illustration above shows the VE in its spherical form, what's also known as a Genesa Crystal — what we might consider as the physically manifest version of vector equilibrium. The image to the right shows the two together to highlight the VE symmetry. Dr. Daryl Langham, a plant geneticist, coined the term genesa in the 1940's and said that this form holds *"the full potential for infinite love, for infinite wisdom, for infinite form, for infinite energy, for infinite power, for the Soul, for eternal time, for infinite velocity, for infinite faith. It has all your goals, your desires, your motivations — even life itself."*

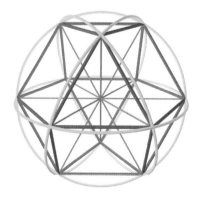

Another way of describing the VE as "the zero starting point for all happenings and non-happenings." It is said that a 24-inch diameter genesa crystal will draw in and condition energy (i.e. create equilibrium) for a radius of two miles. Such a form resides at the center of the Perelandra Center for Nature Research in Virginia, USA,[44] one of my favorite resources for the study of nature intelligence and our cocreative relationship with it.

Expanding on the idea of dynamic toroidal flow centered by stillness, think of the awesome power of a hurricane — a massive vortex of spiraling energy that arises due to the right recipe of temperature, pressure and moisture differentials within a local region of Earth's atmosphere. At its center is stillness, the One Point "eye" of the hurricane. Energy flows cycle upward as warm air and downward as cold air while the entire structure spins with sustained wind speeds ranging from 74 to 156 mph (119-251 km/h) or greater. This highly coherent structure is one of the most powerful forces known to exist on Earth.

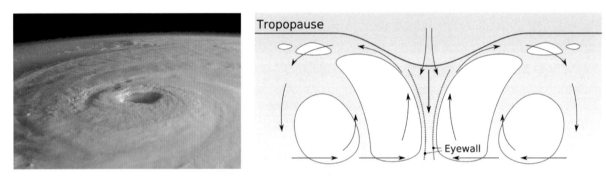

LEFT: Image courtesy of Mike Trenchard, Earth Sciences & Image Analysis Laboratory, Johnson Space Center
RIGHT: By Jannev - Public Domain

As you can see in the illustration, the airflow moves in a toroidal pattern. This is precisely *why* a hurricane is so coherent and stable in its structure — **the flow form of the torus *is the pattern of coherence and stability in dynamically evolving natural systems at all scales*.**

A spiral galaxy, for example, looks very similar to a hurricane, with both exhibiting a vortex pattern around a central axis of spin. Astrophysicists have confirmed the presence of a black hole at the center of galaxies; a fact that Nassim Haramein predicted would be the case well before the first observational confirmations.[45] A black hole is theorized to be a region of space wherein the energy density rapidly converges towards an infinite value — a singularity. While it is typically thought that black holes are a secondary attribute of a galaxy, forming in its center at some point after the initial formation of the galaxy, Haramein's theory turns this idea around.

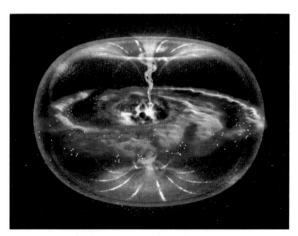

Image courtesy ThriveOn.com

In unified physics, the foundation of all physical form in the cosmos is the PSU-IVM, the ground state level of quantized EM activity that essentially goes to an infinite energy density as it approaches the zerophase state of universal equilibrium at the Planck scale. A black hole's event horizon is the threshold between the convergence towards this zero-point ground state within and the balanced equilibrium of the external object that is centered by the black hole, such as a galaxy (or a star, a planet, an atom, etc.) in relation to the distributed density of the rest of the universe. From this perspective, it is the black hole that is the origin of the form surrounding it, such as a galaxy. The spiraling pattern of a galaxy is a consequence of matter being organized according to the electromagnetic dynamics (i.e. gravitational/mass-energy density gradients) of the space surrounding the black hole, rather than the black hole being a secondary consequence of those dynamics as is theorized in current astrophysical models. With the presence of two "jets" of high-energy EM radiation emitted from the center of a galaxy in alignment with its axis of rotation, we can see quite clearly that a toroidal dynamic is defining the whole structure (as seen in the illustration on the previous page from the film *Thrive*). A galaxy is a coherent and stable structure in the cosmos in the same way that a hurricane is in the atmosphere of Earth, and a hurricane would not form without the presence of its central eye.

The same torus flow process can be seen in many other natural forms, each of which is a fractal expression of the coherence and stability of a dynamic system in balanced equilibrium. These images illustrate the toroidal pattern in an acorn, an apple, a tree, our own human body, and the Earth's magnetic field.

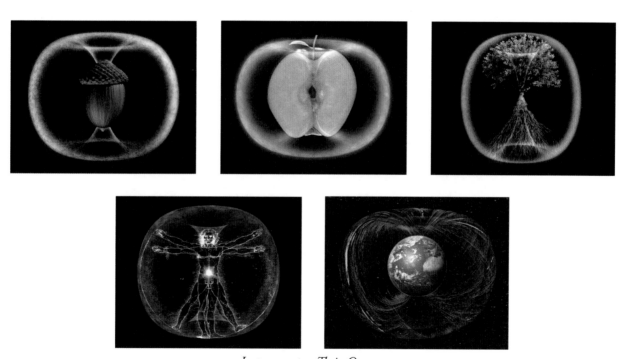

Images courtesy ThriveOn.com

Let's see how the torus fits into our overall model of fractal-hologramic wholeness.

FLOW PROCESS

CHAPTER 17
IT'S TORUSES ALL THE WAY DOWN

A Universe… is a torus.
A Galaxy… is a torus.
A Star… is a torus.
A Planet… is a torus.
A Tree… is a torus.
A Human… is a torus.
An Acorn… is a torus.
A Cell… is a torus.
A Proton... is a torus.
A PSU… is a torus.

There is an anecdote in the field of cosmology about an old woman who stands up at the end of a scientific lecture and proclaims it to be rubbish, saying that the Earth is flat and it sits on top of a turtle. When asked by the presenter what the turtle is standing on, she replies with an air of the obvious, "It's turtles all the way down!"

The unending nature of this argument (i.e. when do we get to the last turtle?) is called the infinite regress problem. If the validation of each iteration is justified based upon the next iteration, there can potentially be an infinite number of iterations. While the nature of this problem is evident and the old woman's reply does not ultimately satisfy as an answer, it does in fact point us in the right direction when considering the overall dynamic integrity of the cosmos across all scales (though to say it's "tortoises" all the way down may be more poetically appropriate in rhyme, if not reason).

The holomovement is a seamlessly unified flow of ever-manifesting-and-unmanifesting activity throughout the entire physical and metaphysical cosmos (i.e. both matter and mind alike). This cosmic flow spans all scales large and small and operates in coherence and integrity throughout. When considering a mechanism by which this coherent integrity can operate across such a vast range of activity, the model that best lives up to the challenge is the dynamic flow process of the torus.

The Fractal Principle of cosmometry simply states that the same pattern is repeated at all scales. In order to do so, there of course needs to be a pattern. While there are many ways we can view the characteristics of movement and flow in nature and the celestial realms, when we "stand back far enough" we can see that they typically resolve into the fundamental pattern of a torus. For example, the spiraling weather patterns on Earth are in part due to Coriolus forces that arise from the sheering interaction of less-dense air with the spinning movement of the more-dense Earth. When viewed locally, we see directional wind currents, high- and low-pressure areas, storm fronts, etc. When we get back far enough and view the movements as a whole, we find that they exhibit an overall torus pattern as the airflow moves from the poles to the equator and back again, as shown in this illustration:

 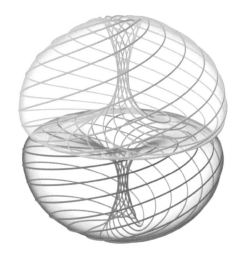

Image courtesy ThriveOn.com

In this case we see a torus flow pattern in each Northern and Southern Hemisphere, making what's called a dual torus system, which arises as a natural consequence of Coriolus forces present in all spinning objects that exhibit fluid dynamics. This is why we see bands and swirls on Jupiter, the distribution of sunspots above and below the solar equator, and the accretion discs of Saturn and other planets, as well as galaxies. The dual torus is a common attribute of fluid dynamic systems, even if sometimes all that we can see is the aggregation of matter at the intersection of the two tori, such as with spiral galaxies.

European Space Agency (ESA)

The torus dynamic is also embeddable, one within another. In the example above, we have a torus flow weather pattern at the scale of Earth's atmosphere. Within that we can have another one at the scale of a hurricane. We can even imagine that within the hurricane is a whirlpool of water as it flows down a street drain. This, too, is one vortex in an overall larger toroidal flow process (though the shape of the torus is not as evident, it is the same dynamic). We now have three iterations of tori nested at different scales. We can also extend this nesting outward with larger torus fields, beginning with Earth's magnetic field. The hemispheric weather torus, hurricane torus, and street drain torus are all nested within it. Earth's torus magnetic field is embedded within the much larger torus magnetic field of the Sun, and it, in turn, is embedded in the galaxy's torus magnetic field…

It is this fractal embedding of tori that allows for the complex dynamics of the holomovement to seamlessly flow as both discrete forms (the individual tori) and together as a unified whole.

As you can see, the pattern of the torus is repeated at all scales in a fractal embedding, one within another. It is this fractal embedding of tori that allows for the complex dynamics of the holomovement to seamlessly flow as both discrete forms (the individual tori) and together as a unified whole. This is exactly the same relationship of undivided wholeness in flowing movement that we saw in the example of whirlpools in a river, though in this case as nested fractals, rather than vortices in a stream.

Although highly simplistic in its portrayal of what the above is describing, the image to the right conveys the idea of nested tori across scales.

Extending this idea to the extremes of scale, the torus may well be an appropriate model for both the Planck Spherical Unit and the Universe as a whole. If so, then from macro to micro, it's nested tori all the way down.

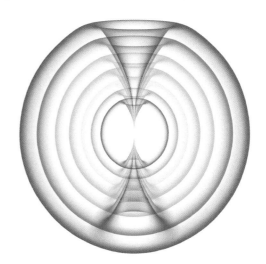

"*The self in a toroidal Universe can be both separate and connected with everything else.*"
– Arthur Young

CHAPTER 18
FEATURES OF DYNAMIC WHOLENESS

In humanity's pursuit of harmonizing with the cosmos, establishing equilibrium and wholeness are of primary concern. Chaotic and fragmented systems yield like experiences of their own making, and these are very much what we are living with in our current social, economic, political, academic, medical, agricultural, environmental and even technological systems. By understanding the qualities of wholeness in dynamic equilibrium found in the torus we have an excellent checklist with which we can measure the integrity of our designs to bring these systems into a balanced and harmonious, and therefore stable, state. Each system can be seen as a toroidal flow process when viewed in its optimal operation, and all of them operating optimally together will inevitably create a profound synergetic wholeness that will naturally and quickly bring humanity into a harmonious relationship with the greater reality of life. The torus flow process is the best model for what dynamic wholeness looks like, and thanks to the innovative work of a few researchers, we have clear insight into the features that describe this flow process, which can aid the design of any and all of our essential systems and technologies.

As mentioned in the previous Section, around the same time I met Nassim Haramein I also met another pioneer in the study of nature's fundamental patterns of wholeness and integrity — Foster Gamble. Since the age of 14, Foster has been researching both the theory and application of the principles and patterns upon which nature establishes and maintains healthy and balanced living systems. He, too, studied Aikido and taught it for many years, and found primary inspiration in the ideas of Buckminster Fuller, as well as Arthur Young (with whom he worked closely for a time), Walter Russell, and many other researchers and innovators.

Along with his wife and creative partner, Kimberly Carter Gamble, Foster created the documentary film, *Thrive: What On Earth Will It Take?* [46] (of which I am an Associate Producer). In simple terms, *Thrive* explores the root causes of global crises we are facing today, and offers a practical path towards solutions based upon understanding and application of fundamental patterns inherent in healthy and regenerative natural systems. The two primary patterns in the Thrive Solutions Model are the 12-around-1 equilibrium of the VE and the dynamic flow process of the Torus. More than anyone I know, Foster is an advocate for the torus as *the* model upon which we can base the design of our technological and social systems in the pursuit of harmonizing with nature and the cosmos.

With my early exposure to Aikido and years of personal practice with a jo staff (a martial arts weapon made from a wooden staff about 50" in length), I had come to realize that the torus is indeed a primary pattern of dynamic flow. I had also been sparked by an inner vision when I was 21 (which I'll describe in the next section) that inevitably led me to contemplation of nature's patterns and greater awareness of the torus, but it was upon meeting Foster (and Nassim around the same time) that the full import of this simple form became clear. Much of the features of dynamic wholeness that follow come from my exposure to his insights and knowledge, as well as those of Nassim, Elisabet Sahtouris, Duane Elgin and others. As you read them, keep in mind how they can be related to systems of any kind when they're in a healthy living process, rather than just describing the dynamics of a torus.

FEATURE:

A torus is made from the medium in which it exists.

A torus is a *dynamic flow process*, not an object. It is an organized and coherent movement of energy within a given medium. A smoke ring is a good example. It's a swirling circle of smoke and air that moves in a defined and stable form. A bubble ring in water is very similar, being made of a swirling circle of water with air inside. It maintains its shape with remarkable definition, and even exhibits the quality of moving through the water sideways without immediately rising to the surface, as is the case with regular bubbles in water. A hurricane is composed of air, water, temperature and pressure, all combined to form a coherent and highly stable spinning structure. In these cases, the dynamic flow of the torus is clearly visible. In others, such as with apples, oranges, cacti, trees, even us humans, its presence is more tangibly represented by the structure, shape, and surface patterns of the objects, as well as the less visible energy flows that inform and integrate them (i.e. sunlight and water intake and respiration in plants; food and elimination cycles in animals). In still other cases, it's the dynamic processes of a whole system that exhibit torus flow, such as found in ecosystems, water cycles, weather patterns, biological systems, etc. The torus pattern is evident, yet it's made up of the specific medium in which it is present. From a design perspective, the flow process of a torus can be conceptually applied to any dynamic system so as to most closely align that system with nature's pattern of coherent wholeness. Imagine an economic system that is modeled upon toroidal flows, for example.

FEATURE:

A torus is self-generating and sustaining.

The simultaneous outward-inward flow of a torus is the key dynamic that defines and sustains its form. When the energy in a system becomes too weak and this dynamic no longer functions with sufficient continuity, the system inevitably collapses. This is obvious when we watch a smoke ring slowly decrease its toroidal spin to a point at which it suddenly dissolves and the smoke dissipates more randomly into the air. The same principle applies to the integrity of an ecosystem. If the in and out flows of a system — such as sunlight and water in plants, or viable food supplies in a habitat — become too diminished, the health and sustainability of the system deteriorates. An economic system is really no different. A healthy living system always displays self-generative attributes of a torus flow process.

FEATURE:

Information and resources are distributed throughout the whole system.

A toroidal flow process has integrity when the movement of energy is present throughout the whole system. Put your finger in a part of a smoke ring and it will immediately lose its circular shape and disperse into the surrounding air. This is because the disruption of flow in one area affects the integrity of the whole. There is no 50% operational torus where the top half is fine but the bottom is not. It's 100% or it falls apart. This would ultimately hold true for the atmospheric and ocean currents on Earth, for example. Too much pollution in either may ultimately affect their toroidal circulation, compromising the integrity of those systems.

When the dynamic flow of energy is seen as information and resources, it's easy to see how quickly a system can collapse when the integrity of its wholeness is compromised by impediment or constriction. Conversely, it's also easy to see how readily a system will come into balanced wholeness when information and resources are flowing freely throughout the whole system. In our present day, nearly every essential system of human endeavor is operating with impediment and constriction, rather than a balanced distribution throughout the whole. It's not hard to see how belief and action based on domination and control for maintaining one's personal and cultural survival has set these compromised dynamics in place. Shifting our worldview to one where wholeness is primary at all scales — from individual, family, community, region, to continental and global — is imperative to establishing healthy living systems, and the distribution of information and resources throughout is a key to engendering this shift.

Shifting our worldview to one where wholeness is primary at all scales from individual, family, community, region, to continental and global, is imperative to establishing healthy living systems, and the distribution of information and resources throughout is a key to engendering this shift.

FEATURE:

Feedback is intrinsic.

As described in Chapter 16, the flow process of a torus exhibits a reciprocating cycle from center point, outward expansion, distribution throughout the toroidal field, and return back in to the center point. This is exactly the nature of a feedback loop, and it is in some ways the most important attribute of a torus and of the nature of the cosmos as a whole.

A feedback loop occurs when energy (or information) is expressed outwardly from a source and returns into that source to be fed back through the system again. An obvious (and sometimes painful) example of a feedback loop is the intense screech of an audio sound system when a microphone is placed in front of a speaker. Sound is picked up by the mic, amplified through the speaker, and then picked up by the mic again and fed back into the speaker… In a fraction of a second this feedback cycle goes from zero to excruciating as a high-pitched squeal causes everyone in nearby proximity to cover their ears as quickly as possible. As not fun as this is, it's a great example of the presence and power of a feedback loop gone wild. Fortunately, nature's feedback loops are more manageable in general (though they too can spin up quickly, such as in the cases of tornadoes and hurricanes).

As it turns out, **feedback is intrinsic to the dynamic functioning of the entire cosmic phenomenon**. In Chapter 11 we briefly touched into the hologramic nature of protons and how the information inside them is equal to the information outside them. Unified physics proposes that the information of *every* proton (location, atomic and molecular interactions, angular momentum, etc.) is present within *each* proton, and they're all communicating instantaneously through a universal wormhole network that connects them through the PSU "aether field". The local characteristics of an individual proton are radiated out to inform the whole, which then incorporates this information in relationship to all protons simultaneously, and then the information of the whole is fed back into the originating proton, which then adapts its behavior according to the feedback of the whole. Nassim Haramein calls this a feedback/feedforward loop. This holofractal dynamic is happening at every scale of physical manifestation, as every manifest entity is composed of an aggregate of protons within atoms within molecules, etc. As such, a dynamic feedback loop is intrinsic to the entire cosmic experience, which makes sense when we consider that it's highly likely that such a mechanism would be present within the seamlessly integrated whole system we call Universe. While this may challenge the ideas of reductionist scientists who hold that randomness is intrinsic and there is no such higher-level function of order, it's not too surprising that it would be overlooked when analysis is focused on parts (fundamental particles) rather than wholes (fundamental patterns).

The torus is a fundamental pattern of wholeness as a flow process that exhibits a reciprocal out-in-out-in exchange of energy-matter-information fractally embedded across all scales micro to macro. The feedback/feedforward mechanism maintains cosmic integrity as galaxies, stars, planets, humans, cells, atoms share a nested toroidal flow coordinating local conditions at each scale with universal conditions throughout all scales. Imagine applying this idea to something like our modern-day media systems. Presently our mainstream media channels are pretty much a highly filtered one-way agenda, the primary feedback of which is called consumerism. The Internet, on the other hand, is very close to achieving this idea, yet there are impediments and constrictions imposed by both the quest for control and dominance, as well as the lack of a clear model of harmonious wholeness that inhibit its fulfillment. Fortunately, there are innovators who understand this model of wholeness actively seeking to design new systems that can bring the medium (the media) into alignment with this cosmic feedback/feedforward principle. It's easy to see how profound a shift it will bring for the advancement of humankind and our relationship to life on Earth and beyond when we have an accurate and ongoing feedback mechanism in place.

This feature of intrinsic feedback is closely related to the concept of Reciprocal Relation between the Implicate and Explicate Orders as proposed by physicist David Bohm, which we'll explore in the next chapter.

FEATURE:

A torus is both autonomous and integrated with its environment.

As we've touched upon a few times, a torus or vortex is both a distinct entity unto itself and a seamless part of a larger system, such as are whirlpools in water. Ultimately that larger system is the entire Universe (which itself is likely a torus within an even larger system, a metaverse), and yet for practical application of this principle it's more useful to "think locally." Imagine the town or city you live in. It has a distinct area that defines its boundaries between "inside" and "outside". These are, of course, conceptual boundaries that generally permit inflow and outflow of people, goods, resources, currency, ideas, etc. Within this defined area are systems of governance, education, commerce and security that are intended to operate on behalf of the town or city as a whole, and to do so autonomously as much as possible. They are located, though, within a larger area called your state, province or country, themselves defined by the same concepts of boundaries and social systems. There is a fractal scaling of dynamic systems of flow and function in these embedded structures, with each entity (town, city, state, province, country) seeking autonomy in its operating processes while innately being connected to larger systems (as well as connected town-to-town through these larger systems). In the optimal functioning of a healthy living system as modeled on torus flow dynamics, this kind of autonomy at each level is what engenders integrity for the interconnected whole.

The previous features all come into play here to make this work. When a given level (such as a town or city) is self-generating, shares information and resources throughout, and has accurate and continuous feedback about its strengths and weaknesses, it has the opportunity to operate autonomously in pursuit of its own integrity of wholeness. When this is achieved it becomes empowered to regulate its own dynamics of complexity while being appropriately coordinated with the dynamics of the larger environment in which it exists. It becomes a healthy part of a larger whole, able to negotiate its own interests in right relationship with those of the other parts and the whole that they all comprise — wholes within wholes. This is, in fact, the way our bodies operate when in optimal health. It is this kind of empowerment through autonomous self-generation, self-regulation, coordination, resource sharing, reciprocity and feedback at all scales that makes for a vibrant and healthy flow process, the hallmark of a whole system in balanced equilibrium.

These features offer a mere glimpse into the breadth and depth of how the dynamics of the torus can inform our pursuit of harmonizing the systems we create with the rest of nature and the cosmos. The features and principles of healthy systems as fundamental attributes of a living universe have been extensively considered by Elisabet Sahtouris,[47] Duane Elgin[48] and others. Application of these principles to the design of our human systems is of paramount importance to our evolutionary success at this critical juncture in our shared journey.

FLOW PROCESS

CHAPTER 19
IMPLICATE AND EXPLICATE ORDER
IN RECIPROCAL RELATION

American physicist, David Bohm, was the most avid early proponent of a holographic model of the universe. Highly respected in the physics community and a leading pioneer of plasma physics, he was also seen as a renegade whose thinking outside the typical closed-system box gave him a unique perspective that was free to explore every assumption of physics with fresh eyes. Bohm spanned a wide range of research and philosophical inquiry, including collaborating closely with Karl Pribram in his consideration of the brain's functioning as a holographic field phenomenon, and exploring esoteric and spiritual dialogues with both J. Krishnamurti and His Holiness the Dalai Lama. For Bohm, cosmic wholeness was the primary context in which to investigate the principles of physics, and this wholeness was (is) of a seamlessly and totally unified nature, which, as previously mentioned, he called the Holomovement. The cosmos is to be seen as a wholly unified and continuously emergent flow of energy, meaning and consciousness.

In Bohm's theory, ever-emergent holomovement has two primary domains within which it orders and organizes itself — the pre-manifest, unseen, background field called the **Implicate Order**, and the manifest, experiential foreground field called the **Explicate Order**, which is the cosmos as we know it. He likened the Implicate as an immense underlying sea of energy and information, and the Explicate (specifically, the quantum activity) as an excitation of small waves rippling upon its surface. Sound familiar? Using the water analogy again, one could accurately equate this to a literal ocean of water with an immense unified ordering process (ocean currents) underlying a constantly moving surface of waves and interference patterns.

These two realms, the implicate and explicate, are in what Bohm called **Reciprocal Relation**, with each one informing and influencing the other in the ongoing manifestation process. At the quantum level, sub-atomic particles (electrons, for example) flicker in and out of existence at a very high rate, emerging into the explicate and returning into the implicate. As they do, the information gained by the particle while in the explicate manifest state is carried back (enfolds) into the implicate state, influencing the underlying totality of background information in its ordering process. The implicate, in turn, influences the energy and information of the particle as it re-emerges (unfolds) into the explicate manifest state, influencing and changing its ordering process... and on and on it goes. In Bohm's words:

> *"Rather than suggesting a continuous entity that moves "through" time and space, the image of ordered enfoldment-unfoldment allows for a view of the electron as a perpetually emerging explicate structure, temporarily unfolding from an ordered implicate background, and then rapidly enfolding back into this background, in an ongoing cycle. By extension, the whole of experience can be understood as a flow of appearances resulting from such a cycle of enfoldment and unfoldment."* [49]

This enfolding-unfolding reciprocal information exchange occurs in nested scales of mutual influence, *"even between macroscopic processes and those at the atomic level, indicating the complexity of the pathways through which the qualitative infinity of nature may manifest."* [50] The dynamic flow process of the torus is an excellent model to depict this reciprocal relationship and nested mutual influence.

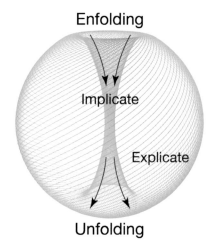

From all that we've explored to this point, it's possible to equate Bohm's Implicate Order to the ground state PSU-IVM holofield and the Explicate Order to the dynamic toroidal fluctuations that comprise experiential reality. The totality of the hologramic Implicate Order (the Absolute Hologram) informs the locally expressed forms of the Explicate Order (the Relative Hologram) in a feedback/feedforward exchange of reciprocal relation in nested fields of mutual influence. Bohm's model fits well in our emerging cosmometry model and the theories of unified physics.

Upon deep analysis of the apparently inexhaustible variety of qualities of nature, Bohm saw no reason to limit the potential for new qualities to innovate at any time and any scale and dimension of physical and metaphysical reality. This is what he called the **Qualitative Infinity of Nature**. Because of this infinite creative potential of the cosmos, Bohm allowed for all so-called scientific laws and fundamental principles (that are held to be sacrosanct by academics and scientists) to have the potential to be transcended and made obsolete by the emergence of a new qualitative context. The speed of light may be held as an absolute universal constant in a relativistic context, with nothing able to travel faster than it, yet in a holographic context, the potential is present for superluminal, and even instantaneous, information exchange, as is now experimentally proven in the study of quantum entanglement.

> *"I would say that in my scientific and philosophical work, my main concern has been with understanding the nature of reality in general and of consciousness in particular as a coherent whole, which is never static or complete but which is an unending process of movement and unfoldment...."* – David Bohm, *Wholeness and the Implicate Order*

CHAPTER 20
TAPPING THE SOURCE AT THE CENTER

Protons spin, and spin, and spin, and spin… forever, as far as we know. To date there is no experimental evidence of a proton decaying. Although there are theories that attempt to predict that they ought to, not one of them has led to an experiment that proves them to be correct. In our current models of physical reality at the atomic level, there is nothing of any tangible consequence to suggest that protons will be disappearing from the universe any time soon. In fact, the proposed estimates for the *half-life* of a proton are in the range of 10^{34} to 10^{36} years;[51] the estimated age of the universe itself is a mere fraction of this time at 10^9 years. While it seems to be met with a rather large degree of oversight in the general field of scientific inquiry, **the fact that protons seem to be spinning without an end in sight is certainly one of the most remarkable attributes of the cosmos**!

In physics, the Laws of Thermodynamics generally state that every dynamic system loses energy through a variety of factors, such as friction that causes heat, and eventually succumb to increasing entropy until the system collapses in a state of chaotic disintegration.

Apparently, protons didn't get this memo.

The Conservation Laws also state that energy can neither be created nor destroyed, only transformed from one state to another, and that because of entropy (i.e. heat loss), we'll always get out less energy from a system than was put into the system. From all that we can tell, it seems protons didn't get this memo either. Protons have been spinning forever and they have never slowed down.

These laws of physics are based upon a concept invented by scientists called a "closed system" wherein the experimental parameters are within rigorously defined limits, outside of which there is no relevant influence upon the system. In the closed system model, the Laws of Thermodynamics hold true, and they've proven very useful in the engineering of technologies to predict the efficiency of a given system relative to energy input-output ratios (with output always less than input). Well, it seems the deviant proton hasn't much concern for such notions, as it appears there is no consideration of energy input-output differences at this most fundamental level of physical reality. They just keep going and going and going. How could this be the case in the face of the tried-and-true Laws of Thermodynamics? Obviously, there's something different going on at the atomic level that does not adhere to the physics of a closed system. Or so it seems.

In current models of the cosmos, space is generally considered to be an empty vacuum; therefore, there is only the energy of atoms and photons of light available for the ongoing process of manifestation and transformation of the physical universe. All of the energy-matter that is going to be created has been created and is simply changing from one form to another. That's all there is and all there will ever be, like it or not. This model has recently hit a rather large wall, though, as physicists have come to realize that the observable universe as we know it comprises only about 4% of what it takes for it to work the way it does. In other words, the observable and measurable energy-matter dynamics of the total universe are not sufficient to describe the behavior of the whole system. Something unseen and undetectable is needed in order for it to behave the way it does, otherwise galaxies would spin differently than they do or even fly apart due to their spin forces, and the universe would not be expanding the way it apparently is. These unseen forces that comprise the other 96% of the universe are known, of course, as Dark Matter and Dark Energy. Dark Matter is needed to add the gravitational force that holds together a spinning galaxy, and Dark Energy is needed to provide an accelerating push to the expanding universe that overcomes the collective gravitational pull of all of the galaxies, which should otherwise slow it down and lead towards contraction.

The model we're exploring based upon unified physics turns this whole idea inside out. Space is actually a vast source of energy out of which the 4% universe as we know it is emerging.

A model of empty space will come up empty handed (an all too literal pun, I know) when attempting to explain where this other 96% of the universe comes from. As we've hypothesized, though, space is not an empty vacuum; it's an unfathomably abundant plenum! It's so abundant, in fact, that the idea of it has long been rejected because it doesn't match experimentally observable reality (though proof of the Casimir Effect[52] suggests otherwise, potentially demonstrating the influence of quantum vacuum fluctuations upon the physical world, and even producing photons from the plenum though the Dynamical Casimir Effect[53]).

The model we're exploring based upon unified physics turns this whole idea inside out. Space is actually a vast source of energy *out of which* the 4% universe as we know it is emerging. Not only is there room for 96% more energy-matter potential in it, there's far greater than that. Remember, in just a *single cubic centimeter* of space there's an estimated 10^{93} grams of quantum vacuum energy density, with the entire observable universe having an estimated mass of only 10^{55} grams. So, there's a lot of headroom available from an energy-potential standpoint when viewed from this perspective. We can see why early researchers in quantum physics felt the need to remove these large values from their equations for what was deemed "empty" space (which were actually called "nasty infinities" because the energy density of 10^{93} is a renormalized value of what otherwise goes to infinity) and put boxes around systems in order to close them to derive workable laws. Since this vast energy potential couldn't be detected, it generally wasn't incorporated, even though the theoretical models being used indicated its presence.

The Planck-scale electromagnetic oscillations that make up the PSU-IVM field are indeed way out of the range of experimental detection, as we've seen earlier, yet there isn't anything to contradict the theory that they are there. With this Planck field as the ground state energy potential (in zerophase equilibrium), we can then begin to consider the *resonant harmonics* (like in music, noted here) of energy dynamics that emerge from this source potential and come into form as electromagnetic fluctuations (detectable across the EM spectrum), atomic and molecular structures (which are electromagnetic interactions), and the macro structures we're familiar with in our physical reality — the 4% observable universe.

Which brings us back to the proton and its endless spin. While researchers are diligently attempting to find some indication that they're decaying, the pesky protons keep indicating that they're not. And since protons are what make up the 4% universe, perhaps it's useful to consider why this is so, and just how they tap into enough energy to spin through existence while seemingly disobeying the Laws of Thermodynamics.

In unified physics theory, protons are an aggregation of Planck Spherical Units (PSUs) co-moving within a compact spherical structure. It's best not to imagine a proton as a solid particle, but rather as a spinning vortex within the surrounding PSU ocean — as a torus, in fact. This torus is at a size that balances the internal energy density of the proton with the external energy density of the universe, as we saw in Chapter 11. It is a fundamental harmonic on the electromagnetic scale from Planck to Universe that is the resonant balance point between the two; a toroidal sphere in the fractally embedded cosmic music of the spheres.

A torus is made from the medium in which it exists, and in this case the proton torus is made of electromagnetic energy internally, at its surface, and in the surrounding EM field. As such, it is tapped directly into the source potential of the entire universe — the zero-point PSU-IVM holofield. The toroidal vortices converge at a point of singularity that taps the infinite potential of the holofield, which is already moving at the speed of light (since it is light), and this zero-point movement spins the proton with an inexhaustible supply of energy. As well, there is no friction to introduce entropy since it's in a state of superfluid superconductivity, therefore it just keeps spinning and spinning and spinning...

Given this model, we can see that, despite appearances, the Conservation Laws are not being violated. A proton isn't spinning endlessly without a known energy source; it's spinning endlessly within a vast energy source from which it (and therefore the entire universe) is manifest — an energy source that until now was unacknowledged or unknown. Protons are resonant harmonic oscillators that tap this vast energy source directly without the detriment of mechanical components that give rise to friction, heat and entropy, as is the case with our modern energy-generating technologies. Can the proton serve as a model for us to base new energy-generating technologies on? Can we, at our scale of experience within the grand cosmic scheme, do the same thing that the protons are doing without violating the Conservation Laws?

The answer seems self-evident at this point: why not! Why couldn't we apply the same concept to the development of technologies that create a toroidal field of electromagnetic energy spinning at a high frequency that is a resonant harmonic of the PSU-IVM energy potential so as to induce a current that taps this cosmic source and converts the zerophase potential into a dynamic local energy source? There is no reason why not, and in fact, it is purportedly being done in laboratories around the world (and if we're lucky (or just smart), we'll see these zero-point energy devices emerging into the world before too long).

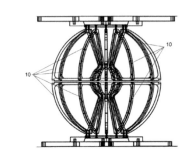

While it's not the purpose of this presentation to provide technical specifications for these new energy technologies, searching online can yield a wealth of information, and you can also review the patent for Nassim Haramein's *Device and Method for Simulation of Magnetohydrodynamics*,[54] which is specifically modeled upon this exact toroidal fluctuation dynamic interacting with the underlying electromagnetic holofield. Across the board, it is not surprising to find that nearly all of the designs for such technologies are based upon the torus.

Imagine having a small device that generates unlimited, non-polluting energy for your home with no dependency upon an extensive and vulnerable power grid. Imagine having cars, planes, trains (and even extraterrestrial transportation vehicles!) that never need refueling. Imagine all of your electronic devices operating continuously without need of recharging or being plugged in. It's truly a new paradigm of sourcing energy that is literally at our fingertips.

Schematic and 3D rendering of Haramein's Harmonic Flux Resonator

With the advent of energy-generating technologies based upon the torus flow process in resonance with the vast energy potential of the plenum, humanity will have taken a massive step towards harmonizing with the cosmos. The shift from burning, exploding and fissuring of non-renewable, polluting and radioactive materials, to tapping the source directly to access unlimited energy with no detrimental waste material is profound to say the least. Every aspect of our society will be affected when we realize there is no shortage whatsoever of the most essential component of our technological and social systems — energy. And our shared worldview will make a dramatic shift from one based upon scarcity, domination and control (which have led to our current systemic crises), to one based upon abundance, distribution and cooperation — the attributes of a healthy living system as modeled by the torus.

As pie-in-the-sky as all this may sound, and as outside the Laws of Thermodynamics the zero-point technologies may seem, perhaps this conceptual overview of the cosmometry and physics of toroidal resonance will provide a logical foundation upon which to see the merit of applying cosmomimicry of the endlessly flowing energy of a proton to our own energy generating capacities.

And what about Dark Matter and Dark Energy? How do they fit into this picture?

Dark Matter is the name given to a hypothetical form of matter that is required to account for the gravitational spin dynamics of galaxies, altogether comprising approximately 85% of the mass of the universe. In the unified physics model, this mass (and its associated gravitational effect) is attributed to the spin of the co-moving Planck field that makes up the galaxy — the non-visible and undetectable PSU's (the volume information or entropy) that are co-moving in a vortex centered by singularity, a small portion of which (surface information or entropy) we see as baryonic matter — the galaxy. As a simple analogy, imagine spinning a cup of coffee with a spoon, then adding milk. Before you add the milk, you don't see the water molecules spinning in a vortex. Adding the milk makes the spin visible. Analogous to the galactic model, the milk represents the visible matter of the galaxy and the coffee represents the co-rotating Planck field, which altogether combine to create a tensegrity effect that accounts for the total gravitational dynamic. The curvature of the PSU aether field comprising the total galactic volume produces gravitational effects, as does the matter we observe as the galaxy.

Dark Energy is the name given to an unknown energy source that is needed to account for the accelerating expansion of the universe, as seen in astrophysical observation. This energy is required to overcome the collective gravitational pull of all the galaxies, which should otherwise slow the expansion and end up in a universal contraction, leading to the "Big Crunch". The unified physics model offers a theory for the origin of both dark energy and dark matter, as well as for the so-called Big Bang that started everything in motion in our universe in the first place.

In their 2019 paper (originally presented in 2015 at the Royal Society in England) entitled *Resolving the Vacuum Catastrophe: A Generalized Holographic Approach*,[55] Haramein and Dr. Amira Val Baker resolve the long-standing problem of the 122 orders of magnitude difference between the vacuum density at the quantum scale and the vacuum density at the cosmological scale, informally known as the "vacuum catastrophe". Their premise is quite simple: imagine taking a proton and expanding it to the size of the observable universe. The Planck density inside the proton (10^{55} grams/proton volume) becomes universally distributed, and when the density is recalculated, the result is approximately 26.5% of the critical density, which is the percentage assigned to dark matter (i.e. dark matter is 26.8% of the critical density). Thus, dark matter is essentially the volume entropy of the universe in terms of PSUs.

Next, Haramein and Val Baker calculate the surface entropy when expanding a Planck voxel (PSU) to the size of the universe. Obviously, the surface entropy increases while the density decreases. When the density is calculated at the scale of the observable universe, they find an exact solution for the critical density. So, essentially, the volume entropy gives dark matter and the surface entropy gives the critical density, with the difference between the two being dark energy.

Now imagine a proton escaping the outer boundary of our universe. When it exits the cosmological density, it is no longer in a state of near equilibrium between its internal 10^{55} gram holographic mass and the 10^{55} gram universal mass. The internal pressure would instantly cause it to rapidly expand, forming a new universe — the conditions for what we call the Big Bang. In such a case, the universe is expanding because of a pressure gradient that is still in the process of equalizing.

Additionally, both Haramein and cosmologist Jude Currivan propose that there is an informational aspect of universal expansion, wherein the total information content of the universe is constantly increasing, thus requiring a growing volume of pixelated spacetime within which to accommodate this informational evolution. Currivan goes so far as to restate the Laws of Thermodynamics as Laws of Infodynamics, summarized in her paper, *A New INSCIght of INformational SCIence* (paraphrased here from the original text):

Restating the 1ˢᵗ Law of Thermodynamics to a 1ˢᵗ Law of Infodynamics

The 1ˢᵗ Law of Thermodynamics states that the total energy of a closed system is conserved. Given the hypothesis that our Universe is a closed/isolated system, and that energy and matter are equivalent ($E=mc^2$), then the total energy-matter of our Universe is conserved. As Quantum Theory is a description of universal and quantised energy-matter, this is its most simple and generalized statement.

And, given that information is physically real and can be expressed as energy-matter, then information expressed as the energy-matter of our Universe is universally conserved, leading to the 1ˢᵗ Law of Infodynamics, which states that information expressed as the total and quantised energy-matter of our Universe is conserved.

Restating the 2ⁿᵈ Law of Thermodynamics to a 2ⁿᵈ Law of Infodynamics

*The 2ⁿᵈ Law of Thermodynamics states that the total entropy of a closed system always increases over time. The entropy of a closed system is a measure of its energetic microstates. To reflect the expanded concept of entropy from this initial thermodynamic association to a measure of the informational content of a system, it is suggested that this new understanding is accordingly differentiated as **intropy**. Given the hypothesis that our Universe is a closed/isolated system, that relative time and space are combined as invariant space-time, and that space-time began in a state of lowest intropy, then the total intropy of our Universe always increases over space-time. As Relativity Theory is a description of space-time, this is its most simple and generalized statement.*

Our Universe is manifested holographically with digitized information pixelated at the Planck scale and encoded on its 2D boundary/brane. Thus, time flows and space expands to intropically express ever more informational content within space-time. The flow of time itself is the intropic accumulation of the informational content of our Universe, leading to the 2ⁿᵈ Law of Infodynamics, which states that the informational content/intropy of our Universe expressed as space-time always increases.

*Essentially, the 1ˢᵗ Law of Infodynamics enables our Universe to exist and the 2ⁿᵈ Law enables it to evolve. Together the two reveal a Universe that essentially exists **to** evolve. And in showing that the two Laws are, respectively, expressions of Quantum and Relativity Theories, they point the way to how these two descriptions of energy-matter and space-time may be naturally reconciled.*

In a personal conversation with me, Currivan elaborated that in every Planck-scale moment the universe adds another set of information that is encoded into the expanding field of spacetime, and that the expansion of space and flow of time *is* evolution, without which there would be no evolutionary experience of consciousness. Through the coherence of consciousness, we are, as is the entire Universe, in fact, adding to the intropic informational content of the universe in every moment.

CHAPTER 21
TOWARD A UNIFIED MODEL

Flow process, dynamic pulsation and zerophase equilibrium — three components of one phenomenon: fractal-hologramic-synergetic wholeness. For all that has been explored to this point with its seeming complexity, there is an underlying simplicity in the cosmometry being described. The Torus, Jitterbug and Vector Equilibrium are attributes of cosmic geometry at the foundation of manifest form and flow at all scales throughout the universe.

In Chapter 2 we began to illustrate the basics of this foundational cosmometry with three fundamental patterns of energetic articulation: Radials, Rings and Spirals.

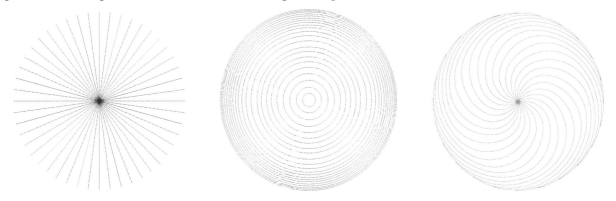

Combining all three creates a unified pattern:

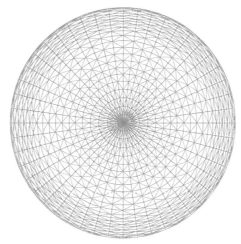

These are, of course, *idealized* expressions of energetic articulation in perfect symmetry, and this is actually an important aspect of the exploration of cosmometry. While the dynamics of natural form and flow are often remarkably close to these idealized patterns, they are just as often not so in their appearance. This foundational simplicity leads to a vast complexity of fractal permutation that creates the wonderful diversity we experience on Earth and beyond. It is by studying the *ideal simplicity* that the doors of perception open so that we can find these fundamental patterns within the diversity of form and flow.

To that end, our exploration of the VE, Jitterbug and Torus has laid the foundation for a fundamental 3D model of wholeness that I offer as an idealized reference of energetic articulation, which I call the **Unified Model of Cosmometry**.

The two-dimensional radial-ring-spiral pattern can be seen as the cross-section of a three-dimensional model that includes all three components, like this:

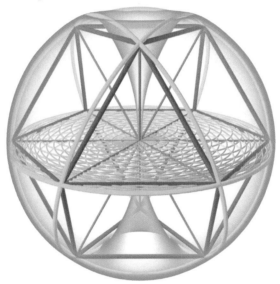

We now have the basis for a Unified Model that includes:

- The zerophase Vector Equilibrium (orange) with its zero center point, 12 inner vectors, and 24 circumferential vectors (all together, the **Radials**), shown as both regular VE and spherical VE, or Genesa Crystal (green);

- The Torus flow process (blue) as the form of dynamic equilibrium with its two polar vortexes meeting at the zero center point and its outer circumference at the same diameter as the VE, with **Rings** (blue-green) indicating the internal circular/spherical wave front and nesting of this pattern (like rings on water);

- And the **Spirals** (yellow) indicating a fundamental fluid-dynamic pattern found throughout the generalized field both inside and outside the defined VE-Torus space, in this case shown as a Double Spiral.

The Unified Model of Cosmometry is *the most* idealized version of the fundamental patterns when in balanced equilibrium and symmetry. In essence, we might say it's an *integrated zerophase model* of all three fundamental patterns of energetic articulation — Radials, Rings and Spirals. By this I mean that the VE, Torus and Double Spiral are the three fundamental patterns that define the primary reference of wholeness in cosmometry. Every system in the cosmos is ultimately based upon all three as one unified model.

> *It is by studying the ideal simplicity that the doors of perception open so that we can find these fundamental patterns within the diversity of form and flow.*

The Jitterbug transformation introduced in Chapter 14 is not depicted in this model. We will come back to it in Section 5 when we explore Structural Integrity and see how it is the basis for the first level of resonant complexity arising from dynamic pulsation — the Platonic Forms. First let's explore the fundamental Field Pattern that in→forms the manifest universe with the most efficient and harmonic ratio of fractal integrity — the Golden Ratio of Phi.

Section 3 Endnotes

42 Oregon Ki Society Instructors.
    http://www.oregonki.org/about-instructors.php

43 http://www.merriam-webster.com/dictionary/torus

44 See *Cocreative Science* by Machaelle Small Wright.
    http://www.perelandra-ltd.com

45 Haramein, Nassim, "The Harmonic Sphere Flux Resonator"; 1997.

46 http://www.thrivemovement.com - Where you can watch the film *Thrive* for free.

47 Sahtouris, Elisabet, *EarthDance: Living Systems in Evolution,* iUniverse (October 2000).

48 Elgin, Duane, *The Living Universe: Where Are We? Who Are We? Where Are We Going?,* Berrett-Koehler
    Publishers (April 1, 2009).

49 *The Essential David Bohm* (pp. 78-79). Taylor and Francis.

50 IBID (p. 10).

51 "Proton lifetime is longer than 10^{34} years", Kamioka Observatory, ICRR, The Univ. of Tokyo.
    http://www-sk.icrr.u-tokyo.ac.jp/whatsnew/new-20091125-e.html

52 "What is the Casimir Effect?", University of California Riverside.
    http://math.ucr.edu/home/baez/physics/Quantum/casimir.html

53 Wilson, C.M., et al. *Observation of the Dynamical Casimir Effect in a Superconducting Circuit.*
    https://arxiv.org/abs/1105.4714

54 https://resonance.is/resonator/

55 Haramein, N. and Val Baker, A. (2019) *Resolving the Vacuum Catastrophe: A Generalized Holographic
    Approach.* Journal of High Energy Physics, Gravitation and Cosmology, 5, 412-424.
    https://doi.org/10.4236/jhepgc.2019.52023

SECTION 4
FIELD PATTERN

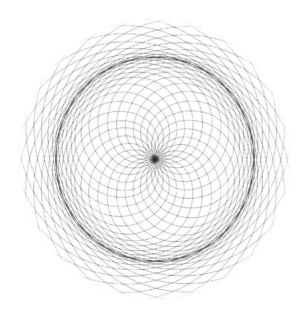

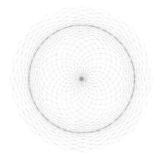

SECTION 4
FIELD PATTERN

"Out beyond ideas of wrongdoing and rightdoing,
there is a field. I'll meet you there."

This poetic evocation is a translated passage from the ecstatic writings of the 13th-century Sufi mystic, Jalāl ad-Dīn Rumi. In the simplest of terms, Rumi is pointing us toward a meeting place in our hearts and minds that transcends a polarity of thought so common in the human journey, that of right and wrong and the inevitable judgment that accompanies such thoughts. He invites us to meet in a field that is beyond these ideas. This field is present and available to us right now, a place where we meet each other in our innate wholeness.

His invitation is potent in light of our imperative passage from disharmony to harmony as we must whole-heartedly and open-mindedly face and embrace the critical challenges present in our world with rigorous discernment about the integrity of our "doing", while meeting each other in a greater field of mutual understanding. This understanding is beyond the ideas of wrongdoing and rightdoing. It is founded upon a worldview that recognizes the intrinsic wholeness of life and the inevitable inter-connectedness of all things, and that the effects of one's doing impact all doings in a feedback loop of action and consequence.

From all that we've seen thus far, it is becoming apparent that this "field of thought", this state of being, is actually our true and inherent nature, just as it is the true and inherent nature of everything being manifest in the cosmos. It seems that the ideas of right and wrong are primarily a concept of the human mind as it's not evident that such ideas are present in the trees that crash down upon each other, or in the transfer of life force from mouse to coyote. It is obvious that nature is constantly striving for balance, for a dynamic equilibrium that enables a living system to thrive, and when that dynamic goes to extremes the system will either collapse or "course correct" into a new state of balanced integrity. Nature's interest is in seeking balance and integrity beyond right and wrong. Standing in a field in nature, literally, is meeting Rumi face to face. While there is much "doing" in our world that we might readily point our fingers at as "wrong" while patting ourselves on the back for being "right", it is essential at this time that we hold a wider view, acknowledge the larger consequences of our actions and take a deep look at the natural and societal systems that we inhabit to see that they are clearly in a state of dynamic extremes. As such, they will either collapse or we will engage in a course correction to establish a new state of balanced integrity. That integrity can only be based upon the intrinsic integrity of the universe as reciprocal flow in dynamic equilibrium. In the grand scheme of things, whichever way it goes will be beyond right and wrong; it will simply be a matter of integrity.

It's time to meet in that field.

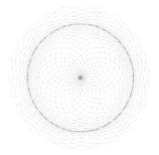

CHAPTER 22
THE FIELD AND THE PATTERN

Rumi's field is one of mind and heart, a metaphysical field of consciousness that is non-local, without a physical location in space. It is really more of a feeling than it is even an idea, a feeling of peaceful connection within ourselves that can extend throughout all of nature, Earth and the entire cosmos. In some ways it is easier to *feel* the concept of a field than it is to *think* the concept. Perhaps this is why the words "feel" and "field" are so similar?

While the *field of consciousness* and the feeling aspect of our experience of it will be explored later, it is pertinent at this point to acknowledge that everything we are exploring is as much about the mind and consciousness as it is about physical reality. The "one thing" we call energy-matter-information is these "two", mind and matter, in the unified state of wholeness that is the cosmos. There is an intrinsic intelligence within the cosmic structure as information is shared hologramically at all scales. Through our remarkable faculties of mind we have the capacity to discern how this cosmic information field is structured — to see the patterns that "in→form" matter and energy as it manifests the physical universe. It is this field of form and flow that we are now venturing in to.

There are numerous definitions for the word field. Of all of them, this one is most closely related to the kind of field we're exploring:

> *a* : a region or space in which a given effect (as magnetism) exists.[56]

It's very simple and provides an example of a fundamental force, magnetism, as defining a specific region or space under consideration. The region of a magnetic field's effect is easy to see when made visible with iron filings, as shown in this familiar image:

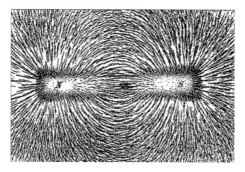

A clear pattern can be seen that is the effect of an otherwise invisible energy dynamic (that is, in fact, toroidal). It is precisely this kind of *field effect made visible as a pattern* that is the basis for our exploration of the in→forming (the coming into form) of energy-matter-information as seen in nature and the cosmos.

Key to this exploration is the discernment of patterns. Cosmometry is the study of fundamental patterns, structures, processes and systems that are inherent in manifestation at all scales within the cosmos. In the previous section we delved into the Flow Process of the torus as a fundamental expression of energy dynamics fractally embedded across all scales. In Section 2: Starting From Zero, we ventured into the prime system of the Vector Equilibrium and Isotropic Vector Matrix (Buckminster Fuller defines these as a system in Synergetics, rather than as a structure). The next section will highlight the Structural aspect of form and function. For now, our attention is on what we call the Pattern, which as described in Chapter 2 is what may be considered as a 2-dimensional representation of 3-dimensional phenomena that we can use to illustrate basic forms of energetic articulation.

For example, the above patterns can be correlated to particular forms found in nature, as seen here:

Top Row: Radiolarian (triangle), Pyrite Crystal (square; Rob Lavinsky, iRocks.com – CC-BY-SA-3.0),
Hibiscus Flower (pentagon, pentagram), Snow Flake (hexagon)
Bottom Row: Dandelion (radial vectors; Photo by Greg Hume), Seashell (offset radials),
Water Ripples (rings), Nautilus Shell (spiral), Sunflower (double spiral)

These patterns are clearly visible in each case, and they all are present due to fundamental attributes of energetic articulation as energy-matter-information comes into form.

While these examples show specific forms, they are simply special-case "instances" of patterns that can potentially be found at any scale. The patterns are not dependent upon any specific size, color, location, material, etc. to define them. Rather, they are a generalized abstraction of energy dynamics that can be found in many different instances. Buckminster Fuller referred to this generalized abstraction as Pattern Integrity. His familiar illustration of this concept is a series of different kinds of string and rope tied together (cotton, nylon, twine, thin, thick), and a simple knot that can be shifted across the different strings and rope. The knot is a pattern integrity that exists independent of which kind of material it's made from. As we just saw in the last section, a torus is just such a pattern integrity. It is a universal form that is made from the medium in which it exists. The torus form itself is independent of the medium as a generalized pattern.

At the end of Section 3 we introduced the Unified Model of Cosmometry as a primary reference within our exploration of cosmometry, proposing that it provides a basic *integrated zerophase model* of the three fundamental patterns of energetic articulation — Radials, Rings and Spirals. The Unified Model consists (in its most simple construction) of the Vector Equilibrium, the Torus, and the Double Spiral, correlating to the radials, rings, and spirals respectively. As we proceed into our exploration of the Field Pattern aspect of cosmometry, we'll bring our focus to the third component in the model — the Double Spiral.

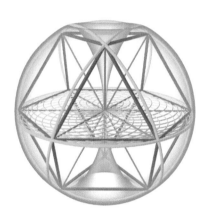

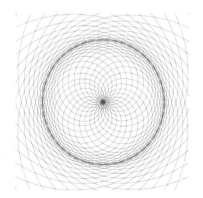

"We can no longer think of reality as little building blocks separated by an empty space. We now know there is no such thing as empty space and that physical objects, including us, do not exist in isolation, but are part of this holistic web of interconnectedness in which fields and relationships are primary." [57]
– Dr. Rollin McCraty, HeartMath Institute

But first we must turn our attention to one of the most remarkable attributes of the Field Pattern that is so intrinsic to the cosmos across all scales it's obviously of primary relevance to the in→forming of energy-matter-information — the Golden Ratio of Phi.

FIELD PATTERN

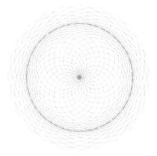

CHAPTER 23
THE GOLDEN RULER

If ever there was a blatantly obvious pattern within the form and flow of the cosmos it is that which is based upon the Golden Ratio of Phi. From massive galaxies to tiny atomic structures and everywhere in between, the Phi ratio is found happily waving at us with such ubiquity that it's not possible to gloss over it, though many a scientist has tried. There are those, in fact, that even relegated to "being in the religion of Phi" the more enthusiastic of us who happily waved our hands (with literal irony due to their Phi proportions) in recognition of this remarkably universal fact. Of course, the age-old fear in the orthodox scientific mind is that someone might suggest the presence of an "intelligent design" at work in the formation of the universe, and the all-too-prevalent appearance of Phi can often evoke that sort of allergic reaction. It can be hard to discern where science ends and religion begins in the face of it.

And yet, the ubiquity of Phi lives on. The question, then, is why is this "golden" ratio so prevalent? Clearly it plays some fundamental role in the in→forming of energy-matter-information; a kind of higher-order organizing principle that does, indeed, suggest a higher-order of intelligent design at play. Would identifying this cosmic role affirm the influence of an *intelligent designer*? Or might it simply be a matter of an intrinsic intelligence within the fractal-hologramic information feedback loop of the quantized cosmos? Either way, somewhere, somehow, a "decision" was made by something other than us humans that this humble little ratio would be used *everywhere*, so perhaps the inquiry may inform both possibilities. The concept of intrinsic intelligence within the energy-matter-information network will be explored in Section 7. For now, let's look at some facts about Phi…

As was introduced in Chapter 4, the ratio called Phi (denoted by the Greek letter Φ) is simply stated as 1.618 to 1. That is, when something is given a unit value of 1, another something that is 1.618 larger is said to be in the Phi ratio. This simple diagram illustrates this relationship:

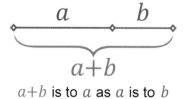

$a+b$ is to a as a is to b

Line segment *b* in red is equivalent to 1, and *a* in blue is 1.618 longer than it. Conversely, if segment *a* is given a value of 1, then segment *b* is .618 smaller in length. This is a reciprocal ratio, often distinguished by using a lower case "p" as in phi. **Phi** is a ratio of 1.618, and **phi** is a ratio of .618. **Phi** is scaling **larger,** and **phi** is scaling **smaller**. It is, therefore, a basic scaling ratio. (For ease of reading we'll use the uppercase Phi as the generic term for the ratio.)

Even though our amazing minds can come up with a mathematical formula that produces a never-ending value of Phi, the cosmos is not concerned with that. What the cosmos is concerned with is whole-number quanta — the quantized nature of energy-matter-information at the foundation of our exploration.

As also mentioned in our earlier introduction to Phi, it is a self-similar ratio, meaning that each iteration of the Phi ratio contains another larger iteration. In the illustration on the previous page, if *a* is given a value of 1, then *a+b* (the length of the whole line) is equal to Phi, or 1.618 larger than *a*. So *a+b* is to *a* as *a* is to *b*. The Phi ratio, then, is not only a scaling ratio, it is a *fractal* scaling ratio. Our simple definition of a fractal — the same pattern repeats at all scales — is exhibited in this self-similar ratio.

So, simply put… **Fact 1** is that **Phi is an inherent fractal-scaling ratio found within the design of the cosmos**. The word "design" in this context means the *observable patterns* found in natural systems of form and flow. We'll see numerous examples of these patterns shortly, but let's first continue with a few more Phi facts.

Fact 2 is that **Phi is a ratio that is independent of any specific unit of measure** (what is technically called a dimensionless number). As such, the Phi ratio can potentially be found in any and every attribute of cosmic dynamics, be it size, distance, weight, temperature, angle, velocity, etc. This doesn't mean that Phi *will* be found in every physical attribute; there are many dynamic factors at play in the universe and Phi is simply one of them. It just happens to be a remarkably prevalent one, so it stands out as inviting considerable inquiry. (Indeed, there are many books written about Phi, and many more websites devoted to it, from all of which something may be learned.)

Fact 3 is that **the mathematical derivation of Phi produces an irrational number**:

$$\frac{1 + \sqrt{5}}{2} \approx 1.6180339887498948482045868343656381177203091798057 62862\ldots$$

…on and on and on ad infinitum.[58] As such there is no "absolute" Phi ratio, only an approximation of it. It turns out, the cosmos is quite happy to use an approximation of Phi. Even though our amazing minds can come up with a mathematical formula that produces a never-ending value of Phi, the cosmos is not concerned with that. What the cosmos *is* concerned with is whole-number quanta — the quantized nature of energy-matter-information at the foundation of our exploration.

This, again, is where the well-known Fibonacci sequence comes in, our Phinary number system:

0   1   1   2   3   5   8   13   21   34   55   89   144   233   377   610   987 ...

Starting with 0 and 1, each new number in the sequence is the sum of the previous two, and the division of any pair of adjacent numbers results in an increasing accuracy of Phi the farther out the sequence we go.

These numbers are found in the patterns of nature with striking regularity (as well as in the ratio relationships of music, as we'll see later). For example, this sunflower seed head has 34 spirals in one direction and 55 in the other:

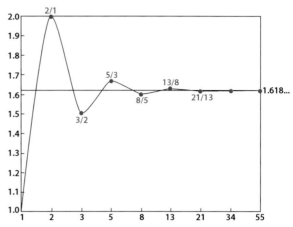

As is evidenced by this, it is more a matter of *quantity* related to Fibonacci numbers than it is a mathematically accurate resolution of Phi. And yet, Phi is present *because* these numbers are present, at least in approximation (55/34=1.61764...).

This is, perhaps, the biggest clue as to how nature is "deciding" to use the Phi ratio so often. Given that the action of energy dynamics is *quantized*, it stands to reason that the quantitative pattern of self-similarity found in the Fibonacci sequence is inherent in these dynamics as an intrinsic relational system. That is, as the quantized dynamics of electromagnetic and acoustic impulses scale from Planck to Universal size, the ratio relationships of quantities correlated with Fibonacci numbers naturally create a specific effect in the in→forming field of energy-matter-information. We see this effect as Phi ratio characteristics within the field pattern of spacetime across all scales. It is, in fact, the fractal-scaling ratio of quantized action that, due to its inherent self-similarity, most efficiently accommodates the unimaginably vast range of cosmic scale with seamless integrity.

So, **Fact 4** is that **cosmic nature utilizes the whole-number ratios found in Fibonacci numbers to approximate Phi**, rather than the mathematically derived irrational number as defined by us humans. (To give the cosmos a bit more credit, though, when we realize that the base unit of quantization is a Planck unit, by the time the Fibonacci numbers get up to our scale in the universe the degree of decimal accuracy becomes exceedingly high!)

It's important to note here that the Fibonacci numbers, as common as they are in nature, are not an exclusive set of numbers that resolve to Phi. On the contrary, we can start with *any two numbers* and build a sequence using the same simple Fibonacci formula (n1+n2=n3, n2+n3=n4, etc.), and when two adjacent numbers in the new sequence are divided, the result will again resolve to an approximation of Phi with increasing accuracy the farther out the sequence we go. Another well-known set of numbers that demonstrates this is called the Lucas series, which is:

$$2 \quad 1 \quad 3 \quad 4 \quad 7 \quad 11 \quad 18 \quad 29 \quad 47 \quad 76 \quad 123 \quad 199 \quad 322 \quad 521 \quad 843 \ldots$$

So why is Phi an unending irrational number when mathematically derived? How does this fit into the cosmic scheme? Perhaps its un-resolvability is what allows for such a wide range of both scale and diversity of material substance in the cosmos to harmoniously interact with an inherent integrity of wholeness. The "wiggle room" exhibited by the quantized approximation of Phi that oscillates on both +/- sides of mathematical Phi allows for the vibratory nature of energy and matter to accommodate itself across scales of size, density, distance, etc. — the "positive and negative asymmetries that propagate the differentials of consciousness," as Fuller said. It may be that mathematical Phi is the underlying zerophase of the spiraling dynamic of the cosmos, just at the Vector Equilibrium is the zerophase of the vector dynamic. And just as the VE will never be seen in any physical sense because it is the zerophase reference, mathematical Phi will also never be seen for the same reason.

Food for thought, as is this amazing Romenescu broccoli that is clearly the winner for making visible the underlying fractal field pattern of Fibonacci-based energy-matter in→formation.

And then there's **Fact 5**, which is that **5 is the number of Phi**, as is certainly evident in the mathematical formula for Phi shown on page 134. All regular 5-fold symmetry is composed of fractal iterations of Phi ratio segments, as can be seen in this illustration of a pentagon (outer lines) and pentagram (star pattern) showing four colored line segments that are all Phi ratio in their relative scaling:

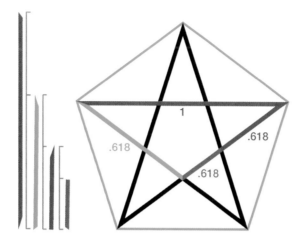

Therefore, every time we see flowers with five petals, or the seed pattern inside of an apple's core, or a starfish, etc., we are literally seeing Phi ratio harmonics manifest in nature. This hibiscus flower, for example, shows just how accurate the harmonic symmetry is:

It is interesting to note that the word "five" begins with the sound of the word "Phi", and could even be spelled "phive" and sound exactly the same. Hmmm…

Is there a Golden Ruler that scribes the measure of the universe in harmonic proportion of beauty, form and function? Maybe the timeless adage "Do unto others as you would have them do unto you" is the philosophical testament of such a self-similar cosmic intelligence.

Let's investigate further…

FIELD PATTERN

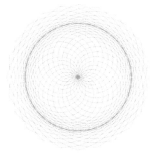

CHAPTER 24
COSMIC INITIATION

My personal curiosity about Phi was initiated on a hot July day in 1980 when I was 21 years old (a Fibonacci number, wink wink ;). It was the first time that I ventured alone to my family's cabin in the remote heartlands of the Adirondack High Peaks Wilderness in northern New York State, eight miles from where we leave the car. I was on a vision quest with spirited youthful intention, my trusty copy of the *I Ching*, and a handful of psilocybin mushrooms. Having consulted the oracle the night before,* in the pre-dawn light I dangled a pendulum over a map of the region and divined where my quest was to be found: a mountain brook whose name sounds very similar to the Sanskrit word for peace. Chanting Shanti Shanti Shanti, I made my way upstream to the highest point I had ever been, where a large swimming hole welcomes a refreshing dip.

Placing the spore medicine in the early morning sun to attune to the rising light, I stripped to flesh and submerged myself in the icy mountain water as a purification ritual, inviting the magic of the day to enliven my journey with insight and vision. As I stood to dry in the warm light beaming through the trees onto a small patch on the rocks, somehow the word got out to the resident butterflies in the area, and for the next half hour I was blessed with a most remarkable experience. One after another they flew in, landed on the rocks by my feet, and proceeded to climb up my legs until I counted twenty butter-flies on me with nearly that many scattered around my feet. Needless to say, I was already in a very altered state after *that* happened, and I even questioned whether the medicine would lift me further or bring me down! After gently shaking my legs and bidding my friends "good day" with immense gratitude, I did choose to continue my journey upstream into realms I had never before ventured. While there were numerous highlights along the way, my quest was fulfilled when far up the brook, which was now a quiet meandering watercourse in the cradle of the Great Range, I sat on a small gravel bank to meditate and was granted this image to the right in my inner vision.

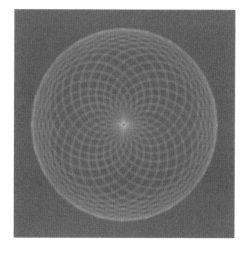

---

*Hexagram 46 – Pushing Upward, changing to 11 – Peace, for those who are interested

It began with two lines crossing at 90°, then slowly receded out as petals formed around the center until my entire inner field of perception was this beautiful double spiral pattern. I knew this was the vision of my quest, and it has been the guiding vision of my quest in cosmometry ever since.

This pattern, which I simply call a Phi Double Spiral, is very common in nature, most visibly apparent in spirals of seed heads at the center of flowers, in pinecones, acorns and cacti, on fruits such as pineapples, and vegetables such as the multi-fractal pattern of the Romenescu Broccoli pictured in the previous chapter.

Over nearly four decades of observation and contemplation in nature following my initial vision of the double spiral pattern, I have come to realize that it is as prevalent as the Phi ratio itself (obviously because they are one and the same thing), and that it is a fundamental field pattern of fluid dynamic motion in nature and the cosmos.

Actually, a more accurate way of describing it is as a fundamental field pattern of *magnetohydrodynamics* in nature and the cosmos. Stating it this way highlights an important distinction that will round out the whole picture of what's being described in this section (and in cosmometry as a whole). While it's easier to reference fluid dynamics that can be readily observed in the flow of water, when it comes to the universal presence of this pattern it is more wholly attributable to the effects of both magnetic (inherent in electromagnetism, e.g. light, gravity) and hydro (fluid, e.g. water, air) dynamics. When we see the double spiral pattern in a given physical form, such as a pinecone, we're actually seeing the signature of the magneto- (PSU, atomic, molecular scales) and hydro- (cellular, organism, ecosystem scales) dynamics. The so-called "difference" between these two is that the magnetic dynamic is universal and non-local (i.e. fractally embedded from Planck to Universal scales), and the hydro is a local fluid dynamic composed of physical matter.

While this distinction has importance in how we view the source of the double spiral pattern when seen in nature, it is again (as is so often the case when describing a fractal-hologramic model) ultimately referring to one phenomenon — a fundamental field pattern found at all scales in the cosmos.

For many years in my quest to understand the qualities of this double spiral pattern I would excitedly open many a "sacred geometry" book, only to find that when it came to a picture of this pattern, typically drawn on top of a pinecone's base, the explanation of it would simply culminate with, "and that's the Phi spiral." This much was already evident to me. What was not were a few key questions I was seeking to answer:

What is the source and role of this pattern in the energy dynamics of the cosmos?

What defines the outer boundary of the pattern when seen in a pinecone (for example)?

What happens to this pattern beyond the outer boundary of the form in which it's visible?

None of the books addressed this level of inquiry, so I was left to my own devices to peel back the veil of nature which offers her aesthetic designs with such blatant abandon yet seems to obscure their origins in what so many have called the "hidden secrets of nature." The irony is that they're not hidden at all! They're put right in front of our eyes every day, and when we politely sit with her and acknowledge her beauty, she readily makes clear that she's hiding no secrets whatsoever.

For my part, my "own devices" came in the form of continual observation of where and how I saw the double spiral pattern in nature, and my eventual love affair with Adobe Illustrator software (which wasn't even a gleam in someone's eye when I first saw this pattern in my mind's eye) that allowed me to explore this pattern for myself. Before we have a look at how the Phi Double Spiral shows up in nature, let's first study the origins and cosmometric attributes of it through an investigation into the Cosmometry of Phi.

FIELD PATTERN

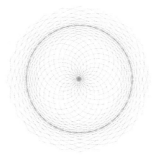

CHAPTER 25
COSMOMETRY OF PHI

To fully comprehend the presence of Phi in the field of space, form and flow, a review of its design origin is in order. The language of Phi is a visual one of proportion, angle, spiral, as well as an audible one of harmonic relationships in sound and music.

In the visual realm of pattern, this image offers a basic illustration with which to commence our inquiry:

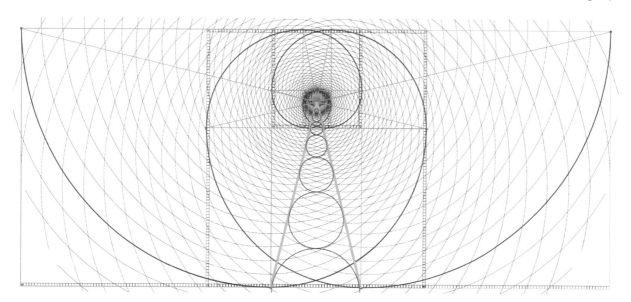

As we'll see, this is essentially a unified blueprint of Phi patterning. To understand this, we need to start from square one (literally) and reconstruct it. It begins with a set of units of scale, in this case very small squares (zoomed in to see the center point of the illustration above).

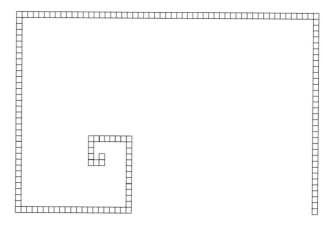

These are arranged so that every 90° turn is at a number of units correlated to the Fibonacci sequence, making a grid of squares that increase in scale by those values (1, 1, 2, 3, 5, 8, 13, 21, 34…).

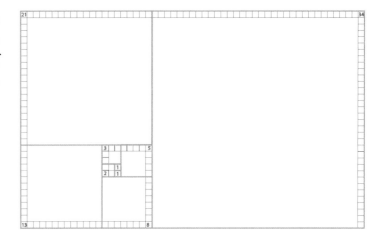

This creates a fractally-embedded series of **Golden Rectangles** whose edge lengths are in the Phi ratio (only two are outlined in this illustration but every rectangle is a golden one, and each is one part of the next larger one).

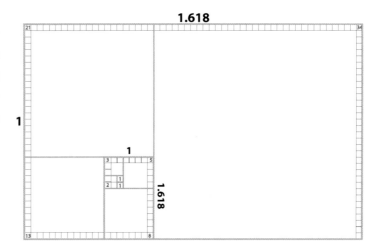

In each of the Fibonacci squares a quarter-circle arc is drawn with a radius equal to the square's edge.

This creates a **Phi Spiral** that is a very close approximation to a mathematically generated one (mathematical Phi does not trace quarter-circle arcs but rather a mathematically "pure" logarithmic spiral).

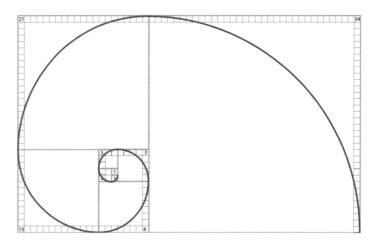

A set of **Nodes** is added to indicate where each iteration of the Phi scaling occurs along the spiral (which will become relevant to our exploration shortly).

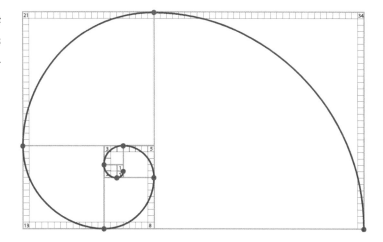

Zooming the image out now, we add lines that connect from the "origin" point of the spiral to each of the nodes (this too will become relevant shortly).

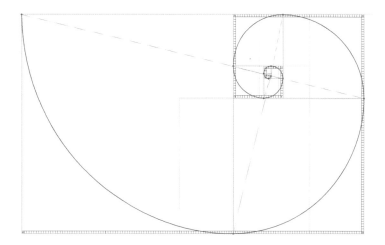

We then "spin" the Phi Spiral to create a Phi Vortex that flows *counter-clockwise* inward to the central origin point.

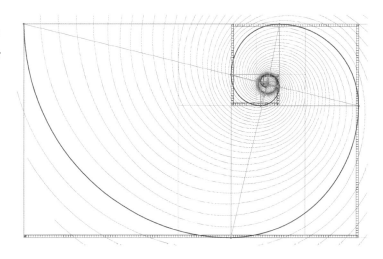

This entire set of squares, rectangles, spiral, nodes, vectors and vortex is then duplicated in the *clockwise* direction of spin:

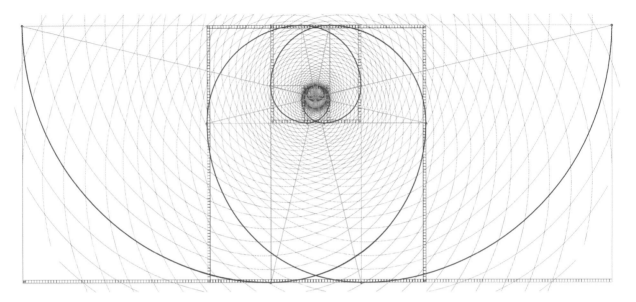

We now can see two Phi Spirals converging towards a common origin point and the combination of the two vortex patterns creates a **Phi Double Spiral** pattern.

The last two components to add that will bring us back to our first illustration are a set of tangential circles that scale in Fibonacci-sized diameter, and the angle that is derived by their increasing size, which I call the **Phi Scaling Angle**,[59] as is shown in this illustration:

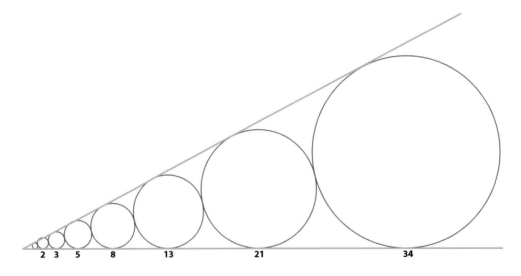

This angle is ~**27.3°** and it is often found in the patterns of nature, as we'll see. What is of great interest to note is that it is also the angle of difference between the two sets of "node vectors" (the orange lines in the above illustrations), which means that the blueprint of the two complementary clockwise/

counter-clockwise Phi Vortices, when overlaid, is offset by the Phi Scaling Angle. Here's the whole blueprint again:

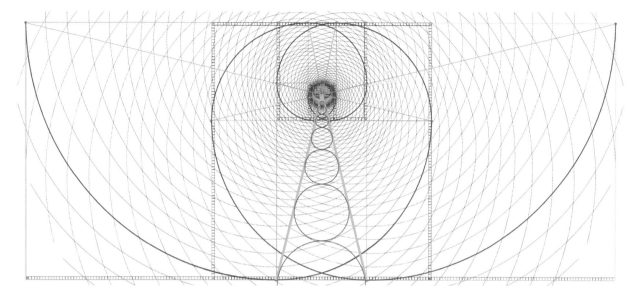

So this one illustration contains a number of basic attributes of Phi:

- **Fibonacci Quantity** (the small square units)
- **Phi Proportional Scaling** (the squares and circles)
- **Golden Rectangles** fractally embedded
- **Golden Spirals**
- **Phi Vortexes** and **Double Spiral**
- **Phi Scaling Angle**

The one other basic attribute of Phi as it is seen in nature that is not included is the **Rotation Angle**, which is derived simply by dividing the 360° of a circle by the Phi ratio: 360° / 1.6180339. This divides the circle into two arcs with angles of 222.5° and 137.5°, both of which can be considered as Phi rotation angles, though the latter angle is often found in the arrangement of leaves on plant stems, called phyllotaxis. In order to maximize the plant's exposure to sunlight, each new leaf is grown at a point rotated 137.5° from the one that came before it. This arrangement provides for a minimum of overlap of the leaves throughout the entire plant structure, thus allowing for a maximum exposure of sunlight to reach the foliage.

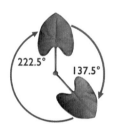

Now that we have a set of qualities of Phi with which we can deepen our investigation, let's see how the patterns illustrated in our blueprint appear in nature, in→forming the Field Pattern.

FIELD PATTERN

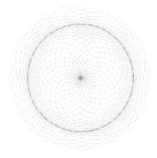

CHAPTER 26
PHIELD PATTERNING

In its simplest form, the Unified Model of Cosmometry depicts three basic cosmometric attributes: The Vector Equilibrium, the Torus and the Phi Double Spiral. These three components share two things in common: a "one point" center, and a spherical circumference.

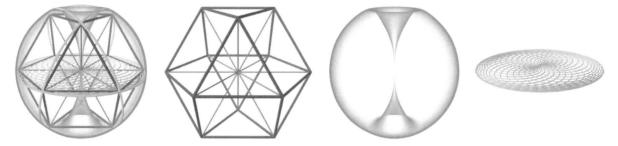

As illustrated, the double spiral is a cross-section slice of the overall toroidal field pattern.

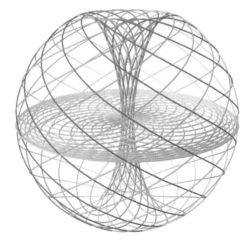

It is important to remember that the Unified Model is depicting one thing —equilibrium — in both zerophase reference (VE) and dynamic manifestation (Torus and Double Spiral). Of the three components, it is the Double Spiral that is most readily seen in nature. The VE is, by definition, non-visible. The torus is most often an implied form (an implicate order, we might say), and the double spiral (or single vortex) is easy to find in the patterns of nature (an explicate order).

Here are a few examples:

A Mammillaria Cactus clearly shows a toroidal double spiral pattern with Fibonacci numbers of 13 clockwise and 21 counter-clockwise spirals.

A pinecone displays the pattern as well, in this case with 8 and 13 spirals.

This pineapple not only shows the double spiral around the fruit torus, it is also present in the pattern of the leaf growth at the top. Though not always immediately apparent, the growth of many plants' leaves occurs in a double spiral pattern.

Here, for example, is a spruce tree branch. Looking closely at the pattern of the bare twig we can see that the needles (which are the leaves of the spruce tree) are arrayed around the branch in a double spiral pattern.

The newly emerging cone of the same spruce tree continues this theme (and in fact does so as a fractal iteration of the entire spruce tree, carrying its unique genetic makeup in its seeds).

These two images show the Phi vortex in a fluid-dynamic motion:

A red smoke flare makes visible a vortex of air that curls off the wing tip of an airplane. The yellow lines are all Phi spirals highlighting the vortex pattern converging towards a distinct center point.

At a much larger scale of about 400 miles diameter, here we have two images of Hurricane Katrina, one with spirals overlaid to highlight the Phi vortex again.

And here we see the same thing at a vastly larger scale, that of a galaxy about 90,000 light-years across.

While the airplane and hurricane vortices are manifestations of aero- and hydrodynamic movements, the dynamics of electric and magnetic fields in interstellar plasma give shape to galaxies. Across great scales from tiny cones to massive galaxies, we see the influence of magnetohydrodynamics in the formation of spiraling flows patterned upon the Phi vortex and double spiral. Keep in mind that everything we are looking at is a visual representation of what are otherwise invisible patterns of energetic articulation, emerging from the superfluid aether field. As we can see, these patterns scale fractally in a self-similar manner, and that is exactly the essential nature of the Phi ratio and its role in cosmic energy dynamics.

In the last three images above, you may have noticed that the vortex patterns all include a circle within them (in the case of the hurricane, it's the eye's outer boundary). Even the cactus, pineapple, and pine and spruce cones all end up defining a circular boundary in their form. This boundary, it turns out, is inherent in the formation of a Phi vortex and double spiral when it arises from whole number quantization as found in nature. It is what I call the Phi Boundary Condition.

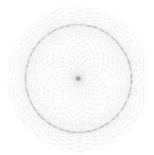

CHAPTER 27
PHI BOUNDARY CONDITION

As mentioned earlier, my contemplation of the Phi Double Spiral pattern led me to three questions that remained unanswered for many years, these being:

What is the source and role of this pattern in the energy dynamics of the cosmos?

What defines the outer boundary of the pattern when seen in a pinecone (for example)?

What happens to this pattern beyond the outer boundary of the form in which it's visible?

In most geometry books (whether "sacred" or not), the Golden Spiral is typically depicted as either a single spiral or as a few spirals traced over the pattern of a pinecone. There is nothing obvious about the characteristics of a single spiral or a few traced spirals that offer insight into the pursuit of answers to these questions. Then the day came when I learned how to make a Phi spiral in Adobe Illustrator software using the method described earlier, and it occurred to me to "spin it" into a vortex pattern. This was accomplished by simply duplicating the first spiral and repeating it around a common central axis point. As soon as I did so that first time I knew that the second and third questions above had suddenly been answered. Repeating the spiral with enough iteration brought to light a new feature that I had never seen before in any other illustration — a very clear circle appears in the pattern.

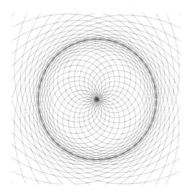

The circle you see in this illustration was not drawn by me independent of the spirals. It simply emerges as a feature of the double spiral pattern. It is, in fact, a synergetic effect of a whole that is unpredictable from the parts when taken separately, so it is not in any way apparent when just looking

Pure Mathematical Phi Does Not Create Boundary Condition

When a Golden Spiral is generated using a logarithmic function based upon the mathematically derived value of Phi and "spun" as we've done with the Fibonacci spiral, a beautiful double spiral pattern appears, but there is no boundary condition within the pattern. Without the quantized Fibonacci values, there are no Nodes along the spiral (or we might say there's an infinite number of nodes, perhaps). This illustrates that pure mathematical Phi is the zerophase of angular momentum, meaning that it is the zero reference around which the approximation of Phi found in Fibonacci-derived spirals oscillates but never ultimately achieves, other than when returning to stillness and nothingness.

at one or a few spirals. Seeing this for the first time was a powerful rush of revelation for me as I sat staring at this beautiful new attribute that clearly defines a distinct boundary within the pattern. Suddenly I had a frame of reference for considering what defines the outer edge of a pinecone, and what happens with the energetic pattern beyond that edge.

Needless to say, I was extremely excited about this discovery, which I came to call the **Phi Boundary Condition**, and immediately began to dive in further to see what else was waiting to be revealed about it.

Very quickly the next compelling piece of information jumped out at me. As I worked with the double spiral in Illustrator and the vectors that were selected became highlighted, the points of segmentation along the paths, called anchor points, became visible. Something significant about them caught my eye. At the center of the pattern is the first anchor point for each path, then along the paths are two more anchors before the paths all converge together to form the circle, and this is *exactly at the third anchor point out from the center*. This illustration shows how that looks in Illustrator (with one vortex set highlighted in blue and the other in green to make it more apparent):

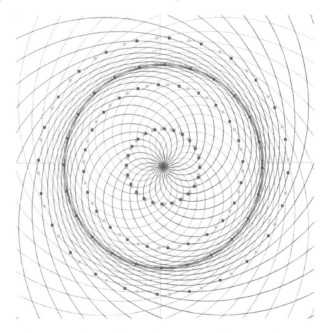

These anchors are located at the point where each quarter-circle arc that makes up the Phi spiral meet, so each point defines a segment along the spiral that is a ratio of Phi larger and smaller than its immediate neighbors. These points I call **Nodes**. We can see them when zoomed in to the very central axis point of our original blueprint illustration, with the Phi Boundary Condition circle appearing exactly at the third node out (the point at the center of spin is considered as Node 0).

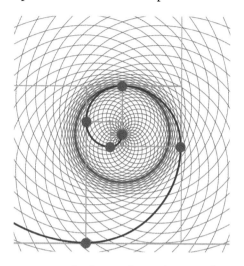

Again, the circle is not drawn on separately. It is where the spiral vectors converge and overlap each other before extending outward, as far as I know into infinity without repeating another circle.

So, within the Phi vortex and double spiral pattern there's now a distinct boundary between inside and outside, the Phi Boundary Condition. Within the boundary is a very familiar pattern seen in many plants (though as we'll see in a moment, they incorporate one more variation into the pattern). Outside the boundary is a continuation of the pattern with no further boundary distinction. In answer to two of my original questions: A *natural boundary limit to the manifestation of form* is defined that answers the second one (*What defines the outer boundary of the pattern when seen in a pinecone?*), and *the extension of the pattern ad infinitum* answers the third one (*What happens to this pattern beyond the outer boundary of the form in which it's visible?*). The first question about the source and role of the energy dynamics will be addressed later, but let's continue our study of the Double Spiral and Boundary Condition with a couple more examples of how they in→form the field patterning of energy-matter-information in nature.

SUNFLOWER EXHIBITS TWO FRACTAL SCALES OF PHI SPIRALS

The sunflower seed head is the poster child of the Phi Double Spiral pattern. Everyone is familiar with it, and the pattern it displays is clean and clear. Except one thing… the two spirals (clockwise and counter-clockwise) look different. One is very sharply curved and the other much less so. If they're both Phi spirals, why is it that they look so different? That question perplexed me for some time until one night I had a sudden flash of insight.

In my exploration of the Nodes and Boundary Condition I had tested whether the phenomenon of the boundary circle repeated fractally at all scales. In order to have a fractal-hologramic model, which is a criterion being sought throughout all my explorations, the pattern ought to repeat at any and every node along the spiral. This meant that when a given node is chosen to be the center point of the spin, then exactly three nodes out from it a boundary circle will appear as predicted. This does, in fact, hold true. So, for example, when I choose Node 3 as the point around which to spin the spiral, the circle will appear at Node 6. This illustration to the right shows this to be so. (Note again that the first node at the start of the spiral is considered Node 0.)

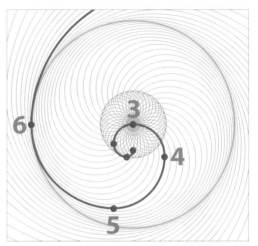

When spiral is spun at Node 3, Boundary Condition appears at Node 6

As a principle, then, **each node along the spiral can be a center axis of spin, and in every instance a new boundary condition is created that is a Phi ratio larger than the previous one**. The spiral itself does not change, and in fact there is only one source spiral that is common to all fractal iterations (because we can spin the same spiral at any of its nodes). So, the model is both fractal and hologramic in that regard. This illustration shows two scales of the boundary condition, one centered at Node 3 (green) and the other centered at Node 5 (red). The **blue** spiral is common to both vortexes. The scale difference between the two boundary conditions would be by a factor of 2 in this case (two iterations of Phi larger).

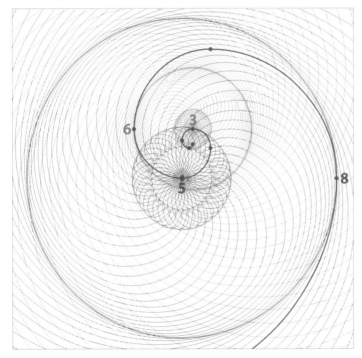

"The entirety of this electric universe of motion is expressed in spirals. Every spiral in nature is centered by a hole. Every spiral is a continuity of rings. All nature is made up of spiral sections, or rings."
– Walter Russell

Which brings us back to the sunflower's differing spirals.

It was about 3 a.m. on a hot night on the Big Island of Hawaii in 2008 and I couldn't sleep due to having a fever. I was staying over at The Resonance Project Foundation campus (located there at the time) the night before Nassim Haramein was hosting an international group of scientists for a research summit called Uni-Phi, and to my surprise that prior afternoon he asked me if I would like to make a presentation to the group the next day. Nassim had also discovered the phenomenon of the boundary circle independently, yet his deep pursuit of physics did not afford him the time to investigate it further. Seeing how I had developed the model with extensive illustrations, he felt it would be of value for the scientists to have a peek into these realms of Phi and geometry.

As I lay awake that night contemplating my presentation, I thought of the discrepancy between the two spirals seen in the sunflower seed head… how was I going to explain that? And then it came to me: the spirals are two fractal scales of Phi, one with a smaller vortex and boundary condition, the other with a larger one with only a portion of the vortex showing in the seed pattern. I immediately fired up my computer and began testing this idea by spinning Phi vortices at different nodes and comparing them to the curves in the seed pattern, and sure enough I quickly found a match with vortex spins that were **two nodes** different in scale. My hunch was correct!

It is, of course, much easier to see this than to read about it…

The steeply curved set of spirals, of which there are 34, has a boundary condition that matches the diameter of the seed head.

34 clockwise spirals

Does Phi Precede Pi?

The well-known ratio of Pi — the ratio of a circle's circumference to its diameter — is another irrational number, approximated as 3.14159… when mathematically derived. Given the vast number of circular patterns and spherical forms in nature (bubbles, planets and stars being the most common (well, certainly protons are the most common)), it's an interesting question to ask at what decimal value does nature cut off the infinite value of Pi and close the circle? Given that circles and spheres are the result of spin dynamics, and that all spin is spiral in nature, could it be that the spiraling attribute of Phi that creates a circular Boundary Condition precedes Pi in the formation of circles and spheres in nature? Perhaps the whole number Fibonacci quantization that nature uses to form spiral energy dynamics is the true origin of natural circular and spherical boundaries, and of Pi itself.

The gently curved spirals, of which there are 55, are showing only a portion of a bigger vortex with a boundary condition that is two iterations of Phi larger than the seed head boundary. As you can see, this boundary is approximately the same diameter as the sunflower's beautiful yellow petals.

Sunflower image by Oliver Feiler
https://kiza.eu/

This phenomenon of two different spiral curves is found in every instance (from my observation) of the Phi Double Spiral when seen in plants, not just the sunflower. There's always one set of spirals that's steeply curved, and the other more gently curved. And they're typically in Fibonacci quantity pairs (like 34 and 55). We now know that when we see this **we're observing two scales of Phi Vortexes and Boundary Conditions interacting in a harmonious relationship of fundamental energy dynamics**.

These illustrations show both spirals and vortices overlaid together:

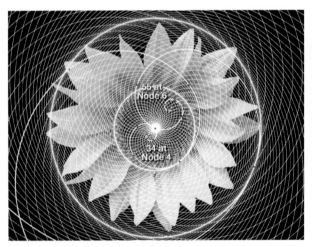
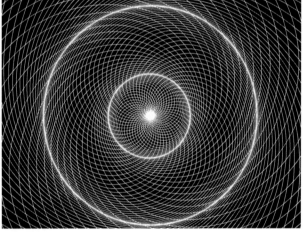

On the left we see the two source spirals spun at different nodes, one at Node 4 and the other at Node 6. Notice that the source spiral is exactly the same for both. Spinning it at different nodes simply makes for two scales of vortex and boundary condition. The image on the right shows the true energy pattern of the sunflower's Phi Double Spiral, with the boundary conditions being two fractal scales different in size.

I am in deep gratitude to the Sunflower deva for teaching me these great lessons in Phi spiral cosmometry!

Now let's check in with an Apple...

APPLE SEEDS DISPLAY PHI DOUBLE SPIRAL AND PENTAGRAM SYMMETRY

Like all plants and their fruits, an apple is a torus, and being a torus there's a chance we might be able to see the presence of the Phi Double Spiral pattern in its design. Of course, not every plant or fruit will be as clearly symmetrical and obvious in the display of this pattern as the sunflower (most are not, actually). In the case of an apple, the double spiral pattern is not apparent either on the outside surface or within the structure of the fruit inside. It is valid to wonder, then, whether this pattern is at play at all in the design of an apple. It's when we cut an apple in half horizontally that the story begins to emerge.

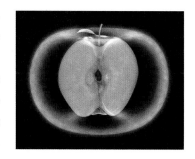

By Rasbak
commons.wikimedia.org

Everyone who has done this has seen a wonderfully symmetrical arrangement of seeds within the core of the apple. There are five of them (yes, a Fibonacci quantity), and they're evenly spaced around the central axis of the apple torus in a pentagram pattern. You might recall **Fact 5** about Phi, which is that five-fold geometric symmetry contains Phi ratios in its proportions. This alone shows us that the underlying energetic blueprint of an apple has Phi at its core, literally! The overall torus shape has a specific resonant five-fold symmetry within its structure.

What of the Double Spiral, though? Is there any evidence of its presence in this harmonious seed design? While it may not jump

out as obvious at first, it turns out that indeed there is. Each of the five seeds is held in a protective shell that has an elegant petal shape, somewhat like a candle flame, and this same shape is present at the center of a Phi Double Spiral. As you can see, when a double spiral pattern is created with 24 spirals in each direction (which accommodates pentagonal symmetry), we can see a very close match with both the internal petal forms to the seed shells, and the boundary condition with the outer surface of the apple. In the case of these seed shell spirals, the two curves are the same and therefore share a common boundary circle.

All of the examples in this chapter are, of course, obvious symmetrical ones. While nature displays this level of ideal patterning quite often, it is also very obscure in the shape and habit of most plants. Nature is wildly variable in energy dynamics and diversity is a well-known hallmark of ecosystems' success. It would be presumptuous of us to think that these patterns ought to always be visible, and if they're not then they don't apply. What is being proposed here is that these are *fundamental patterns*; idealized renderings of Phi-based toroidal field dynamics that can be considered present in the underlying energy dynamics of form and flow, even when not overtly apparent.

Let's explore a few other contexts wherein the Double Spiral pattern is evident, though the shape of the form is quite different than what we've seen so far.

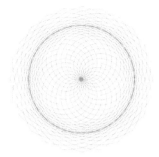

CHAPTER 28
EVERYTHING INCLUDING THE KITCHEN SINK

A pinecone provides a wonderful example of the Phi Double Spiral as both a "2-dimensional" pattern when looking at its base, as well as a complete toroidal field pattern with the spirals running throughout the internal form and defining the arrangement of the seeds. It becomes clear to see the interplay of this pattern between form and space as the pinecone expands, as pictured. This interplay is one of the first clues about the source and role of Phi in energy dynamics. The form we see is very much informed by the space itself, which makes sense when we remember that the space it not empty but rather a highly energetic field of electromagnetic vibration with a base resolution of a Planck unit.

Pratheep P S, www.pratheep.com

The interplay of space and form occurs across all scales with the Phi ratio providing a self-similar continuum of proportional relationship and seamless integration. As an example, let's shift our perspective from the scale of a cone to that of a whole tree and see how the torus and double spiral pattern present themselves.

BARKING UP THE RIGHT TREE

While the variety of trees and their unique shapes is an awesome study in creative design (as is true for all phyla of flora and fauna), they all have one thing in common; a form above ground that captures the energies of sunlight and carbon dioxide (CO_2), arising from and anchored by a form below ground that captures water and minerals as nutrients for growth, sustenance and hydraulic structure. These dynamics alone demonstrate the interplay between the form and the space it is manifest within. They also demonstrate the toroidal flow process as intrinsic to this interplay. In the case of trees, though (and all rooted plants), they do so in a dual torus system, which as we've seen is a fundamental attribute of many dynamical energy systems.

The above-ground system of leaves, branches and trunk harvest sunlight and CO_2, seen in the illustration on the previous page as a blue torus flowing inward at the top, while the below-ground system of roots draws water and minerals inward from the bottom of the magenta torus. We can imagine the ground-level interface between above and below as where the two tori meet. Of course, these two dynamics distribute the energy and nutrients throughout the entire tree, so this dual torus system is ultimately contained within a single torus flow process that encompasses the entire tree (an example of fractal embedding of tori). The overall flow process in this case is illustrated as the incoming water and nutrients at the bottom of the single torus, with the outgoing oxygen represented by the vortex at the top of the torus.

What of the double spiral? It's not as immediately evident in the overall shape or branching of a tree as it is in the pinecone and other plants. The pinecone, pineapple and cactus show us the double spiral pattern wrapping the outer surface of the torus (and permeating through it as in the pinecone). In the sunflower we see it almost flat, much like the image of the double spiral cross-section within the torus. To find its presence in a tree we need to take a deeper look at the torus.

The image to the right offers a view inside a torus where we can see the central column of vortex flow that defines the axis of the toroidal field. The outer double spiral pattern curves inward through a vortex, wraps around the axis column as it flows through the center, and then moves outward through the other vortex in a regenerative cycle. Does that central axis double spiral remind you of something tree-like?

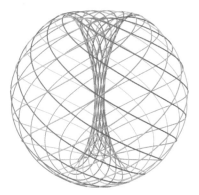

Indeed, the trunk of a tree is this central axis of a torus, and on many trees it is quite easy to see the beautiful basket weave pattern of the double spiral wrapping its entire surface. The trunk of a White Ash tree provides a very clear example. The pattern is evident from its base all the way up the trunk, even extending throughout the branches. In essence, a tree is showing us the fractal space within a torus field as the trunk, branches, twigs and leaves extend throughout this field to form a structure within a toroidal flow process. Is the double spiral pattern actually of the Phi ratio? Being neither flat like a sunflower nor round like a cactus, but rather a tube shape, how can we tell? Remarkably, this is one example of where the **Phi Scaling Angle** becomes apparent. A closer inspection of the basket weave pattern reveals an underlying symmetry that is based upon this angle, as seen in the image on the right.

The same pattern and Scaling Angle can be seen in the bark of this coast redwood tree found in the Henry Cowell Redwoods State Park in California:

Remember, the Phi Scaling Angle is found in our original Phi blueprint as the difference between the two directions of vortex spin, clockwise and counter-clockwise, what is technically called chirality.

Obviously, not all trees display such a clear double spiral pattern on the trunk and branches, and their overall shape is more often very asymmetrical and "distorted", looking nothing like a torus. And yet the underlying field pattern can be considered present, even if not in its ideal visual pattern, as it is in the case of this Date Palm tree where both the trunk and canopy show the double spiral pattern.

Tree trunks also provide a view into the integrated pattern of Radials, Rings and Spirals that we began our journey with back in Section 1. We can see evidence of the double **spiral** in the outer bark pattern. Everyone knows that trees have growth **rings**, which can be readily seen when a trunk is cut cross-wise. Also visible are **radial** cracks that appear when the wood begins to dry out after being cut. This highly weathered log shows the rings and radials very clearly. The central axis of a torus that is the trunk of a tree contains all three patterns as an integrated whole.

 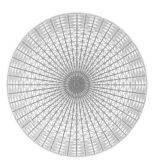

Photo: Michael Gäbler

FROM WOOD TO WATER

Over the years I've often wondered what action in the universal flow of energy causes the double spiral pattern to appear. Certainly, it was apparent that it's directly reflective of the torus flow process. There was something more that I was looking for, though, something that would offer an insight into what dynamic of energy flow was causing the double spiral itself to appear, whether in the obvious form of a torus or not. An insight into the answer came one evening as I was washing dishes after dinner. We all know how mundane that task can be day after day, and I was absentmindedly going at it when suddenly my innate Double Spiral Radar lit up. There on the surface of the chopping block that I was washing was a spectacular double spiral pattern being created by the water flowing over it!

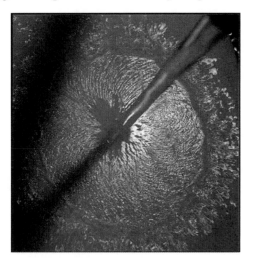 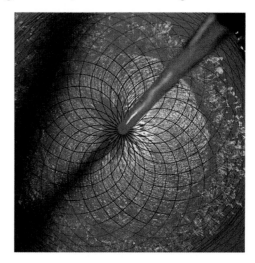

Of course, the dishwashing came to an abrupt halt as I put all of my attention onto this riveting discovery. Here was a dynamic fluid motion making as clear a double spiral as I had ever seen. I had intuited that the pattern in plants and trees was related to the fluid energies of water and air they are so intimately in relationship with, and even the daily spiraling Earth-Sun influence, and yet their static-looking appearance seemed to freeze this pattern in time. Perhaps they're not frozen in time but that what we're seeing in plants and trees is a longer flow of time making the same pattern as the sink water.

I had intuited that the pattern in plants and trees was related to the fluid energies of water and air they are so intimately in relationship with, and even the daily spiraling Earth-Sun influence, and yet their static-looking appearance seemed to freeze this pattern in time. Perhaps they're not frozen in time but that what we're seeing in plants and trees is a longer flow of time making the same pattern as the sink water.

This in itself is a compelling idea, but what really piqued my interest that evening was not only the double spiral pattern on the chopping block, but the vector of water that was streaming onto it. The sink faucet was making a distinctly directed flow of water, a vector of energy, which was meeting a different medium of a greater material density (the chopping block). The most circular double spiral pattern would appear when the water vector was at a 90° angle. When I would change the angle, the pattern would still be there but just stretch out in a more oblong shape.

Could the *flowing-energy-vector-meets-different-density-medium* dynamic seen in my kitchen sink be the answer to my question? Is this what's happening throughout the cosmos? It certainly is interesting to note that pinecones, cacti, apples, flowers and trees all form at an angle (often perpendicular) to their source, be it a branch as with cones or the ground as with cacti and trees. Even a hurricane has its central axis of spin perpendicular to the ground. And the Phi-spiraling accretion disc of a galaxy is commonly at 90° to the axis of its powerful plasma jets, which certainly appear as very focused vectors of energy defining the central axis of a torus field. Perhaps the gradient shift from a galaxy's high-density center (considered to be a black hole) to the less dense field of gases, stars and planets that comprise the accretion disc gives rise to the visible spiral vortex in a manner similar to the double

Source: NASA

spiral spread of the water on the chopping block? A question I invite astrophysicists to ponder…

WHERE THE OCEAN MEETS THE SHORE

Having had the good fortune of living for many years in Santa Barbara and Santa Cruz, California, and on the Big Island of Hawaii, I've been blessed to spend many a day walking on sandy beaches where the ocean meets the shore. I've long held that water is the most explicit visual example we have of the underlying fluid-dynamic of the cosmos. Nassim Haramein and other physicists[60] have proposed that the invisible medium of space is a superfluid "aether" of electromagnetic fluctuation, the dynamics of which are similar to what we experience with water. It is interesting to note that water itself is invisible, for it's only the optical effects of water's reflection and refraction, or another material in the water like sand, that make its dynamics visible. It seems water is truly a fractal manifestation of the geometry of space at our level of perception. And one thing is for sure at a beach; if you want to study the dynamics of fluid motion, there's a never-ending rhythm of wave after wave after wave to fill your cup.

Sandy beaches offer us a unique environment with a singular opportunity to catch a glimpse at our scale of perception into the fine granularity of the quantized structure of space. Although extremely crude by comparison, the bazillion grains of sand can be likened to the Planck-scale voxels, the PSUs, that fill all space, according to unified physics theory. (Loosely speaking, a grain of sand is near the midpoint between the Planck and Universal scales). Their size and density make them both easily affected by the forces of ocean waves and currents, and "solid" enough when aggregated to hold the effect of those forces in sculpted forms and visible patterns. In a way they're like the atoms and molecules of water itself, an aggregate of discrete units moving together in a fluid motion; water and sand merging as one dynamic with the "after image" left behind on the beach for us to study, or just simply contemplate its beauty.

FIELD PATTERN

While there are many wonderful examples of water's creative artistry imprinted in the patterns of sand, there is one in particular that has caught my eye on numerous occasions — a very clear and precise basket weave pattern. This pattern appears after an ocean wave breaks onto the shore, climbs up the sandy slope, and then gently flows back into the ocean. It's this last phase of its journey on land that creates the basket weave pattern.

These detail images confirm what I suspected… the angle of the basket weave is the Phi Scaling Angle, exactly as it is in the tree bark.

 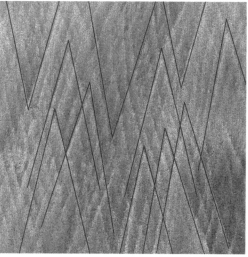

The pattern is, in fact, a *very large* Phi Double Spiral! It is stretched out across a flat surface where the less dense medium of water meets the denser medium of sand. This is the same phenomenon I saw on the chopping block in the kitchen sink, especially when I angled the surface so that the water's pattern was stretched in one direction. In effect, the wave pulling back out into the ocean is doing the same thing. We now have two fractal scales of the same pattern caused by the same interaction of water with a denser medium.

Although it's difficult to see due to the rapidly changing roll of a wave as it's cresting, I believe that this same basket weave dynamic also occurs in the water as it lifts, curls and spreads into an extended surface area that is the forming wave. The expanding motion requires a means for the rapidly shearing water flow to spiral in a coherent manner, doing so in both spiral directions.

Even the surface of the ocean itself exhibits this basket weave pattern (shown with a few Phi Scaling Angles highlighted)…

Compare that with the bark of the Ash tree we saw earlier…

I trust you can see more clearly what I mean when I say this is a fundamental Field Pattern.

FROM WATER TO STONE

As energy dynamics coalesce from the micro world of atoms to form the macro world of our physical reality, there is an intimate relationship between rigid crystalline structure and malleable fluid motion. Even a solid granite boulder was once in a molten state. In this one we can see that it, too, was at one time a flowing liquid with a distinct basket weave striation pattern that's now crystallized in its ancient legacy. While the angle of the weave is obviously not the Phi Scaling Angle, quite interestingly it does appear to be very close to double that angle (our binary scaling ratio).

Why would that be so? A question I invite the geologists to ponder…

SEEING THE LIGHT

In what may be the most essential demonstration of this phenomenon of the Phi Scaling Angle, in the midst of writing this book my friend and colleague, Clay Taylor, published an online article[61] presenting his study of the refraction of sunlight through an optical glass sphere. The premise for his inquiry is that a sphere is the most universal and primary form, and that by studying the refraction of sunlight we may come to understand properties of the way light and form interact that are more universal in nature (the sun is at such a great distance as a light source that the rays are, for all intents and purposes, consistently parallel rather than introducing parallax due to using a closer proximity light

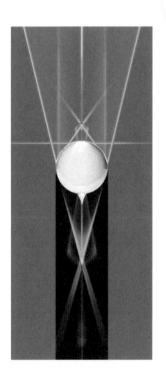
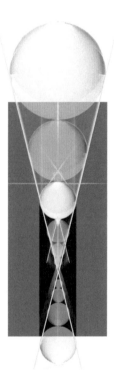

source). In this image he created to illustrate the consistent effects of refraction he was observing, it is easy to see that the Phi Scaling Angle is intrinsic to this most fundamental relationship of light and form. The first image is his original. In the second image I've added spheres that are scaling in Phi ratio, illustrating the origin of the Phi Scaling Angle, as seen in Chapter 25.

As fascinating and informative as this all is, what does it have to do with us? Is there any way we can see this field pattern in the design of our physical form and flow? As usual, it all depends on how you look at it.

THE EYES HAVE IT

Yes, that's an often-misused cliché, but in this case I mean it literally. The eyes, it turns out, do have it. Have a look…

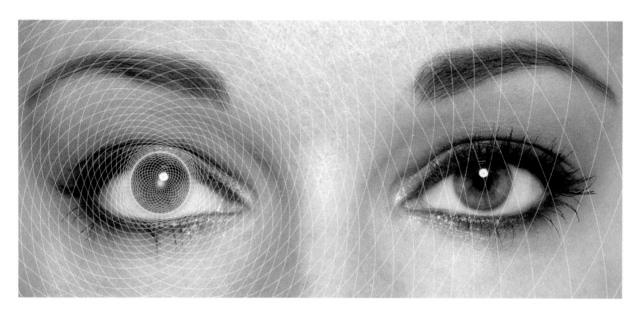

The most obvious toroidal form in our body is our eye; the receiver of Light that carries information, illuminating our vision in a feedback loop of perception and perspective — the windows into and onto our worldview, defining one of the most essential "boundary conditions" in our relationship to life. Look closely at the contours of the eyelids, the arc of the eyebrow, the curve of the bridge of the nose. From simple appearances, it certainly does look like the dynamic formation of our eyes and facial features surrounding them incorporate this fundamental double spiral design. Of course, we can map the double spiral over both eyes to reveal the dual symmetry, but I've chosen not to in this case so as to make it easier to see the pattern with a minimum of complexity.

Is there rigorous analysis or mathematical validation of the biophysics behind such a distinct correlation? Not that I am aware of. For my part, observing these patterns so vividly present in nature and seeing how they in→form energy-matter-information manifestation at a basic and universal level is compelling enough to warrant such deeper analysis.

FIELD PATTERN

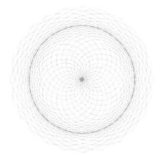

CHAPTER 29
ANGLES, PROPORTIONS, YOU AND ME

The influence of Phi on the formation of the physical universe is undeniably evident and remarkably prevalent. Even when looking for it simply through the lens of the Phi Vortex and Double Spiral pattern, it's readily observable from the great expanse of galaxies to the dual-torus currents of global atmosphere and ocean dynamics that spin hurricanes and leave basket weave signatures in the sand… and on to the revolutionary imprints of Sun-Earth spirals seen in the bark of trees, the pattern of plants, and the fractal seed-bearing vehicles of cones and fruits. In some ways, the spiral attribute of Phi is the most obvious one in nature. There are a great many more examples of it to be explored, and yet there are other attributes that help us deepen our perception of just how ubiquitous this Golden Ratio is in the structure of form and process of flow that co-exist at all scales. Let's delve a little deeper…

SCALING ANGLE

We've seen the attribute of the Phi Scaling Angle intimately associated with the double spiral pattern, finding that it is in fact the intrinsic angle that defines the chirality or spiral "handed-ness" of energy-matter interaction, somewhat like a differential angle in our original Phi blueprint. It is not too difficult to find examples of this angle in nature "on its own" though (in quotes because that's just a characteristic of what's visibly apparent, whereas we might rightly assume that the double spiral energetic is still operating in the formation process of these examples).

This Spruce tree exhibits an overall form that closely constrains to this angle over many years of growth. Notice how the angle is present in its branches as well, displaying a fractal symmetry of the scaling angle throughout.

We know from earlier examples of the spruce cone and needles that the double spiral pattern is present throughout the tree's growth processes. It appears that the tree is demonstrating the interplay between the left- and right-handed spirals in its overall form with the Phi Scaling Angle making this interplay visible.

Shifting from wood to water again, this beautiful red starfish and its seashell friends share the same angle as the spruce tree.

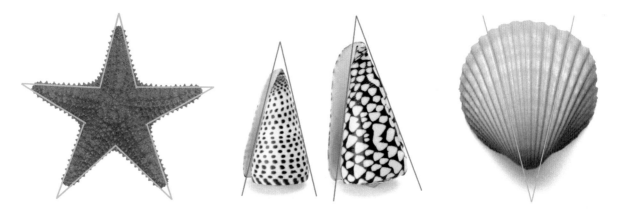

This spiral shell clearly seems to not be complying with our convention, though…

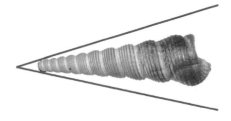

… until we realize its growth angle looks to be one-half of the scaling angle.

From seashells to she-shells, it appears this modern mermaid reveals that the human form has a distinct affinity for Phi scaling proportions. Even the double spiral curvature is evident (although it's prudent to acknowledge that this example is possibly a bit cheeky for some).

Which brings us to the presence of Golden Ratio proportions in the human form.

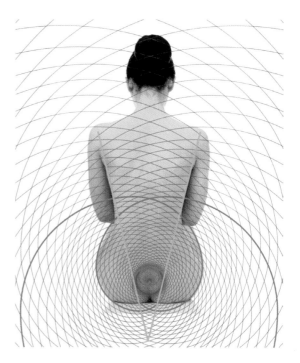

PHI PROPORTIONS

The simplest attribute of Phi is that of proportion in a ratio of 1:1.618.

This is, of course, the primary attribute upon which all others are based. While spirals and scaling angles do not explicitly exhibit this simple ratio relationship, it can be found in the structural system of our bodies in very straightforward ways. A few examples are shown in the proportions of the human skeleton in the illustration to the right. Note, as well, the two green scaling angles aligned with the ribs and femurs.

It is also well known that the scaling of the bones in our fingers is in close approximation to the Golden Ratio.

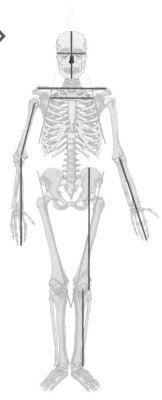

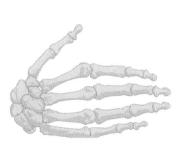

Why would our skeletal structure have Phi proportions? What functional role might it play in our physiological order? When it comes to capability and diversity of movement, we humans possess a unique and highly optimized structure that enables us to perform an incredible array of activity that the rest of the planet's species do not innately demonstrate a capacity for. From ballet to bicycling, playing musical instruments to playing tennis, the movements of our hands, arms, legs and torso exhibit a remarkable integrity of wholeness and harmony in coordinated mastery. What is the common thread of movement within our diversity of activity? Spirals. The ability to curl our fingers and grasp an object is directly a function of the Phi spiral. The same holds true for the curling of our arms and legs, and the twisting movement of our pelvis. All of these rotations are aligned with Phi proportions within the physiological structure of our bodies. While it's obvious that there are proportional variations of body structures in humans, and even more so within the vast diversity of other species, there certainly appears to be a harmonic relationship with the Phi ratio within our basic structural system. Curl your fingers now and you'll witness this intrinsic spiraling harmony that offers such a vast range of potential right at hand!

At the deepest levels of biological structures within our bodies' cells we also find evidence of Phi proportions, as seen on the next page in the spiral pathways of microtubule channels that cycle in Fibonacci values of 3, 5 and 8, and within the proportional structure of the DNA-B molecule.

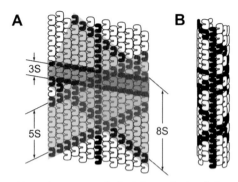
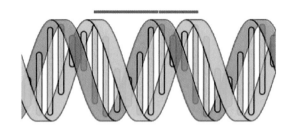

Extending microtubule A-lattice hydrophobic channels… results in helical winding patterns matching Fibonacci geometry.[62]

And one of the most fascinating instances of the double spiral pattern is found right at the center of our brain — the shape of the pineal gland. Its name is in recognition of the fact that it looks very similar to a pinecone, as was illustrated by Renée Descartes who referred to the pineal gland as the Seat of the Soul.[63] This rather humble little appendage in the middle of our heads has some remarkable properties that may tie it into a kind of universal holographic vision, which we'll explore in Section 7.

BACK TO THE BASICS

What is the origin of all this Golden Proportion throughout the cosmos? And what really is its function within the energetic dynamics of form and flow? Considering these questions requires us to go back to the very basics.

As we've explored, at the base resolution of the cosmos is the field of Planck Spherical Units — the PSU-IVM — that are electromagnetic oscillations in a state of equilibrium arranged in what may be called a 3-dimensional Flower of Life pattern. Since ancient times in many cultures, the Flower of Life pattern has been present in iconic symbolism found in various temples, perhaps the most mysterious and oldest of which is imprinted on a rose granite block at the Osireion Temple in Abydos, Egypt, where I took the picture below. It seems evident that many cultures were clued into this fundamental understanding a long time ago!

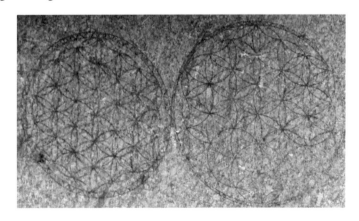

As seen in Chapter 9, this pattern is a 2-dimensional isotropic vector matrix wherein the circles are overlapping each other in hexagonal triangulation to be all-space-filling. It is this zerophase equilibrium symmetry that Nassim Haramein utilizes as the fundamental cosmic geometry for unified physics theories. And it is at this primary level of energetic articulation that we find our first instance of the Phi ratio coming into play, and it does so in complement to our other primary scaling ratio, the 2:1 octave.

As this illustration shows, the *overlapping* circle packing inherently contains the octave-doubling ratio of .5:1 (left). When the isotropic array is organized with *tangential* circle packing as Buckminster Fuller explored (right), the same proportional relationship is now a Phi ratio. Quite remarkably, our two fundamental systems of quantization, the Binary and Phinary, find their origin within the same isotropic symmetry.

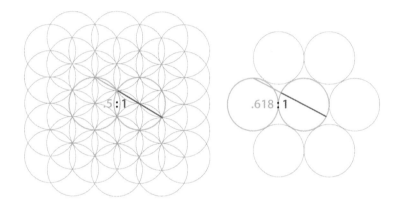

This may perhaps be correlated to a difference between the space-filling symmetry of the overlapping PSU-IVM's electromagnetic standing-wave interference pattern (the Planck-scale zerophase equilibrium state, which in Section 2 we showed has intrinsic octave scaling), and the non-space-filling atomic and molecular structures that are more associated with crystalline geometries and physical form (the non-equilibrious physically manifest state).

It is quite noteworthy that the **Phi Scaling Angle** also appears in this very basic level of energetic symmetry as the angle correlated with the tangential circle arrangement.

Even in the most fundamental geometric relationship of a triangle in a circle we find a phi ratio of **.618:1**. (The same holds true for a tetrahedron within a sphere, and in fact, the point of the phi segment that touches the sphere's surface is at the resonant latitude of 19.47°.)

As we can see, the Phi ratio is inherent in the very geometry of space from which all things arise. And it is this simple statement that leads us into the investigation of my original question about what the role and function of Phi is in cosmic energetics. While the answer resonates in me as being true, it's not what I was initially expecting!

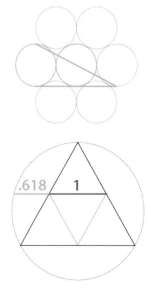

A glimpse into the hexagonal symmetry of the 3D Flower of Life PSU-IVM

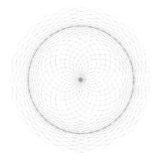

CHAPTER 30
DAMP IT ALL!

What is the source and role of this pattern in the energy dynamics of the cosmos?

For decades I've mused upon this question as I contemplated the many ways in which the attributes of Phi appear in nature. From spiral to angle to rotation to proportion, the ubiquitous presence of Phi suggests that the varieties of its expression are founded upon a fundamental, and universal, principle. For some reason, the cosmos incorporates this ratio in the energy dynamics of form and flow across all scales, even embedding it into the most basic cosmic geometry — the Platonic forms — as we'll soon see.

The self-similar quality of Phi clearly indicates that it plays a role in the fractal aspect of cosmic manifestation. It appears that this self-similarity allows for a harmonization in the scale (at the very least) of form and flow across the vastness of space, from Planck to Universal. This vast scale expanse also contains an equally vast gradient of energy density, from the low-density distribution of "dark energy" at the universal scale (called the Cosmological Constant, $\sim 10^{-30}$ gm/cm^3), to the high-density equilibrium ground state (the PSU-IVM, traditionally called the Planck Density, $\sim 10^{93}$ gm/cm^3); a gradient spanning 122 orders of magnitude. (See Chapter 20 for an explanation of the resolution of this vast energy density discrepancy, known as the "vacuum catastrophe" in physics.)

Discovering the Phi Boundary Condition, which defines an inside/outside component to the vortex and double spiral energy patterns, oriented me towards Phi's role as having something to do with delineating the relationship between form and space, specifying the necessary limits that make form possible. It's as if Phi is more fundamentally an attribute of the space itself, and that the visible manifestation of it we see in form is a secondary outcome. This is similar to the idea that the Octave Doubling ratio found in the IVM structure may in→form the crystallization process of snowflakes, which are directly related to the IVM cosmometry with their common hexagonal symmetry. Energetic resonance with these ratios may be *a priori* to the manifesting form. Given that the cosmos is one big ocean of vibration, just as is music, it stands to reason that vibratory resonance and harmonic structure is inevitably a key aspect of how Phi contributes to the definition and proportion of form within the formlessness of space. As Albert Einstein said, *"Physical objects are not in space, but these objects are spatially extended. In this way the concept empty space loses its meaning."* [64]

The primary system that describes relationships of resonance within a spectrum of energy frequencies is the harmonic structure of music. Standing wave patterns within a single musical tone, such as a vibrating string, contain a very specific set of harmonic ratios, called overtones, which define the tonal quality of the sounds we hear. These ratios define frequencies of resonance that are in whole-number relationship with the fundamental frequency we hear from the string's vibration. These same resonance relationships also exist within the musical scale, with the interaction of many notes creating a complexity of interference patterns that form a rich sonic tapestry we experience, for example, as Beethoven's 9th Symphony and its cosmic polar opposite, Roll Over Beethoven. If Phi is somehow involved in delineating the whole-number ratio vibratory interactions of music, which is a direct correlation to the vibratory interactions of energy-matter formation within space, what is its role?

The answer to this came as both a surprise and an "of course" aha moment for me. You might say it was staring me in the face the whole time I was observing nature's Phi patterns, though I hadn't yet changed my perceptual orientation to see it.

Credit for this insight is due to the pioneering research of Richard Merrick who, through inspiration of intuitive visions early in his life, pursued a quest to understand the harmonic structure of sound and how the musical system it defines in turn informs our psycho-physiological ability to perceive and enjoy music. While the breadth of his research is too great to sum up in this writing, the core of it is centered on his study of the basic standing wave pattern of a single tone when vibrating through a round cylinder. In very simple terms, this is what he found…

As mentioned above, a single musical note, no matter what instrument makes it, is actually composed of a collection of frequencies that are in very specific and well-defined whole-number harmonic ratio relationships. Without going into the technical aspects, the root note we hear has a series of overtones that are in ratios of 2:1, 3:1, 4:1, 5:1, etc. These overtone frequencies are where the energy of the root tone (the actual vibratory energy) finds greatest resonance within the spectrum of sound frequencies that are higher than the root tone. The frequencies of these overtones of resonance are the same for each instrument, but they differ in strength (amplitude) and phase (interference pattern) relative to each other from instrument to instrument, thus giving each instrument its unique quality of sound, called timbre. These frequencies can be thought of as the *foreground* of the manifesting tone, the energetic vibration in resonance that we hear. What Merrick came to realize as he analyzed the standing wave pattern of the harmonic overtone series is that this foreground resonance is in very specific relationship to a *background* of non-resonant "gaps" between the overtones. These are areas in the standing wave interference pattern where the energy goes towards stillness and silence rather than resonance, what is called damping. It turns out that this damping function is directly correlated to the Phi ratio within the overall interference pattern. What Merrick discovered is that *Phi is what damps energy back to zero*, and in so doing it actually makes possible the resonance of the overtones, *providing the necessary limits to their resonance* that would otherwise bleed over into each other and resonate wildly out of control if not constrained in this way. In other words, within an acoustic standing wave interference pattern,

Phi is defining the natural boundary conditions between the foreground resonating frequencies and the background silent space between them.

Phi's role is to damp the energetics back to zero!

This remarkable insight put everything into perspective for me. My questions about *what defines the limits* of a pinecone's double spiral interference pattern, the double spiral in water and basket weave in sand and tree bark, the forms and patterns of seashells, starfish, etc., became resolved with the concept that Phi is providing the damping function within all cosmic energy dynamics — the boundary condition that eliminates enharmonic frequencies so that the resonance of form and flow is optimized within its background environment of space.

So, for example, when we're looking at the double spiral pattern below, instead of seeing it as the physically manifest component, consider it as the empty space between the physical form, just as it appears as empty space within a pinecone and sunflower.

What Merrick discovered is that Phi is what damps energy back to zero, and in so doing it actually makes possible the resonance of the overtones, providing the necessary limits to their resonance that would otherwise bleed over into each other and resonate wildly out of control if not constrained in this way.

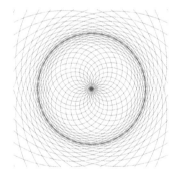  

The double spiral pattern is showing us how the energy is damped back into zerophase equilibrium so that the manifesting form can have a defined limit of physical resonance. Something needs to provide this function, otherwise the cosmos would spin out of control into a chaotic sea of overly excited resonance, and Phi appears to be fulfilling this role (hence the name of this chapter.)

Merrick proposes this idea as a fundamental principle of cosmic nature in what he calls **Harmonic Interference Theory**. His research shows that our very physiology exhibits the incorporation of this principle, with the shape and function of our auditory system (ears, cochlea, etc.) being a direct result of this damping principle of Phi. Even the proportional structure of our skeletal system is defined by the *spaces* between the bones that are where the Phi ratio damps the energy, providing specific limits to the form and scale of the bones.

Merrick's book, *INTERFERENCE: A Grand Scientific Musical Theory* (available for download at www.interferencetheory.com), covers the technical aspects of Harmonic Interference Theory in depth.

His explanation of Phi damping in relation to all cosmic dynamics is so effectively stated that I'm including here an extensive excerpt from the chapter called Perfect Damping, with permission from the author.

"When musical tones vibrate they always assume the form of a standing wave. Within the standing wave, energy reflects and resonates in equal and opposite directions, causing the formation of sympathetic whole number harmonic waves. Without the stabilizing effect of standing waves, there would be no sound and we would have no ears. Indeed, we would not even exist without the structuring properties of standing waves resonating at every level of our reality from the quantum level beneath atomic matter to the cellular structure of our bodies.

At the same time, without harmonic damping to control the resonance of standing waves, atomic structures could not bond, planets would not have formed and life would not have evolved. Unbridled oscillation would have rent asunder any attempt at coherent organization of energy, leaving a cosmos full of free particles with no way to stick together. Fortunately, we find ourselves in a place where resonance and damping are perfectly balanced; producing a harmony we are able to hear with our own ears.

The most important thing to realize about standing waves is there is no room for fractional or enharmonic wavelengths. A standing wave simply cannot be sustained if there is any wave partial that is not a whole number multiple of the fundamental. In fact, the sympathetic vibration that produces a musical tone will cease to exist if such a frequency is introduced. To keep this from occurring, a standing wave naturally polices itself and annihilates enharmonic frequencies that may attempt to form during resonant vibration. The question of course is what mechanism causes this to occur?

The police action inside a standing wave can be found in the proportions located in the background space out of which whole number wave frequencies resonate. As we already know, this background is the result of Fibonacci proportions as they converge adjacently to the golden ratio. We can even see how this affects the spacing of gaps that form between the first sixteen partials in a harmonic standing wave.

In Figure 41, gaps form in the standing wave of a single tone at simple harmonic proportions — the locations where enharmonic Fibonacci proportions have been thinned out — thus, enabling the wave energy of the fundamental frequency (shaded heavy lines) to be shared between all of the co-resident wave partials. Without this thinning process, there would be no gaps and the tone would not have the necessary space between whole number harmonics within which to vibrate.

Figure 41 - Standing wave of the first sixteen harmonic partials

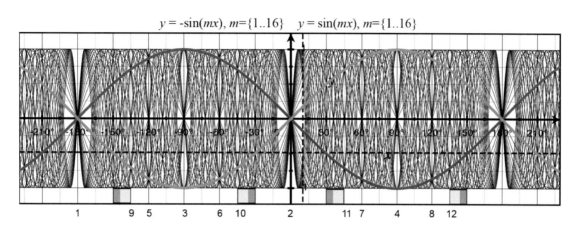

In the diagram, the first 16 vertical gaps are numbered along the bottom according to visual gap size. Unlike the earlier spectral analysis of two tones, the gaps in a single tone follow an evenly divisible pattern of halves, fourths, sixths and twelfths, thereafter shrinking in toward the convergent nodal points located at multiples of 180° on the horizontal axis. The last four gaps, numbered 13 through 16, can be seen to occur at a point inside the $\pi/12$ spaced grid lines (at the border in the small shaded bars at bottom). In fact, they occur at about the proportion of a small golden ratio between the grid lines. So why, you might ask, is this important?

Well, beginning with the 13th gap in the harmonic series, each subsequent concordant gap becomes increasingly smaller than $\pi/12$. This occurs naturally as harmonic waves approach the denser interference regions near the nodes where resonance damps down to zero. Here the waves become compressed, less resonant and increasingly dissonant, thus creating a dense barrier around each node that captures and contains the inner coherence of simple harmonic proportions in the numeric range {1..12}, such as 3:2, 4:3 and 5:4.

In other words, the semi-transparent area either side of the node measuring $\pi/12$ in width is a place where enharmonic frequencies cannot resonate as easily, thus fading away to leave mostly clear space around the nodes at 180° (π) multiples. Inside this protective envelope, each wave partial then has the slack it needs to vibrate in its own space while sharing the vibrating medium with other harmonics. Outside this sonic barrier, the harmonic waves begin to interlock, dampen, become frozen and ultimately crystallize. More than a nice explanation of a musical tone, we can find the same behavior everywhere in nature.

For example, a bird egg can be defined as twelve sinusoidal harmonics encased in an outer damping shell. To prove this point, take the length of the 10π /12 non-damped region in the preceding standing wave as a proportion of its total displacement of 2 to yield the ratio (5π /6) : 2 or 1.3090. This number happens to exactly match another theoretical geometric model of the egg by Carlos Rojas based on cubic proportions of the golden ratio: Φ^3 : 2Φ or 1.3090. And, when we cross-reference this number to a survey of 34 species of bird eggs, we find the average length to width proportion to be about the same at 1.3097. As illustrated in Figure 42, the average dimensions of a bird egg closely match the same theoretical Φ-damping proportions of a standing wave.

Figure 42 - Harmonic damping in an eggshell

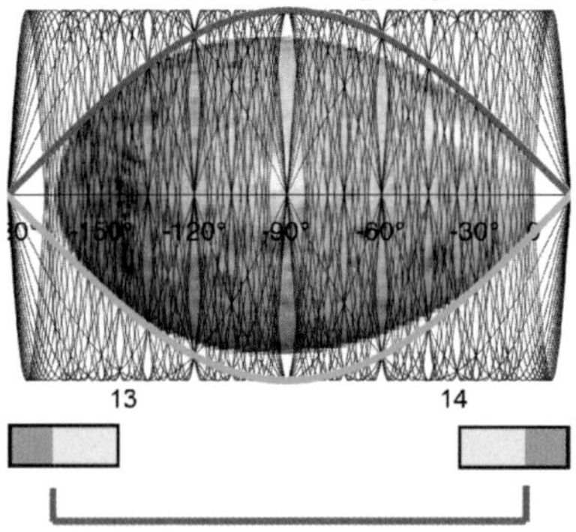

The pressure of Fibonacci proportions converging to Φ inside a harmonic standing wave is the only possible explanation for the physiological structure of the common egg, though how this occurs as a property of DNA has yet to be fully understood. Perhaps Aesop's little fable of The Goose That Laid the Golden Eggs (with origins tracing back to the Egyptians!) is not so much about alchemy or gold metal as it is an allegory involving the role of the golden ratio in the shape of the humble egg.

Intrinsic to this wondrous process of perfect damping are the qualities of symmetry, reflexivity and whole number structure of space. But it is the force of natural damping that provides coherence and prevents "overly exuberant" resonance from forming fractional waves. Beginning with the 13th convergent gap at the ratio of about 1.3, the golden ratio acts as a kind of physical container to keep standing waves from simply exploding. But how would modern science explain this strange relationship between "unlucky 13" and the golden ratio.

Ironically, in the field of acoustics, the one thing you do not want is a standing wave. In a performance hall or home theatre, acoustic engineers go to great lengths to construct spaces and use materials that act to cancel standing wave reflection so that the original sound and music is propagated cleanly. Since reflection can occur between any two parallel surfaces, it is important to choose proportions and angles that eliminate this possibility. Of course, eliminating reflection is hard to do in a rectangular theatre or box speaker enclosure where every side is parallel and a potential reflector of standing waves.

In the field of amplified speaker design, there is a long-known secret about how to keep unintended standing waves from forming. Sealed box enclosures are always built with interior proportions approximating the golden ratio and its inverse, such as 0.62 × 1.0 × 1.62. These proportions are widely considered anti-harmonic and optimal for eliminating standing waves inside a speaker box. This works because standing waves cannot form when reflected at or near the proportion of the golden ratio or its inverse. Similarly, rooms and auditoriums built in this proportion will not echo and, along with non-reflective materials, avoid extraneous dissipation or cancellation of the original sound energy that can occur in interfering waves…

So why does this work? Because Φ is an infinite irrational number that cannot be evenly divided by whole number ratios to sustain a standing wave and co-resident harmonic partials. As the Fibonacci series diverges from the harmonic series after 13:8 (=1.625), it begins to converge infinitely to Φ (≈1.61803) between harmonic proportions, thereby Φ-damping all enharmonic partials in the standing wave. In this way, the golden ratio is the perfect damping force that attenuates physical resonance in nature and enables the formation of whole number harmonic proportions in a standing wave.

If we had to sum all this up in one concept, it might go as follows. The golden ratio acts as a "strange attractor" for the Fibonacci "growth spiral" that then "wraps around" the harmonic series beginning with the thirteenth partial to contain resonance. Wave partials based on Fibonacci ratios from thirteen up die out as they get ever nearer to Φ. Within this natural damping field, the first twelve harmonic waves can then resonate into geometric shapes. One of the great philosophical truths of all time is that the harmonic and Fibonacci series have been working together like this from the very first moments of our universe to create organic structure and imbue it with flexibility.

The role of damping in flexible organic systems can even be found in our own anatomy. A January 2003 article in The Journal of Hand Surgery entitled "The Fibonacci Sequence: Relationship to the Human Hand" found that the proportions of the Fibonacci series could describe the equiangular proportions between the midpoint spaces of joints in the spiral of a clenched hand. For the first time, this report suggested that Fibonacci proportions might have something to do with the space or gap between bones rather than the more popular notion that it defines the proportions of the bones themselves. Of course, the small gaps in our joints are precisely what give us the freedom of physical movement.

Fibonacci proportions in life act to damp and contain unrestrained harmonic growth, accounting in some way for every gap, crevice, slice or cavity found in any life structure. If we characterize the Fibonacci series as a surgeon, the golden ratio would be its infinitely sharp scalpel. The material silence of these gaps is the very thing that enables our joints to flex and articulate, thus allowing the purposeful movement necessary for survival. Just wrapping the Fibonacci spiral of our hand around an object is itself a damping action upon whatever we grasp.

And while it is usually overlooked, the "silent" space separating harmonics is as important as the energy itself. In our perception of sound, it is the separation or "articulation" between overlapping waves that actually enables us to distinguish one tone from another and maintain our auditory attention level over time. Without these gaps as predictable "signposts," sound would be an unrecognizable sonic roar. We would not have survived to speak and understand language, much less enjoy the diversity and differentiation required of music."

In this simple yet comprehensive summation, we find that there is an intimate "always-and-only co-existing" (as Bucky Fuller would describe it) interplay between the foreground dynamic activity of energy in whole number (quantized) harmonic ratios of musical resonance, and the background containment of this dynamic activity in Fibonacci number Phi ratio damping to stillness and silence. The Binary (Octave) and Phinary (Fibonacci) number systems, which are so similar in their fundamental values (e.g. 16 and 1.6), weave interference patterns of resonance and stillness in the hologramic energy dynamics of the cosmos, defining the form and flow of universal manifestation. Decimal values of Phinary fractal self-similarity (Fibonacci resolution approximating 1.618…) oscillate around whole number values of Binary octave structure (8, 16, 32, 64, etc.) in a cosmic musical holomovement. The irrationality of pure mathematical Phi assures both the wiggle room for resonant vibration at all scales and the damping of this vibration all the way to the Planck scale zerophase ground state from which the vibration arises.

The Binary (Octave) and Phinary (Fibonacci) number systems, which are so similar in their fundamental values (e.g. 16 and 1.6), weave interference patterns of resonance and stillness in the hologramic energy dynamics of the cosmos, defining the form and flow of universal manifestation.

This last point is one that must be highlighted — that resonant vibration *arises* from the zerophase state. In the years following his writing of *INTERFERENCE*, Richard Merrick came to also understand that the process of resonance formation is *additive from* Phi-damping *to* resonance, rather than solely due to subtractive damping of enharmonic frequencies.

Phi-damping removes non-resonant frequencies in a subtractive process that converges towards mathematical Phi in ever-increasing accuracy as the Fibonacci numbers increase in magnitude, creating a **Phi-Damping Well** of ever-higher frequencies (smaller wavelengths) that theoretically continue to infinity (i.e. the infinite irrational value of mathematical Phi).

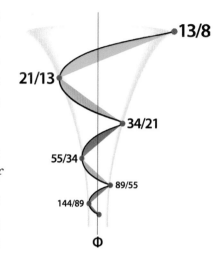

Merrick came to realize that the harmonic tones we hear as resonant sound do not pre-exist the Phi-Damping Well but rather *form out of the well itself.* The fundamental tone we hear (such as when a guitar string is plucked) is the result of higher frequencies **heterodyning** (when higher frequencies combine to produce lower frequencies through constructive interference), such that the whole-number harmonics and fundamental tone *emerge from* this additive process. They are the *result* of Fibonacci partials bubbling up recursively from Phi to define the harmonic resonance of the fundamental and overtones, in tandem with the damping that provides the structure (i.e. boundary condition) within which the emergent resonance becomes stable and coherent. **So the order of coherent processes in nature is: Phi-damping >> Fibonacci attenuation >> harmonic formation >> resonance.** This is the case not just in coherent resonance of sound but for coherence of all form at all scales.

In a paper by S. Giandinoto, R. L. Amoroso, and E.A. Rauscher (the latter of whom co-authored papers with Nassim Haramein) entitled *Incursion Of The Golden Ratio Φ Into The Schrödinger Wave Function Using The Φ Recursive Heterodyning Set,*[65] the authors *"demonstrate that Phi is... intimately related to the quantum realm by virtue of its presence in the quantum mechanical wave function...* [the basis for their demonstration being] *derived by solving the Schrödinger Wave Equation and the use of the Phi recursive heterodyning set of wavelengths."* By using the same Fibonacci heterodyning process as described by Merrick, the authors show that quantum mechanical wave functions that are intrinsic to all manifest reality (being the basis for all atomic and molecular characteristics) directly correspond to the same resonance and damping process found in musical resonance. In their conclusion, the authors state, *"this paper has demonstrated that individual wavelengths and/or frequencies are actually a summation of an infinite number of wavelengths or frequencies."* In other words, **the manifest universe emerges from the Planck-scale aether field as a constructive process of quantum wave functions heterodyning Fibonacci frequencies in smaller-to-larger wavelengths to form whole-number harmonic resonance that we ultimately hear as sound and see as physical form** (the Acoustic attribute of our cosmometry exploration). Haramein's model of unified physics is based upon this same premise of harmonic resonance bubbling up in fractal scales from Planck to Universal, with his Scaling Law for

Organized Matter[66] (written in collaboration with Elizabeth Rauscher and Michael Hyson) showing Phi ratio relationships throughout.

Independent researcher, Dan Winter, also proposes this function of Phi heterodyning from the Planck scale in what he calls Phase Conjugate Implosive Charge Compression.[67] In this chart he depicts values of size and periodicity for physical phenomena — ranging from the hydrogen atom to the Galactic Year — that are determined by multiplying the Planck Length (or Planck Time) by powers of Phi. For example, three radii of hydrogen are determined by Planck Length x Phi to the 116, 117, and 118th powers (e.g. 1.6×10^{-35} meters x 1.618^{116}).

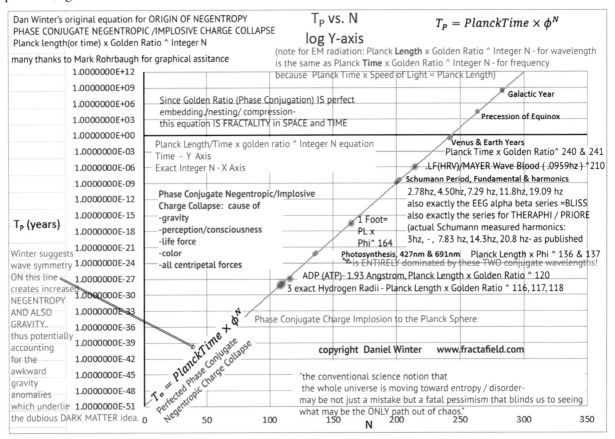

To put the above in everyday terms, Phi is involved in both the emergence of form (i.e. the pinecones physical seed structures that we can see — resonance), as well as defining the boundary condition the form exists within (the space between the seeds and the outer boundary of the pinecone itself — damping).

Merrick has determined that there is a threshold of resonance and damping effects at the 13:8 Fibonacci number pair (which correlates precisely with the octave ratio in the harmonic structure of music we'll explore in the next section), such that Fibonacci ratios above 13:8 (e.g. 8:5, 5:3, 3:2, 2:1) provide the founding partials for further heterodyning of other whole number harmonics that share the fundamental's energy, while those below the 13:8 threshold create the damping locations that provide the containment necessary to establish coherence.

Phi-Recursive Heterodyning

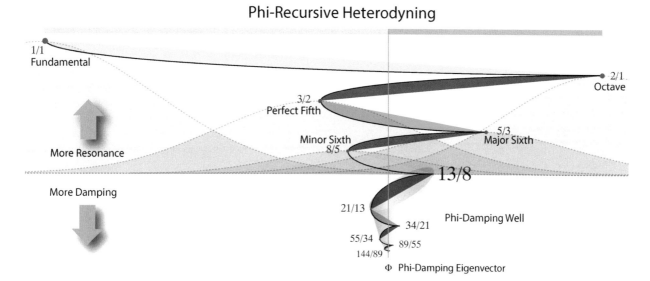

This illustration from Merrick shows the relationship of increasing whole-number resonance above the 13:8 threshold and increasing damping below it.

It is noteworthy here that, given the Fibonacci proportionality of the Phi-Damping Well, it stands to reason that the damping vortex would match the Phi Scaling Angle in its whirlpool of convergence.

In Section 3, we saw that the coherent flow process of a Torus provides a model of seamless fractal embedding across the vast range of cosmic scale. As we know, a torus has two vortexes that converge toward a central still point — the *space* that defines the torus shape. Are these the same Phi-Damping Wells that are found in standing wave patterns of sound? Are musical tones resonating fields of toroidal energy flow?

In Section 6 we'll explore the emerging art and science of Cymatics that provides a visual resource with which to study the geometric flow and structure of acoustic interference patterns in a liquid medium, such as water. It is evident from studying these patterns that there's a dynamic interplay between the actively resonating energetic flows and the zones of stillness in between them that combine to make astoundingly beautiful geometric forms (in the image to the right, for example, the zones of stillness are the lighter highlighted patterns). Given that the foundation of our cosmic model is based upon a superfluid medium of electromagnetic energy, and that both

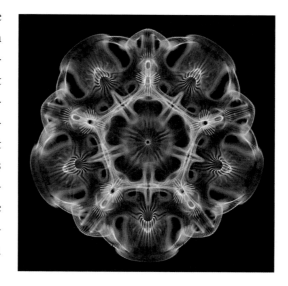

water and the sound waves that travel through it are fractal harmonics of this medium, it makes sense that the study of Cymatics may offer great insight into the form and flow dynamics that comprise all physical manifestation in the cosmos.

In preparation for that journey, though, we must first circle back to where we left off at the end of Section 2: Starting From Zero, when we introduced the origin of dynamic pulsation within our overall cosmometry model — Buckminster Fuller's Jitterbug motion of the Vector Equilibrium. Cosmometry is the study of the Patterns, Structures, Processes and Systems of energy dynamics as they manifest in the universe. We've seen how the Flow Process of the Torus appears in nature as the Field Patterning of the Double Spiral, and how this and other attributes of the Phi ratio are inherent in the energy dynamics that weave the interference patterns of form and the space between form.

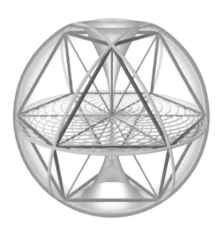

The Unified Model of Cosmometry (seen to the right and introduced at the end of the previous section) offers a simple basis for illustrating an integrated relationship between the zerophase Vector Equilibrium, the Torus, and the Phi Double Spiral. It's time to bring our attention back to the Vector component of this model and see how the dynamic Jitterbug oscillation is not only the source of structural resonance in what are called the Platonic Forms, it also inherently offers a context for the emergence of our very familiar 3-Dimensional perceptual framework and reveals even more the presence of the Golden Ratio of Phi in the Structural Integrity of cosmic design.

Section 4 Endnotes

56   http://www.merriam-webster.com/dictionary/field

57   Dr. Rollin McCraty, quoted in HeartMath Institute Newsletter, June 2016.

58   See this website for Phi carried out to 5,000 decimals:
    https://www.cs.arizona.edu/icon/oddsends/phi.htm

59   Acknowledgement goes to Robert Hutchins who also discovered the significance of the Phi Scaling Angle independently.

60   "If Spacetime Were a Superfluid, Would It Unify Physics—or Is the Theory All Wet?", by Clara Moskowitz, ScientificAmerican.com, June 18, 2014.
    https://www.scientificamerican.com/article/superfluid-spacetime-relativity-quantum-physics/

61   Taylor, Clay, "Spherical Refraction - The Magnetic Relationship Between Light and the Universal Shape", February 7, 2017.
    https://www.artofclaytaylor.com/single-post/2017/02/07/
    Spherical-Refraction---The-Relationship-Between-Light-and-the-Universal-Shape

62   Penrose, Roger, PhD, OM, FRS, and Hameroff, Stuart, MD *Consciousness in the Universe: Neuroscience, Quantum Space-Time Geometry and Orch OR Theory*, Journal of Cosmology, 2011, Vol. 14.
    http://journalofcosmology.com/Consciousness160.html

63   "Descartes and the Pineal Gland", Stanford Encyclopedia of Philosophy, 2005 (revised 2013).
    https://plato.stanford.edu/entries/pineal-gland/

64   Einstein, A., *Metaphysics of Relativity*, 1950.

65   Giandinoto, S., Amoroso, R. L., Rauscher, E.A., *Incursion Of The Golden Ratio Φ Into The Schrödinger Wave Function Using The Φ Recursive Heterodyning Set*, Advanced Laser Quantum Dynamics Research Institute.
    http://science.trigunamedia.com/fractalsynth/GiandinotoAmorosoRauscher.pdf

66   Haramein, N., Rauscher, E.A., and Hyson, M. *Scale Unification - A Universal Scaling Law for Organized Matter* (2008). Proceedings of the Unified Theories Conference. ISBN 9780967868776.
    https://resonance.is/research-publications/

67   Winter, Daniel, *Fractal Space Time*
    http://www.fractalfield.com/fractalspacetime
    "Scaling Law of Time" calculator in Google Sheet: https://drive.google.com/
    file/d/0B1e1ytUD-G6RMVFnRVY1VW44Z2M/view

SECTION 5
STRUCTURAL INTEGRITY

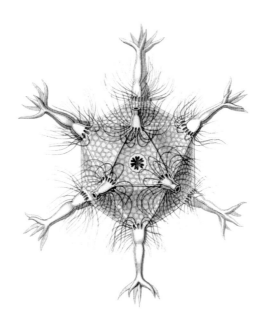

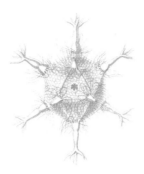

SECTION 5
STRUCTURAL INTEGRITY

Tension.

What arises in you when you read that word? Does it evoke a feeling of some sort, a reaction in your mind, emotions, body?

Clearly there is a lot of what's called tension in our world and in the hectic complexity of daily modern life, and it's typically considered to be not very good for us. To lessen this tension and the stress associated with it, we're offered through media channels a barrage of ways to soothe it, from pills and pain relievers to alcohol and fantasies of white sand beaches. And yet somehow the tension in life always seems to remain present.

We speak of "tensions running high" between people, armies, nations, with the implications tending towards conflict and fighting if the tensions escalate. In the face of fear and danger we inevitably tense up, feeling an overall contraction in our body, in our gut, as we prepare to deal with the circumstance at hand. Even when we wake up from a night's sleep, we can feel the tension in our muscles as we start to move, stretch and activate our body to step into a new day.

These experiences of tension have a negative connotation associated with thoughts and feelings we'd prefer to avoid. There is a flip side to tension, though, a simple fact that places the presence of tension in a whole new context:

Life and the Universe we live in would not exist without tension.

That's right, without tension in your body you would be a useless pile of floppy skin and jumbled bones. Without tension in the atomic and molecular realm there would be no matter. Without tension in the cosmos there would be no cosmos. Perhaps it's of use, then, to reframe our understanding of tension and come into a more whole and harmonious relationship with the role it plays in the dynamics of life. There is not a single system in the world that does not contain tension, be it an organism, an ecosystem, a family, or a society. As such, tension clearly holds a key function in the integrity of these and all systems. Too much or too little tension can introduce instabilities, pushing systems towards the extremes of disequilibrium. Tune a guitar string too tight and it will snap. Tune it too loose and it will lose its resonant tone. Give it just the right amount of tension and it will ring out in harmonious beauty of sound and song — a feedback loop of resonance and integrity. More than an analogy, this same dynamic is literally true for all vibrating mechanisms in the universe, which as we've come to realize is everything there is. **The cosmos and all systems within it are an orchestra of instruments playing an eternal symphony of universal resonance.**

So, what does all this tension have to do with Structure? As it turns out… everything.

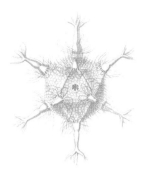

CHAPTER 31
TENSEGRITY

"All structures are tensegrity structures from the solar system to the atom…
Everything we call structure is synergetic and exists only as a consequence of
interactions between divergent (compressional) and convergent (tensional) forces."
– Buckminster Fuller, Synergetics Dictionary[68]

In 1949, Kenneth Snelson introduced Buckminster Fuller to an innovative method of building geometric forms. Snelson was an art student in a summer program at Black Mountain College in North Carolina, and Fuller was a professor teaching about his synergetic geometry. His innovation was to incorporate a continuous line of tension (utilizing thread, string or wire, for example) that wrapped around the ends of rigid struts and stabilized the whole system into a geometric form, even though the struts were not touching each other. The struts were actually "floating" independent of each other, serving the role of compression members, while the thread of tension connected them together to form a stable geometric structure. The interplay of a continuous line of tension with discontinuous "islands" of compression is what caught Fuller's eye. For him at that time, Snelson's innovation provided a key insight into the fundamental dynamics of the energetic-synergetic geometry he was exploring — tension is what creates the structural integrity of all atomic elements, and therefore of all physical manifestation. It is this "tensional integrity" that Fuller came to call Tensegrity. (Unfortunately, Snelson's original contribution to this insight became buried for many years under the prodigious magnitude of Fuller's personal mission, and he didn't entirely agree with Fuller's perspective on the subject, yet it's important to give credit where it's due.)

Stereographic image of a tensegrity structure.
Cross your eyes to overlap the images and see it in 3D.
Source: Cmglee [CC BY-SA 3.0]

In his study of the tensegrity of energetic geometry, Fuller came to realize that **the forces of tension and compression always-and-only-coexist in all structures and systems**. Tension begets compression and vice-versa. The nucleus of atoms — composed of protons and neutrons — are bound by a so-called "strong force" of tension (which unified physics theory shows is actually gravity at the atomic scale, i.e. quantum gravity) that compresses the nucleus into a stable structure. The same holds true for all molecular structure, wherein the individual atoms (islands of compression) are held together by the same dynamics of tension-compression tensegrity. Scaling this up, all structure — from the mineral and biological forms here on Earth, to the Solar System, interstellar constellations, galaxies, galactic superclusters, and the universe as a whole — is a product of the coexisting tension-compression dynamic. The fundamental difference between Snelson's and Fuller's tension-compression models and cosmic dynamics is that **the models use a string or wire to induce (i.e. represent) tension, wherein the cosmos uses electromagnetism and gravity to accomplish the same**.

When we shift our perspective from the "objects" of form to the relationships of energy dynamics, it becomes possible to see how the three components of Cosmometry, Unified Physics and Music are each a lens through which we are describing one thing.

Why is this important in our exploration of cosmometry? How does it relate to the fractal-hologramic model of cosmic manifestation?

In the pursuit of defining a model of wholeness that may contribute to a more accurate description of the workings of the cosmos, the concept of tensegrity offers a framework upon which to shift our perspective from focusing on the compression components (i.e. the "particles" of reductionist science) to the pattern integrity of the tension component. It is commonly accepted in physics that at the quantum-atomic scale, there is actually no "matter" as we know it. There's only the energy dynamics of electromagnetic interactions in ever-changing standing wave patterns. These standing wave patterns are, literally, the presence of the cosmic hologram, just as a holographic image is formed by standing wave patterns of coherent laser light. Within this vast ocean of electromagnetic energy dynamics is the constant interplay between tension and compression that manifests as the physical universe. Atoms are standing wave patterns of electromagnetic energy that combine into larger geometric constellations of standing wave patterns called molecules, that in turn combine together in larger standing wave patterns we call matter — yet it's all the same dynamic occurring in a self-similar fractal manner. The only difference is the degree of compression, or density, that the tension component manifests, and that's an attribute of the geometry of atoms and the molecular structures they create. **It is this tensegrity of energy-matter-information that is the basis for the structural integrity of the cosmos.**

When we shift our perspective from the "objects" of form to the relationships of energy dynamics, it becomes possible to see how the three components of Cosmometry, Unified Physics and Music are each a lens through which we are describing one thing. And when we shift from a worldview of parts and particles seen as separate from each other to one of relationships of parts in synergetic wholeness, we open the way to apply the same principles that comprise cosmic wholeness and structural integrity into the dynamics of our own relationships, personally and for humanity as a whole.

Tension, then, becomes our ally as it provides intrinsic feedback about the integrity of a structure or system, be it a musical instrument, an economic system, or a society. There's really no difference when it comes to the dynamics of tension-compression that create or destroy all harmonic resonance in the universe.

Let's see how the concept of "intention" relates to the in→tension — the inward tension — that is the originating impulse in the transformation from zerophase equilibrium to manifest form. This brings us full-circle back to the Vector Equilibrium and its remarkable attribute of dynamic Jitterbug oscillation, introduced at the end of Section 2.

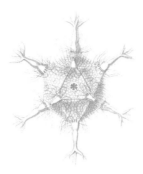

CHAPTER 32
IN→TENSION AND THE JITTERBUG

At the foundation of our working model is the universal field of electromagnetic energy in equilibrium — the Planck-scale Isotropic Vector Matrix. We might, in essence (or possibly in fact), think of this as the coherent laser light that plays the same role as it does in the making of a holograph: that of the "reference beam" that interacts with the interference pattern of the light reflected off of an object to create the holographic image. **The PSU-IVM is the ground state from which all manifest form and flow arise, these being a consequence of the shift from zerophase equilibrium to dynamic disequilibrium — the fluctuations of light and sound that we know as the observable universe.** In the zerophase state, we can say that the tension-compression dynamic cancels out; therefore, there is no density differential being expressed as what we call matter (i.e. no collective spin). It may also be said that the tension-compression dynamic goes to infinity, just as the energy density is theorized as going to infinity when the quantized structure of space reaches, and goes beyond, the extremely high frequency of the Planck scale. From this perspective, we could propose that the tensional integrity of the PSU-IVM is at a maximum value, and as such this universal field or aether has a high propensity towards returning to its zerophase equilibrium state following the movement of a disequilibrious fluctuation within it.

OK, that was a mouthful. What I'm suggesting here is that the tension within the PSU-IVM is extremely high, therefore it is readily prone to returning to its state of zerophase equilibrium. The cosmos is a vast sea of movement that occurs in spirals, vortices, rings, spheres, vectors and arcs. All of these manifesting attributes of cosmometry are tensegrity structures due to the fact that there is now an observable tension and compression dynamic at play. It is this shift from zerophase tensegrity to manifest tensegrity that is seen to originate in the Jitterbug motion of the Vector Equilibrium, and the first direction of movement is inward towards its center. As a proton spins, for example, it creates a spherical tensegrity structure within the PSU-IVM field that defines a curved topology at a scale some 20 orders of magnitude larger than the Planck Spherical Unit. Considering this, we can imagine the triangulated 4-dimensional Isotropic Vector Matrix "collapsing" inward from its universal equilibrium state into a localized area of tension-compression that forms a geodesic tensegrity structure — a spherical proton. The twelve points that form the VE spiral inward together towards the center point, creating a constellation of tension that very quickly assumes a new state of resonant equilibrium, that of an Icosahedron, which is the basis for geodesic domes and spheres… and protons.

The icosahedron is one of the five regular polyhedrons commonly referred to as the Platonic Solids. The fact that they have been called solids for centuries has oriented both scientists and laypersons alike toward a mindset that solid matter is primary in the universe, and as such the pursuit of scientific understanding has focused on parts and particles of so-called solid matter while considering the space between them as a generally irrelevant empty vacuum. With such a strong materialist viewpoint, it's challenging to imagine a model that basically does a 180° turn, **putting the structure of space as primary with the matter we observe being a result of energetic fluctuations within this space coming into resonant symmetries of tension-compression dynamics that create a gradient of energy-matter density**. Our experience of solidity is a consequence of those dynamics at a threshold of molecular density that is greater than that of our bodies. Stubbing your toe on a rock is evidence of this sometimes-painful truth. Dipping your toe into a cool lake is evidence of a lesser-density threshold of tensegrity, that of water. Fundamental to both states is the tension-compression dynamic of the atomic elements and the molecular structures they create. From the supreme density of diamonds to the nearly imperceptible density of air, a density gradient of energy dynamics is all that is at play. The concept of "solid" is only a relative one, for which an entity like a neutrino has no regard whatsoever. It is for this reason that I prefer to use the term Platonic Forms rather than Platonic Solids. They are highly symmetrical energetic forms created by tension-compression dynamics, tensegrity structures, within the vast ocean of energy we call the cosmos — pattern integrities of resonance in the interference patterns of the universal hologram.

The five Platonic Forms are the Icosahedron, Dodecahedron, Octahedron, Cube or Hexahedron, and Tetrahedron. The Icosa and Dodeca (right column) are duals of each other, meaning that their symmetry is complementary, with the points (vertices) of the Icosa positioned in the middle of the faces of the Dodeca, and vice-versa. The same holds true for the Octahedron and Cube (middle). The Tetrahedron is its own dual (left).

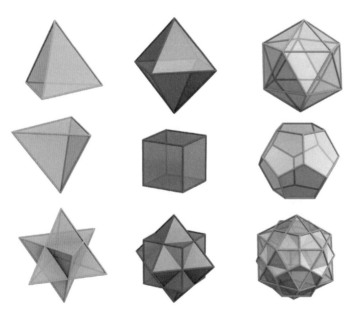

Remarkably, all of the Platonic Forms are resonant symmetries found within the Vector Equilibrium and the Jitterbug motion of dynamic pulsation that it exhibits when it goes out of its zerophase equilibrium state. Let's look at the Jitterbug motion again and see how this works.

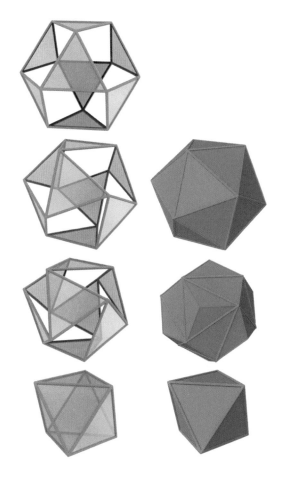

In the illustration to the right, the top image shows the VE in its state of equilibrium, a form also known as a cuboctahedron, which as we've seen has symmetry of both a cube and an octahedron — two Platonic forms accounted for. As we already know, the VE is composed of eight Tetrahedrons, and as well the triangular faces of the VE are symmetrical with the faces of a larger Dual Tetrahedron, as seen below — a third Platonic Form is accounted for. In the equilibrium state, the tension and compression (attraction/repulsion) relationships of the 12 points at the VE's circumference and the one at its center are equal. When a spin dynamic occurs, an inward tension is introduced and the 12 points of the VE's circumference converge simultaneously towards the center. The shift from zerophase equilibrium to manifest disequilibrium creates a tension-compression relationship between these energy nodes that quickly finds a new state of dynamic symmetry, seen in the second row, called the Icosahedron Phase of the jitterbug transformation. Following that are two more resonant symmetries, called the Dodecahedron and Octahedron phases.

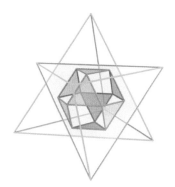

The triangular faces of the VE are symmeterically congruent wih the faces of a larger Dual Tetrahedron

All of the Platonic Forms are accounted for. The primary building blocks of atomic and molecular structure are inherent in the cosmometry of space itself.

Let's explore these symmetries further and see how the Phi ratio is integral to them as well.

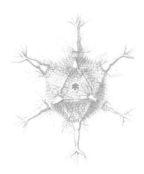

CHAPTER 33
PLATONIC SYMMETRY AND PHI

"By definition, a structure is a complex of energy events
interacting to produce a stable pattern."

This quote from Buckminster Fuller's Synergetics Dictionary[69] reminds us that when it comes to studying cosmic structures, we're talking about *energy events* in resonant tensegrity symmetries, rather than solid materials with struts and faces (though of course, we can make such structures as well). Atoms and molecules that comprise the physical universe are aggregations of energy events interacting to produce stable patterns, and because of their fundamental simplicity of symmetry, they have a strong affinity with the Platonic Forms. **Icosa, Dodeca, Octa, Hexa and Tetrahedral symmetries are at the root of all form and structure in the cosmos**.

ICOSAHEDRON PHASE

From an architectural perspective, the most stable structure that encompasses the largest volume of space with the least amount of surface area is a geodesic sphere. An iconic example of this is the Spaceship Earth exhibit at the Epcot Center in Florida, seen to the right. While its outer curvature appears quite spherical, its underlying geometry is that of an icosahedron. The image below illustrates this relationship. The apparently smooth spherical shape of the Spaceship Earth building is due to the greater degree of triangulation of the icosahedron's faces, making for a greater degree of curvature. Buckminster Fuller spent many years refining the geometry of geodesic structures, calling the degree of triangulation the "frequency" of the structure. Given the exceedingly small size of a PSU relative to the diameter of a proton, the geodesic tensegrity of the proton is at an extremely high frequency, making for a surface that is far smoother than the most highly polished stainless steel or crystal balls. Perhaps this is one reason why protons are observed to be spinning into eternity, free of the entropy

Rstoplabe14 [CC BY-SA 3.0]

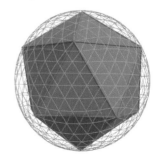

of friction found in the lower frequency structures of the macro world we experience, such as in steel and crystalline molecular structures.

At whatever scale a spherical structure comes into form, it is the result of an inward tension (an intention?) that transforms from the omni-triangulated Vector Equilibrium system, with its four intersecting hexagonal planes of symmetry, to an enclosed curved spatial symmetry based upon the structure of an icosahedron. This is, as we've seen, the first phase of symmetry in the jitterbug transformation. The non-curved (i.e. flat) symmetry of the hexagon, composed of six triangles, becomes the curved symmetry of the pentagon, composed of five triangles.

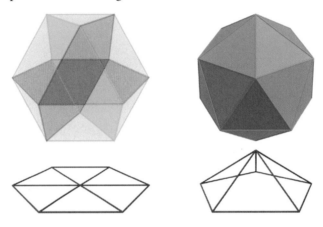

As you'll recall, five-fold pentagonal symmetry is based upon the Phi ratio, so right away as the zerophase potential collapses into a localized icosahedral structure, the fundamental Golden Ratio is present. The shift from non-spatial VE symmetry to spatially enclosed icosahedral symmetry creates a structural framework that inherently introduces the Phi ratio into physical manifestation. As further reinforcement of this idea, there is also a shift from a 4-dimensional framework (the VE's four hexagonal planes, as discussed in Chapter 8) to a 3-dimensional framework, and this is also Phi based. Within the cosmic design of icosahedral symmetry are found three intersecting planes in 90° correlation, and they're all Golden Rectangles. Could it be that our familiar "Cartesian" 3-D perceptual framework is inherent in the very structure of spherical space when it comes into physical form? And could it be that the Phi ratio's damping limit that defines icosahedral symmetry is intrinsic to the definition of our perceptual framework within the physical universe?

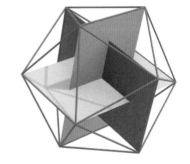

We live on a spherical planet that is made up of an unimaginably large number of dynamically cohered atoms and molecules. The overall gravitational tensegrity structure of the planet is that of an extremely high-frequency triangulated geodesic sphere, the underlying structural geometry of which is an icosahedron. Our physical relationship to this large (relative to our size) planet is such that the readily accepted dimensions of our spatial perception are up/down, front/back, and left/right — an obvious basis for the derivation of the XYZ Cartesian coordinate system. As we stand upon the earth, the central axis of our body is aligned with the gravitational tensegrity that converges toward the center of the planet, what we experience as the up/down vertical dimension. This is the central axis of our personal toroidal field, with its One Point located in the center of our belly. Our body's physical movement is largely constrained to a back-and-forth (front/back) and side-to-side (left-right) range upon the planet's surface. Perhaps this powerful perceptual and motional experience is inherently present due to the underlying 3-D Golden Rectangle symmetry of energy-matter-information in icosahedral tensegrity, literally present within Earth's gravitational form and magnetic field.

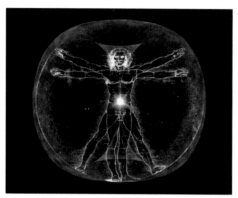

Image courtesy of ThriveOn.com

Is there evidence of 5-fold icosahedral symmetry in organic structures that might support the idea of Phi-damped structural enclosure? We certainly saw this in the core of an apple with its five seeds arranged in pentagram symmetry. There is clearly a 5-fold tensegrity resonance displayed by this pattern, indicating the possibility of an underlying icosahedral organization within the apple's molecular and cellular arrangement.

At the very small scale of biological life we can easily see icosahedral symmetry in both radiolarian (such as *Circogonia icosahedra*, left) and virus (such as HIV, right) structures. In terms of both efficiency and strength, the icosahedron makes an excellent protective shell for their inner contents.

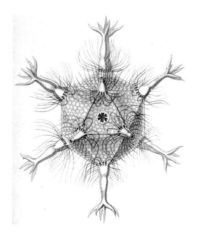
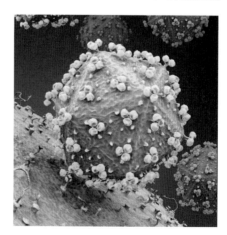

DODECAHEDRON PHASE

As the jitterbug motion continues past the Icosahedron, the next resonant symmetry is the Dodecahedron Phase. This Platonic Form is also composed of 5-fold symmetry, having twelve pentagonal faces. And it, too, contains XYZ symmetry within it, in this case being able to hold both the same three Golden Rectangles as the icosahedron (because they are duals of each other) as well as five regular cubes within the symmetry of its vertices (only one is illustrated here for visual simplicity).

Note that the edge length of the cube is also a Phi ratio larger than that of the Dodecahedron's edge. Hmmm… who's cosmic design inspiration was that! The 4-fold symmetry of a cube fits within the 5-fold symmetry of a dodecahedron in a Phi ratio — five times.

The dodecahedron doesn't stop there, though. It also accommodates the symmetry of the tetrahedron, being able to fit five of them inside as well, their points aligned with the vertices of the dodecahedron.

OCTAHEDRON PHASE

Continuing on with the jitterbug motion, the next resonant symmetry is the Octahedron Phase. This is when the edge vectors of the collapsing VE come together, creating a double-edged octahedral tensegrity structure. This double-edge structure is what Buckminster Fuller likened to double-bonded atomic tensegrity. Being the dual of the cube, the octahedron also exhibits XYZ symmetry. In fact, we can put the same three Golden Rectangles found within the icosahedron inside an octahedron so that their corners all touch the edges of the octahedron in the XYZ axes. When we do, we of course define an icosahedron, and once again yet another Phi ratio emerges: The points where the icosahedron touches the octahedron divide the edges of the octahedron by the Phi ratio!

  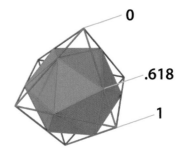

0

.618

1

As we've already seen, the octahedron also encompasses the cuboctahedron or Vector Equilibrium, in this case when its edges are divided at the mid point.

So in the "Octa" symmetry we find both the Binary Octave (halving the edges to define the VE) and Phinary Fibonacci (dividing edges at Golden Ratio to define Icosa) quantized number systems. Remember, the number 8 (octa) is common to both of those number systems. Another cosmic coincidence, to say the least.

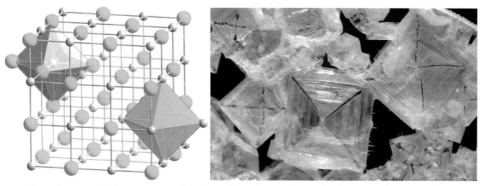

The sodium and chlorine atoms of sodium chloride, or salt, are both arranged in octahedral symmetry within an overall cubic crystalline structure that gives salt its cubic shape. Note that the octahedral symmetry of the two atomic arrays are overlapping each other throughout the structure, highlighting the fact that the geometry is formed by tension relationships rather than solid objects (as the illustration could suggest due to the faces being filled in). Note as well the diagonal lines within the crystals in the photograph that appear to make the octahedral symmetry visible.
[Photograph by the NASA Expedition 6 crew (NASA Image of the Day)
[Public domain], via Wikimedia Commons]

TETRAHEDRON, STAR TETRAHEDRON AND CUBE

The VE's jitterbug motion can continue past the Octahedron Phase to ultimately form a Tetrahedron. Even a physical model of a VE can be transformed into a tetrahedron without breaking apart any of its vertices. Whereas in the octahedron symmetry the VE's edges are double-bonded, they become quadruple-bonded in the tetrahedron symmetry. From a tensegrity perspective, according to Fuller this may explain why the molecular structure of a diamond is so strong, given that its structural integrity is based upon a tetrahedral crystal lattice.

Visualization of a diamond cubic unit cell:

1.

1. Components of a unit cell,

2.

2. One unit cell,

3.

3. A lattice of 3 x 3 x 3 unit cells.

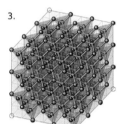

Image by Cmglee - Own work, CC BY-SA 3.0

The tetrahedron is the most basic structural form, and as mentioned earlier, it is the fundamental unit in Fuller's synergetic geometry upon which the "accounting of nature's omni-rational coordinate system" is based. Its dual is itself, creating a "star tetrahedron" structure when combined. It is this structure that portrays the divergent energy dynamic (eight tetrahedra pointing outward, in green below) in complementary relationship to the Vector Equilibrium's convergent energy dynamic (eight tetrahedra pointing inward, in orange), which when combined brings us back to the 64 Tetrahedron Matrix we started with in Section 2.

Inside the star tetrahedron is the symmetry of an octahedron, and connecting its eight points forms the symmetry of a cube. It also is found within the symmetry of the dodecahedron, as seen earlier (two of the five tetrahedra are shown below).

So as we've now seen, all of the fundamental structural forms of cosmic energy dynamics are embedded within each other in a unified tensegrity relationship that is harmoniously integrated with the Phi ratio.

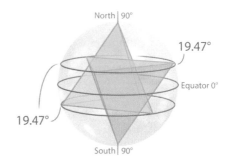

Returning to the spherical tensegrity dynamics, there is compelling visual evidence that the fundamental structural integrity of the tetrahedron is found to be resonant within planetary and solar structures. It is well known that the points of a star tetrahedron touch the surface of a sphere of the same overall diameter at a latitude of 19.47° both north and south of the equator. This is the approximate location of the Great Red Spot on Jupiter, a massive vortex of swirling gas, as well as a latitude of demarcation of some of the overall fluid dynamics of Jupiter's atmosphere. It is also a latitude that exhibits a high degree of activity on the Sun, where solar flares are often located.

Here on Earth it's noteworthy that one of the largest geological structures of the planet, Mauna Loa on the Big Island of Hawaii, has its summit almost exactly at 19.47° north latitude. It is, in fact, the largest mountain on Earth when measured from the sea floor to its summit.

"Combining the volcano's extensive submarine flanks (5,000 m (16,400 ft) to the sea floor) and 4,170 m (13,680 ft) subaerial height, Mauna Loa rises 9,170 m (30,085 ft) from base to summit, greater than the 8,848 m or 29,029 ft elevation of Mount Everest from sea level to its summit. In addition, much of the mountain is invisible even underwater: its mass depresses the crust beneath it by another 8 km (5 mi), in the shape of an inverse mountain, meaning the total height of Mauna Loa from the start of its eruptive history is about 17,170 m (56,000 ft)." [70]

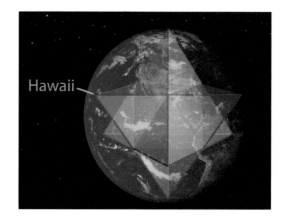

As you'll recall, a tetrahedron within a sphere has a Phi ratio spatial relationship. While there's as yet no scientific verification that these geometric tensegrity dynamics are influencing the geological, solar and Jovian atmospheric phenomena, it is certainly of compelling interest to consider the visible evidence of an underlying tetrahedral standing wave resonance within the macro-scale gravitational energetics of these highly quantized (molecular) structures.

Researchers of these kinds of dynamics have also proposed that there's an energetic grid that encompasses the Earth in icosidodecahedral symmetry.[71] The evidence of star tetrahedron resonance may lend support to this theory given its relationship to dodecahedral symmetry, as we saw ealier. Given that we also saw that the curvature of space into spherical form is correlated to the icosahedron phase of the jitterbug motion, perhaps these theories deserve greater consideration.

ATOMIC GEOMETRY AND THE COSMIC HIERARCHY

The regular Platonic Forms are all intimately related in their symmetry in such a way that they embed one within another, as well as with the VE. It is this embedded symmetry that Buckminster Fuller called the Cosmic Hierarchy, as seen to the right in this color plate from *Synergetics*. These geometries are relationships of energy events — intertransformable systems, as he describes them in the image's text. Fuller proposed that *"all the internal or nuclear affairs of the atom occur internally to the vector equilibrium and all the external or chemical associations occur externally to the vector equilibrium."*[72]

Recognizing that the torus is a fundamental pattern of energy dynamics, Foster Gamble determined that the energy events that make up these intertransformable systems would be toroidal and set out to model the atomic geometry of the Periodic Table of Elements based upon Fuller's Cosmic Hierarchy. In his own words:

> *"I worked with physicist, geometer, computer scientist, Robert Gray, to see if what we had learned would reveal a useful, new understanding of the table of atomic elements, the 92 complex patterns by which spirit, or consciousness, manifests into what we call "matter". We worked with the hypothesis that if the torus were fundamental, then it would probably be the shape of hydrogen,*

the fundamental atom. The next element, helium, would be a double torus, like the Sun itself. And the rest would complexify from there as pressure was added to the tiny structure by the giant stars and supernova in which they are cooked.

Bucky Fuller's Cosmic Octave Hierarchy laid out a potentially predictable series of shapes with each electron as a torus on the outside and each proton as a torus in the nucleus, both connected by a tornado-like vortex of energy.

The Cosmic Octave Hierarchy is to 3-D geometry what the music octave is to sound waves or the rainbow is to light. It begins with the simplest space-containing form, the tetrahedron, and its dual. These two form the cube whose dual is the octahedron. Next comes the icosahedron and its partner, the dodecahedron. And, finally, the vector equilibrium and its dual, the rhombic dodecahedron.

As with so much in Nature, the sequence seems to follow the most efficient, least effort arrangements of symmetry in space. Increasing external pressure creates not billiard balls, but more and more of the whirlpools that show up as electrons on the outside and protons on the inside. As the structure of the atoms become more complex and get heavier, they periodically reach stability in what are called the "inert", or "noble elements": Neon, then Argon [left image below], then Krypton, Xenon, and, finally, Radon. Each of these is characterized by having eight electrons in the outer shell and I believe these eight vortices match the eight outer triangles of the vector equilibrium. And that is why they exhibit equilibrium on their own. They are essentially satisfied or, literally, fulfilled and do not seek to combine with other atoms for stability. As each so-called shell builds toward equilibrium, the pressure creates more and more vortices inside the outer shell, and these form the geometries of the octave hierarchy. The atomic numbers of each inner shell hint that if we could look inside, we could see the sequential forming of the duo-tetrahedron, the octahedron, the icosahedron, and the dodecahedron.

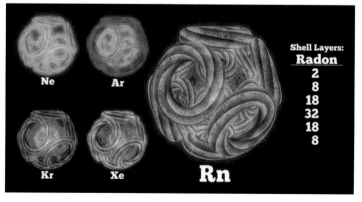

The final elements, like Radon and Uranium, have their outer vortices, or electrons, so far from the pull of the nucleus that they are on the verge of flying off to join other atoms. That seems to explain why they are so volatile and ready to radiate or start a chain reaction as used in the atomic bombs and nuclear fission." [73]

With the Cosmic Hierarchy as their guide, Gamble and Gray successfully modeled all of the noble element geometries according to sixteen fundamental postulates (see sidebar on next page). In the text on Fuller's Cosmic Hierchary image he states, *"[the cosmic hierarchy] may come to be identified as the unified field, which, as an operationally transformable complex, is conceptualizable only in its equilibrious state."* A comprehensive exploration of this model may well prove Fuller to be correct. [Note: Gamble and Gray's work has not been published to date.]

Similarly, in a 1988 article entitled The Geometric Basis for the Periodicity of the Elements, published in *21ˢᵗ Century Science & Technology*, Laurence Hecht presented the pioneering research of University of Chicago physicist, Dr. Robert J. Moon. Dr. Moon also developed a nested hierchary of Platonic Forms as the embedded system upon which he modeled the elements, producing *"a synthetic geometric construction of the periodic table of the elements in such a way as to account geometrically, in a first approximation, for the existence of the 92 naturally occurring elements and many of their physical properties."* [74]

With the perspective of tensegrity being *a complex of energy events interacting to produce a stable pattern*, as Fuller says, we can see how the dynamics of toroidal vortices within the quantized unified field of space would create quantum gravitational tensegrity effects at the atomic level that tend towards the same fundamental geometries as are found at all scales in the cosmos.

To recap this chapter, all manifest form is a result of inward tension that coheres discrete compression "islands" at fractal scales from nuclear, atomic and molecular to crystalline, mineral, cellular, biological, planetary, solar, galactic and universal. The prime foundation of the entire construct is the Planck-scale field of electromagnetism, which is in a state of coherent tension-compression equilibrium (the PSU-IVM). This quantized field "collapses" from the VE equilibrium into tensegrity structures that are most fundamentally resonant with the symmetry of the five Platonic Forms, which can be observed within atomic and molecular structures. These aggregate into the macro structures we see and feel as the physical world, therefore it would make sense that the same symmetries would be harmonically present throughout the entire fractal tensegrity structure of the cosmos.

We can see this to be true from the cubic shape of a salt crystal and octahedral shape of various fluorite crystals, to the icosahedral form of the shells of viruses and radiolarian, the high-density integrity of diamond's tetrahedral lattices, and the potential influence of tetrahedral, icosahedral and dodecahedral harmonic tensegrity in geological, atmospheric and solar dynamics. Octahedral symmetry is even observed at the scale of supermassive galactic clusters, and dodecahedral symmetry is present in the Cosmic Microwave Background of the universe as a whole (as we'll see in Chapter 39). Every one of these structures is an example of tension-compression dynamics creating a specific density of matter that is part of a continuum across a universal gradient of density, and throughout the entire field are the same basic geometric relationships we call the Platonic Forms. These forms are tensegrity structures of energy dynamics, not solids. As we've just seen, these forms are intimately related to each other in embedded symmetry based upon the self-similar Phi ratio, the inherent damping limit that defines form and resonance within space. And all of these forms are inherent within the zerophase system of the Vector Equilibrium and its dynamic "jitterbug" oscillation. Remarkable to say the least!

Given that tension is key to all of this, there must be some way in which we can understand its role in the cosmic play of energy-matter-information as it pertains to the creation (and destruction) of harmonic resonance within form and structure. And indeed, there is, and that's through the principle of Tuning. As we make our way toward exploring the third fundamental "lens" of our inquiry, Music, we must have a basis upon which it correlates to the complementary lenses of Cosmometry and Unified Physics explored thus far. To begin this correlation, let's consider the idea of Tuning the Universe.

Foster Gamble's Fundamental Postulates for the In-Forming of Essence

1) Universe is a continuous, alive and infinite medium.

2) The metaphysical, conceptual "geometry" of balance of the system will always be present and, because it is in equilibrium, it will be invisible.

3) All multiplication happens by division of the wholeness.

4) All form and matter are a function of motion (in the medium), centered by stillness, so action, not matter, is basic, and comes in wholes.

5) All processes evolve through maximum simplicity and efficiency.

6) The simplest distinction creating a self-sustaining entity as motion in and of the medium is toroidal.

7) Since every system is in rotation and embedded in other rotating systems, all movement is helical.

8) All systems are connected, and all centers are one.

9) Complexity builds on combinations and variations of toroidal field distinctions – following fundamental principles of least-effort division of the space medium cohering geometrically around any "point" as center.

10) Each "point" is the center of its system even as it participates in other systems with other centers.

11) There are an infinite number of "points" or "centers".

12) Curvature toward and away from a center is infinite.

13) Within the infinite is the finite and within the finite is the infinite.

14) The structuring of "reality" is fractal and holographic in nature.

15) Quantization of space pre-exists matter.

16) Since the whole must always be in balance, any event, impulse, break in symmetry is always accompanied by its complementary dual (reflected as linear and radial polarity; opposite direction, rotation, charge; contraction/expansion; edge/vertex; fields, alternating shells etc.).

CHAPTER 34
TUNING THE UNIVERSE

I have been a musician my whole life, with my primary instruments being guitar, keyboard and percussion, as well as voice for singing. Along with playing acoustic and electric guitars, my great passion in recent years has been the remarkable (and quite intimidating) drum from India called Tabla. While most every instrument needs tuning at some point, both the guitar and tabla put you into an ongoing, daily, face-to-face relationship with the necessary act of tuning.

As mentioned at the beginning of this section, a guitar has strings that are either tightened or loosened to ultimately resonate at a specific frequency — to be "tuned" to a certain note in the musical scale. A guitar string is a simple example of tensegrity, with one end being fixed in place at the bridge and the other being wound around the peg of a tuning mechanism. The tension of the string between the bridge and the tuning peg (along with the diameter of the string) determines the frequency of sound — the note — that rings out when the string is plucked. Tuning, in the case of a guitar string, is an act of increasing or decreasing the tension of the string, either raising or lowering the frequency (also called the pitch) respectively: the tighter the tension, the higher the pitch. As with all tensegrity structures, there is a limit to how much tension can be introduced into the string, at which point the molecules of the metals used to make the string can no longer hold their atomic bonding and the string snaps.

This is literally an example of how all structures in the cosmos behave when it comes to tensegrity dynamics and the limits of their "tunability". A guitar string is a very visible and audible correlate to the same tension dynamics found in atomic and molecular structures. In fact, in materials science and engineering research the "tensile strength" of a substance (i.e. metal, wood, rope, beam, etc.) is determined by the amount of force it takes to stretch the substance (i.e. introduce tension) before it breaks. It is knowledge of this specific limit of tension that makes possible the ability to construct all mechanical devices with structural integrity.

Our simple and familiar guitar string offers a clear example of the principle of tensegrity as applied throughout the cosmos, for along with atomic and molecular bonds, gravitational tension lines between planetary, solar and galactic structures are essentially doing the same thing. A guitar string is at a fractal scale of length that produces acoustic vibrations that we are able to hear with our ears. Above and below this frequency range exist the same tension dynamics, and therefore the same tuning dynamics. For example, the gravitational tension between Earth and Sun is tuned just to the right amount so that we orbit as we do rather than either flying away from (too little tension) or being pulled into (too much tension) the Sun. The Earth, Sun and all planets in the solar system are harmonically tuned (and as we'll see in the next Section, they are musically so.)

As a musician with an instrument that needs tuning, I have had decades of direct experience of this phenomenon, hearing the rising and falling of a tone as it homes in on the frequency desired. It can be one of the most enjoyable aspects of being a musician, as it feels very satisfying when the tuning "arrives" at the right place. It can also be one of the most frustrating aspects when the tuning gods are not with you! There are many reasons why this is so, such as when your guitar strings have been stretched too many times and are tired of the whole thing and no longer have the tensile strength to hold pitch. No matter how hard you try, the tensegrity is too far gone and the tuning game between you and the universe becomes a losing prospect. Time to buy new strings.

And then there's the tabla.

If ever there was a living, breathing, dynamic medium through which to experience the highs and lows of tuning, it is found in the head of a tabla drum, and for me, it has been one of my greatest teachers of tensegrity and the idea of "tuning the universe."

The tabla consists of two drums, one for each hand — a large one for deeper bass tones, and a small one for higher treble tones. They are traditionally made in India using goat skin for the drum head and a thicker leather hide for the straps that hold the head onto the drum. It is actually just one continuous strap that wraps up and down and around the drum, and it is this strap that puts tension on the drumhead.

The tabla is a tuned drum (the word "tabla" is used as the name for the pair of drums as well as specifically for the small one; the big one is called the "bayan"). This means that the small drum can be tuned to a specific pitch that is in harmonic resonance with the other instruments being played, such as a sitar, bamboo flute, sarangi, harmonium, etc. Looking more closely at the tabla drum, we can see that the straps are also wrapped over a set of round wooden blocks, which provide another source of tension in the overall tensegrity system. They are, in fact, islands of compression in dynamic relation with a continuous tension — the definition of a tensegrity structure.

So there's a drumhead, straps and wood blocks that combine into a tensegrity system that all together result in applying an even amount of tension across the drumhead so that when it is struck with your finger a clear, precise and resonant tone rings out. So how the heck is it tuned?

With a hammer, of course!

Yup, you gotta take the hammer and smack both the wooden blocks and the braided rim of the drumhead to ultimately achieve an even tension across the entire head, the failure of which to do so leaves you somewhat physically and emotionally exhausted! And on top of that, since the head and straps are made of leather and the blocks and body of the drum are wooden, the entire thing is susceptible to temperature, humidity and pressure changes! One day the stars are aligned and all is happily in tune, and the next there's a change in the weather and you're wrestling with the elemental gods of cellular tensegrity and atmospheric influences. There are times when you just want to take that hammer and... but you don't (at least not after the first time you succumb to the urge), instead invoking self-control, patience and fortitude. Lesson #1 in how to live life in tune with the universe. The reward is worth every ounce of effort, though, for there's nothing like the "ping" of a well-tuned tabla.

But what does all this have to do with tuning the universe?

We saw with the guitar string how it gives us a readily observable example of a vector of tension, just as can be associated with the vector tension bonds within atomic and molecular structures, and even gravitational dynamics within the celestial dance. It is very precise, more like a laser beam than a floodlight. The head of a tabla drum reverses this equation. In its case, the tension is spread across a defined area, much like what we call the "face" of a geometric form. In geometry, the suffix "hedron" refers to the face of a so-called solid form, so the word tetrahedron means "four faces" (and hexahedron = six faces, octahedron = eight faces, etc.). Whereas the edge of a form — the vector — is more like a line (the guitar string), the face of a form is more like a field (the head of a drum). Both are tunable, as we've seen, and it is this tunability that underlies the symmetry of resonance that is found in atomic and molecular structures. The crystalline structure of sodium chloride that we saw earlier illustrates this dynamic relationship, with both cubic and octahedral tension vectors defining interstitial fields or "faces" of those geometries.

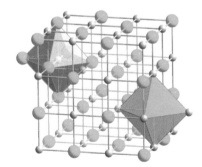

The tensegrity within atoms and molecules is extremely high compared to that of a guitar string or tabla head but the same dynamics are at play. This alone points to a musical relationship within the great cosmic scheme! And yet there's more...

In the next Section we'll dive deeper into the basic harmonic attributes of music and how the tabla head's resonant tensegrity field directly correlates with them, but for the moment let's look at the geometric attributes of the tabla's tensegrity.

The tabla drum has eight wooden blocks across which the single leather strap weaves between a braided ring around the head of the drum and its base. The strap is threaded through the braided leather sixteen times, as can be seen in this image:

This creates a matrix of tension lines that connects all sixteen points where the strap holds the head, like this:

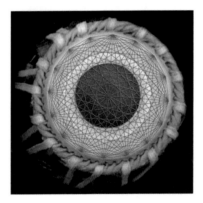

In cosmometry, this kind of 2D matrix illustrates a pattern of relationships, in this case the connection points of the strap encircling the drumhead. In essence, this matrix depicts a field of vectors and nodal points (where the lines intersect) across the whole drumhead that must all come into dynamic equilibrium in order for the tension to produce a clear, resonant tone when the head is struck. When tuning a tabla, the ring of wooden tuning blocks and the encircling braid must be hammered all around the drum so as to even out the tension within the cellular tensegrity of the goatskin (it's remarkable, really, that apparently "dead" cells of animal skin retain such a high degree of tensegrity in their overall structure). Sometimes three-quarters of the head is in pitch, but the last quarter is flat (lower in pitch). Readjusting the tension around the entire head is often the only way to bring it all into balance.

Correlating this to the rest of the cosmos... the drumhead of a tabla (or any drum) is a quantized aggregation of molecules and atoms with a specific tensegrity relative to the material used, such as the goatskin. This is true of every material substance in the cosmos, for everything is a quantized collection of atoms and molecules, each with its own tensile strength. Even liquids and gases are included, though their inter-atomic tension is relatively low and therefore mutable. It is noteworthy, though, that the very familiar element of water has the capacity to be "structured"[75] such that its molecular arrangement becomes more stable and coherent overall. This is, in effect, tuning the water. The molecules establish an evenly distributed tensegrity that results in a geometrically symmetrical resonance, one that is often icosahedral in fact. This is the same principle as tuning a drum or guitar string. The molecules of water are now all vibrating together in a larger resonant whole system.

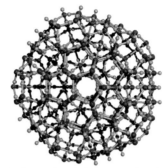

hydrogen-bonded clusters related to icosahedral clustering.
Image by Martin Chaplin
http://www1.lsbu.ac.uk/water/

By DieKlangschale
(http://creativecommons.org/
licenses/by-sa/3.0)]

Think of a crystal bowl — an aggregation of silicon and oxygen atoms in continuous tetrahedral framework. Striking it with a mallet produces a most beautiful clear tone comparable to the beauty of the mineral itself. In nature we find examples of crystals, rocks, and even sheets of ice that will ring with a bell-like chime when struck. While these are the more musical examples of tensegrity resonance in natural structures, the general principle is present throughout all structures in the cosmos, though not as sonically evident. Given the fractal-hologramic nature of the cosmos, tuning a tabla drum is equivalent to "tuning the universe."

But now… let's get personal. Here you are, sitting and reading these words. Your body is mostly relaxed, with a little bit of tension being called forth to hold this book (or whatever you're reading this on).

Yes… tension. The good kind! The kind that makes the existence of the entire universe possible. You are — we are — a tensegrity structure. The muscles, tendons and ligaments within our bodies provide the tension (the continuous tension component) that make it possible for the skeletal system (the discontinuous compression component) to have structural integrity. Within this biophysical tensegrity system are basic geometric symmetries that support balanced wholeness in our physical body. The first image to the right, from the late Tom Flemons of Intension Designs Ltd, depicts the underlying simplicity of this geometric symmetry throughout the entire body. The second image shows what he calls a Tetrahedral Vertebral Mast, depicting tensegrity of the spinal column based upon tetrahedral symmetry.

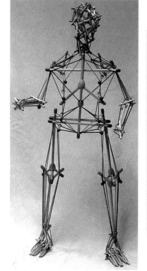

Go ahead and take a moment to stretch out your arms and legs, twist your spine, extend your fingers open wide and release them. That feeling you're experiencing inside? — Tensegrity. What we call "stretching" is literally applying the same action to our muscles, tendons and ligaments as when tuning a guitar string or tabla head. It is how we go about tuning ourselves at the physical level, the lack of which quickly resulting in the uncomfortable evidence of being out of tune — the all-too-familiar aches and pains. This is why stretching and exercising are so important. We, too, must continually tune our instrument! When we don't, the effects are readily visible in our posture. And we need just the right amount of tension. Too much or too little can both have postural consequences.

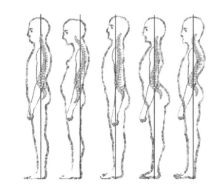

We can also see evidence of biotensegrity within cellular structures. The torus-shaped red blood cell, seen below, has an obvious geodesic tensegrity in the structure of its cell membrane that makes it both strong and flexible.

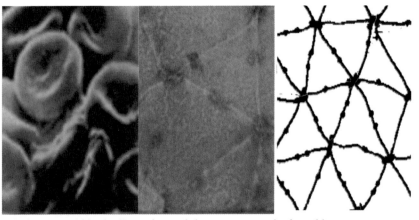

The human red blood cell membrane skeleton is a network of roughly 33,000 protein hexagons that looks like a microscopic geodesic dome. [77]

This is also true within the internal structure of cells, as described in this excerpt from an article from The Ingber Lab of Harvard Medical School:

> *"The cellular tensegrity model proposes that the whole cell is a prestressed tensegrity structure, although geodesic structures are also found in the cell at smaller size scales (e.g. clathrin-coated vesicles, viral capsids). In the model, tensional forces are borne by cytoskeletal microfilaments and intermediate filaments, and these forces are balanced by interconnected structural elements that resist compression, most notably internal microtubule struts and ECM adhesions... Intermediate filaments that interconnect at many points along microtubules, microfilaments and the nuclear surface provide mechanical*

stiffness to the cell based on their material properties and on their ability to act as suspensory cables that interconnect and tensionally stiffen the entire cytoskeleton and nuclear lattice. In addition, the internal cytoskeleton interconnects at the cell periphery with a highly elastic, geodesic cytoskeletal... network directly beneath the plasma membrane... Tensegrity also explains how hierarchical structures may be comprised of systems within systems (molecules within cells within tissues within organs) and yet still exhibit integrated mechanical behavior. In addition, it reveals how robust behaviors, such as persistence, mechanical adaptability, and shape stability, can be generated using "sloppy" parts (e.g., flexible molecular filaments), a key feature of both complex networks and living systems. Thus, tensegrity may represent the "hardware" behind living systems."
— The Ingber Lab, Children's Hospital Boston, Harvard Medical School[76]

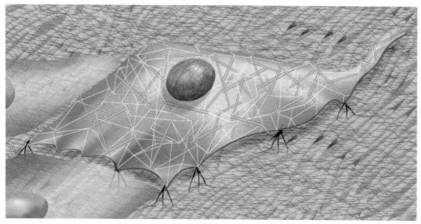

Image courtesy of Donald Ingber

One of the most salient points in this excerpt is the statement that "Tensegrity also explains how hierarchical structures may be comprised of systems within systems (molecules within cells within tissues within organs) and yet still exhibit integrated mechanical behavior." In a fractally-integrated universe, this is exactly what we would expect. The researchers are putting the emphasis of their observations on the pattern-integrity of the whole system rather than solely focusing on the discrete parts, as has been the traditional approach to scientific study. The innumerable quantized (i.e. discrete) islands of compression (atoms, molecules, forms of all kinds) are bound together in a unified field of fractal wholeness. We can then extend this concept of hierarchical fractal wholeness to see how the principle of tensegrity permeates the entirety of cosmic dynamics from Planck to Universal scales, providing the tensional integrity needed for the whole "mechanism" to behave in an integrated, and well-tuned, manner — Structural Integrity.

With this in mind, let us now consider how it does so with a natural tendency for harmony and rhythm as we venture into the next fundamental component of our exploration — Music.

221

Section 5 Endnotes

68   Quotes from Synergetics Dictionary:
http://www.rwgrayprojects.com/SynergeticsDictionary/SDCards.php?cn=17029&tp=1
http://www.rwgrayprojects.com/SynergeticsDictionary/SDCards.php?cn=17065&tp=1

69   http://www.rwgrayprojects.com/SynergeticsDictionary/SDCards.php?cn=17029&tp=1

70   https://en.wikipedia.org/wiki/Mauna_Loa

71   See https://www.goodreads.com/book/show/9040571-earth-grids

72   http://www.rwgrayprojects.com/SynergeticsDictionary/SDCards.php?cn=847&tp=1

73   http://www.thrivemovement.com/spirit-matter-geometry-life.blog

74   Hecht, Laurence, "Mysterium Microcosmicum: The Geometric Basis, For the Periodicity of the Elements", *21st Century Science & Technology*, May-June 1988.
http://wlym.com/archive/fusion/tcs/19880506-TCS.pdf

75   Chaplin, Martin, "Water Structure and Science", London South Bank University.
http://www1.lsbu.ac.uk/water/cluster_evidence.html
https://creativecommons.org/licenses/by-nc-nd/2.0/uk/

76   "Tensegrity and Complex Systems Biology", The Ingber Lab, Harvard Medical School.
https://apps.childrenshospital.org/clinical/research/ingber/Tensegrity.html

77   "Scientists Discover Secret Behind Human Red Blood Cell's Amazing Flexibility", UC San Diego, Jacobs School of Engineering, 2005.
http://jacobsschool.ucsd.edu/news/news_releases/release.sfe?id=484

SECTION 6
MUSIC – THE MASTER CODE

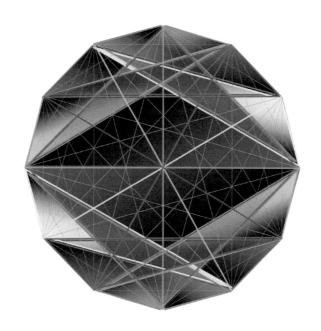

SECTION 6
MUSIC - THE MASTER CODE

"Music is the best."
– Frank Zappa

Imagine a universe without music. When I do this, I get a very stark, emotionless feeling. A bleak emptiness pervades my sense of what life would be like in a world without a musical soundtrack. Fortunately, it's not the case, and for whatever reason it is that we humans are gifted the opportunity to create, play, share and enjoy music here on Earth, and to whatever "divine intelligence" that thought it would be a good idea to include it in the cosmic scheme, I am most grateful. It is truly a kind of miracle that from the nothing of silence emerges the absolutely magical, even mythical, agony-and-ecstasy-evoking possibility we call music.

What's ironic, though, is that music has become so commonplace in our personal and social experience that in some ways we've come to take it for granted as simply an ordinary part of everyday life, especially considering the likelihood that there are literally millions of songs simultaneously playing around our planet in every given moment in our modern digital age. When we get right down to it, though, music is actually one of the most extraordinary phenomena to exist in our human — and cosmic — experience. In fact, when we *really* get right down to it, it turns out we wouldn't even have a human or cosmic experience without the musically harmonic structure of the universe that fractally percolates up to our scale of reality so that we ultimately can dance ourselves silly to it in the privacy of our own home, should we be so unabashedly bold!

The premise we're exploring here is simply stated as this:

The *form and flow* of all manifestation in the cosmos, from atomic dynamics on up, *is a direct consequence of* the ubiquitous presence of the fractal system of harmonic resonance that we call *music.*

Uni-Verse = The One Song = Music

Music as a theoretical framework is a system of relationships. We are fortunate to be able to experience, revel in, move to, and be moved by music without having to intellectually know this system of relationships. Music takes care of the knowing and we get to enjoy the results. While many people

225

who have studied music's relationships have extensively defined its theoretical framework, one of the most important points to realize in the context of our overall exploration is this: **We did not invent music — we discovered it**.

Music as a phenomenon exists in the very structure of the cosmos, given that sound waves (and more broadly, acoustical impulses) exist as an intrinsically natural component of physical matter. We humans, uniquely from the rest of life as we know it to date, have discovered that this phenomenon has a specific set of relationships and that when we combine these relationships we can produce sonic creations of indescribable beauty (and sometimes otherwise, especially if we don't tune our instruments well beforehand). We might say that music is a Divine Gift from the cosmos with the ability to provide endless variation and entertainment through our own invention. We can *invent with* music, but we did not invent music.

As has been said from the beginning of our journey, Music is the third fundamental component of our exploration, complementary to Cosmometry and Unified Physics. In other words, **the cosmic geometry at the foundation of the model describing unified physics is directly correlated to the system of relationships we call music.** They are three lenses describing one cosmic whole. This is because the entire cosmic phenomenon is one of relationships. No relationships, no universe. No relationships, no dynamic fluctuation on either side of zero to experience, observe, talk about and dance to. No relationships, no relativity or quantization.

Fortunately for us the universe is quantized, and it is precisely due to the universe being quantized that we have such a thing as music, just as it is due to quantization that we have a fractal structure that simultaneously and seamlessly divides and unifies the experiential cosmos. **Music is a system of harmonic relationships inherent within the quantized fractal structure of the cosmos**, which we happily experience as sound and song. It is this system of relationships that will be explored in this section, doing so with the primary intention of integrating it with the cosmometry and unified physics presented thus far.

But here's the tricky part… describing music as a system of relationships using words and musical symbols (such as the letters A B C D E F G) is abstract at best for those unfamiliar with the system of music (what's commonly called music theory). And on top of that, after describing the basics of the musical system I'll be referencing a theory that is as yet not taught in common music education! For these reasons I am choosing to stick with the simplest aspects of this system that are foundational to the vast complexity that arises from them. Simplicity is the key here, anything beyond which will become confusing. There are many great researchers into the complexities of the geometry of music that can be explored in depth (some of whom will be referenced on the website at www.cosmometry.com).

My intention is to correlate the *system* of music with cosmometry and physics. The word *system* is italicized here because I want to emphasize a distinction that is of importance in the context of this exploration; that is the difference between viewing music as a *generic system* (of harmonic and rhythmic relationships) and the much more complex study of music theory (which becomes culturally dependent), and even more so the technical mathematical analysis of frequencies and their relationships. Our overall model of wholeness is founded upon simplicity, and that's what we'll aim to maintain as we delve into our third component — Music.

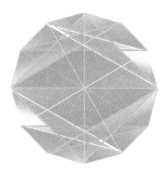

CHAPTER 35
THE HOLOGRAMIC SYMPHONY

"…the engine behind harmonics lies not in stories and mysterious symbols
nor in old mechanics and abstract formulas, but in the universal physics
of a standing wave. Cracking open this bundle of energy should reveal both
the mechanics at work in music and the source of our perceptions of it.
Like the fingerprints of our brain, standing wave patterns hold
the essential clues for how we perceive our world
at the very deepest level."
– Richard Merrick

As stated throughout this book, from a very basic perspective, the universe as we experience it is a dynamic interplay of two fundamental expressions of energy — the electromagnetic and acoustic impulses of Light and Sound (we'll get to the "as we experience it" aspect of this statement in the next section, which is equally relevant to our energy-matter-information totality). While these two energetic expressions exhibit their own unique qualities in the cosmic play, at their foundation they are essentially the same thing — waveforms. These are the discrete frequency "packets" that are the quanta of quantum reality, fractally scaled to our perceptual reality. And as we've seen before, they are mutually compatible and convertible, from acoustic to electromagnetic to acoustic to electromagnetic… with no conflict or discrepancy.

As is well known, the interacting waveforms of these energetic fluctuations create interference patterns, just like we see when pebbles thrown in water create rings that overlap and a temporarily stable pattern becomes visible. These rings are, in fact, pressure waves; the acoustic attribute of the cosmic dynamic. While this experience of intersecting waveforms is a common, everyday one, what's equally common and everyday, though less overtly apparent, is that this is the exact same phenomenon that's occurring throughout the entire universe. Fundamentally, the whole of the electromagnetic and acoustic cosmos is one big ocean of waveforms interacting to create interference patterns.

The key aspect of this insight is that **it's all interference patterns**, so it's essential that we understand what that terms means. The *American Heritage® Science Dictionary* defines it as:

> *An overall pattern that results when two or more waves interfere with each other, generally showing regions of constructive and of destructive interference. Optical interference patterns are analyzed in devices such as interferometers; the acoustic effect of beats is an example of an interference pattern.*[78]

While I'm not a fan of definitions that use the word being defined, this one does describe the qual-

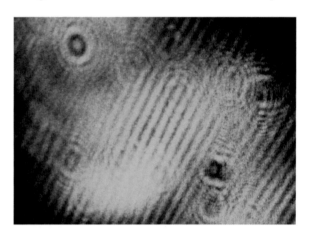

ities of waveform dynamics in both light and sound wherein as the waves overlap and intersect they will either enhance each other (constructive interference) or diminish each other (destructive interference). When this constructive/destructive interference dynamic stabilizes into a regular pattern, we call this a Standing Wave. It is this standing wave phenomenon that is seen when we look at a holographic image on a glass plate and see an interference pattern of light waves, appearing very much the same as rings in water.

Reiterating what was described in Chapter 1, the same holds true for sound waves. In the very simplistic illustration below, we can see that when sound waves from a source (the triangle) fill a room they bounce off the walls, overlap and create a standing wave interference pattern, with the combined result of all the primary and reflected waves converging at the location of our ears (the hexagon). The totality of the sound wave interference is actually present at *every* point in the room, just like the information about the source object is in a hologram. As such, sound is holosonic (complementary to light being holographic).

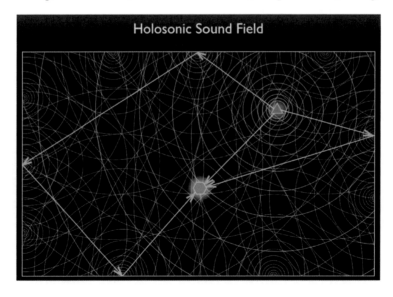

These interference patterns of Light and Sound aren't "analogous" to the cosmic hologram, they ARE the cosmic hologram that we experience as everyday reality — the Sonoluminous Holofield as introduced in Chapter 1. Both light and sound are hologramic in nature, right down to the mundane (*amazing*, actually!) ability to perceive these words with your eyes and hear sounds with your ears. If the general field of spatial reality were not hologramic, these sensory perceptions that we mostly take for granted would not work the way they do.

> *These interference patterns of Light and Sound aren't "analogous" to the cosmic hologram, they ARE the cosmic hologram that we experience as everyday reality.*

This is a vitally important point for our exploration: **The hologramic field is *generalized in space and time*, with the interference patterns of light and sound creating an "image of the whole" at every point in the field.**

This is an expanded perspective from the current scientific model defining the Holographic Principle, which holds that holographic information is present solely on a 2-dimensional surface, like we see on a flat holographic plate, and that our 3-D perceptual reality is a projection from the 2-D surface hologram. As mentioned earlier, a holographic image on a glass plate is actually representing a *slice* of the generalized holographic field of laser light that is present at the location of the plate. In the context of where we're heading in our exploration, this is a critical distinction because we're venturing into the premise that **the interference patterns of sound that manifest as the harmonic structure of Music is what *in→forms* the entirety of our beloved cosmos**. The actual form of physical "stuff", from atomic to universal scales, is defined by the harmonic interference ratios found in music, not as flat 2-D holograms but as emergent forms within a generalized harmonic field of hologramic space and time.

In considering the dynamic relationship between light and sound in the cosmos (or more generally, electromagnetic (EM) and acoustic impulses), it could be said that electromagnetism is the *tension* component that is complementary to the acoustic *pressure* component, for sound is pressure waves. This fundamental relationship is the always-and-only-co-existing tension-compression tensegrity dynamic explored in the previous Section, with electromagnetism as continuous cosmological and quantum gravity (tension) cohering into discontinuous islands of matter (compression).[*] From this perspective, **the physical, material universe from atoms on up is an acoustic (pressure) phenomenon floating in a sea of electromagnetic tensegrity**. In essence, then, the physical universe of form and flow is the same as what we call sound, and as such it is based upon the same harmonic relationships as sound, the primary experience of which we call Music. Not just "conceptually" or "approximately" but *literally* the same as music. And given the convertibility of acoustic and EM waves, this applies to the entire EM spectrum as well; the non-material photonic cosmos is harmonically organized in the exact same way. The cosmos is one big, beautiful Hologramic Symphony.

---

[*] When described in terms of spin dynamics, electromagnetism is the source of both the radiational, centrifugal force of light and the gravitational, centripetal force that compresses into mass/matter.

While the amount of rigorous research required to make a solid case for this premise is vast and technically demanding, thankfully that task has to a great degree been accomplished by Richard Merrick and thoroughly presented in his excellent book, *INTERFERENCE: A Grand Scientific Musical Theory* (available as a PDF download at www.interferencetheory.com). Founded upon the analysis of standing wave patterns of sound, Merrick offers a remarkably comprehensive account of how the interplay of harmonic resonance and Golden Ratio (Fibonacci/Phi) heterodyning and damping in→forms all physical manifestation from atomic to universal scales, as we saw in Chapter 30. For me, his **Harmonic Interference Theory** is equally important and complementary to Haramein's Unified Physics theory, and of course the premise of this book is that along with Cosmic Geometry they're describing one phenomenon — Cosmic Integrity in Harmony with Itself. I will refer to Merrick's research as a prime source for much of what is presented in this section.

But first, we need to start with an understanding of the basics of Music, just enough to provide a harmonic landscape while not overloading our exploration with the vast complexity it can ultimately lead to.

"You have hundreds of feelings that can't be put into words. And that is why I think that, in a sense, music is the highest of the arts, because it really begins where the others leave off."
— C.S. Lewis, *Surprised by Joy: The Shape of My Early Life*

CHAPTER 36
MUSIC BASICS

In our exploration here, we are viewing music as a *system* of harmonic relationships that in→forms cosmic reality. At its foundation, the system of relationships is very simple, and from this simplicity emerges a vast harmonic complexity. In the context of this journey, we're mainly going to stay focused on the simplicity so as to convey how the system of harmonic relationships correlates with cosmic geometry and unified physics. Here are the basics of this system…

OCTAVE

We're already familiar with the musical ratio of an Octave, wherein a sound frequency is either doubled or halved to create the same note in the musical scale, e.g. A = 110 Hz, 220 Hz, 440 Hz, etc. This is the primary ratio found in our Binary Number System introduced in Section 1. To our ears, there is a natural agreement that octave ratios produce the same note, just higher and lower than the reference note. This is a universal experience among most all cultures regardless of what scale is used to divide the octave.

12-TONE CHROMATIC SCALE

A quick survey of musical scales and styles around the world reveals that there are many ways in which the sonic landscape can be interpreted. The harmonic structure of South Asian music and the microtonal scales of Middle Eastern music, for example, offer a variety of ways in which the soundscape can be divided into harmonic relationships. While the study of musical scales around the world is a culturally informative venture, for our purposes we're choosing to orient our exploration around the familiar 12-tone scale most typically associated with Western classical and contemporary music. (Note: Since we are viewing music solely as *a system of harmonic relationships*, the 12-tone designation is equally pertinent to all 12-tone tunings, such as Just intonation and Equal Temperament.)

An octave as our "container" is divided into twelve parts, so for example the frequency spectrum between 220 and 440 Hz is divided into twelve notes. In music this is called the Chromatic scale.* The twelve tones of the Chromatic scale are given symbolic labels using the first seven letters of the alphabet.

---

* It's noteworthy that chromatic is also used in reference to light in scientific terminology.

In order to label twelve notes, these letters include designations that are either *sharp* (♯, a higher tone) or *flat* (♭, a lower tone). So you can see in the illustration below that there are seven notes in white (A B C D E F G) and five notes with the added sharp or flat symbols. The relationship between each note in the twelve-tone sequence is called a half step or semitone (e.g. A to A♯).

A	A♯	B	C	C♯	D	D♯	E	F	F♯	G	G♯	A
	B♭			D♭		E♭			G♭		A♭	

7-TONE DIATONIC SCALE

As seen above, the seven basic notes (in white, just like the white keys on a piano) comprise what's called a Diatonic scale — the familiar Do Re Mi Fa Sol La Ti Do (with the second Do an octave higher than the first). In this case it creates a C-Major scale, with C as the first note in the scale, followed by D (Major 2nd), E (Major 3rd), F (Natural 4th), G (Perfect 5th), A (Major 6th) and B (Major 7th). Each note in the scale is an *interval* related to the first or root note (as labeled in the parentheses) and can also be designated using numbers such that, in the Key of C, there's:

$$C = 1 \quad D = 2 \quad E = 3 \quad F = 4 \quad G = 5 \quad A = 6 \quad B = 7 \quad \text{(with octave } C = 8, D = 9, \text{ etc.)}$$

Within the 12-tone system of music there are twelve 7-note Diatonic "Keys", all of which have the same basic interval structure. So each note in the Chromatic scale can be the 1st note of a Major Diatonic scale, just like C above — 12 Keys consisting of 7 Notes, Do Re Mi… simple basics.

5-TONE PENTATONIC SCALE

Within the seven-note Diatonic scale is a sub-set of five notes called a Pentatonic scale. Numerically, these notes are the 1st, 2nd, 3rd, 5th, and 6th. It is a simple and familiar scale used in all musical genres. In a video that can be readily found online, vocalist Bobby McFerrin demonstrates very effectively that the Pentatonic scale is deeply ingrained in our psyche (and by implication, our physiology).[79]

TRITONE INTERVAL

With the 5-note Pentatonic scale as a sub-set of the 7-note Diatonic scale, we have two tones still to account for: the 4th and 7th. These two notes have what may be one of the most fundamental interval relationships in music, second only to the Octave. This is the interval called a Tritone, named this because the interval spans three Whole Tones (e.g. in the key of C: F (4th) and B (7th) are three whole steps apart — F • G • A • B). Here's why this is important…

A Whole Tone (or whole step) consists of two Half Tones (half steps); therefore a Tritone interval consists of six half steps. There are twelve half steps in the 12-tone Chromatic scale, which means that **the interval of a Tritone is exactly half of the 12-tone scale.** In other words, the two notes of a tritone are symmetrically opposite from each other in the 12-tone scale. From the perspective of dividing an Octave, the Tritone is exactly in the middle (e.g. for octave C to C, the Tritone is six half-steps away at F♯). This means that in the basic system of music **there are six pairs of Tritones**, as can be seen color coded in this illustration (A/D# A#/E B/F C/F#, C#/G D/G#):

As we'll soon see, this Tritone relationship is a fundamental duality in the music system that defines a double-torus dynamic in its most basic structure. (It is also another example of the Binary system at play, dividing the octave in half.)

FRACTAL SCALING IN OCTAVES

Everything we've seen above — the 12-tone **Chromatic** scale, 7-note **Diatonic** scale, 5-note **Pentatonic** scale, and six **Tritone** interval pairs — occurs within every octave of the sound spectrum. The exact same *relationships* of the basic music system are fractally scaled by octaves, so while the frequencies of the specific tones are halved and doubled, the system remains consistent. The same pattern repeats at all scales — our definition of a fractal. The image to the right depicts the ten octaves of sound that we humans can hear, with each set of seven dots half the size of the previous one (the last three octaves are so small it's not so easy to discern them in this graphic, but they're there).

Octave scaling is true not only for the acoustic spectrum of Sound but as well for the electromagnetic spectrum of Light. Our familiar seven-color "visible light spectrum" is literally one octave within the vast range of the EM spectrum that spans from Universal to Planck scales.

HARMONIC OVERTONES – WHOLE NUMBER RATIOS

The final part of the basics of the music system that's relevant to our exploration is called the Harmonic Overtone Series. Every sound that is made — be it from a guitar string, a trumpet, a car horn, a human voice — consists of a root tone, called the Fundamental, and a series of higher frequency tones that are in resonance with the Fundamental, called Overtones. The overtones are structured in a very specific series that is the same no matter what the sound source, but they vary according to strength (amplitude) and phase (constructive or destructive interference). This is what gives musical instruments (and all other sounds) their unique tonalities, known as timbre. Using the simplest possible scheme, the quantized nature of the cosmos defines these overtones solely according to **whole number ratios** — 1:1, 2:1, 3:1, 4:1, 5:1, 6:1, etc.

This illustration shows these ratios as subdivisions of a fundamental vibration, such as a guitar string:

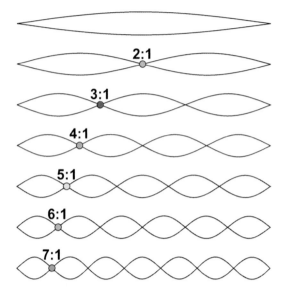

The harmonic overtone series spans a large frequency range, covering four octaves in the first 16 overtone "partials" (as they're called), and defines within the interference pattern of a single tone the harmonic structure of the Diatonic scale (with the addition of the minor 7th). The first 16 overtone ratios and their respective interval notes are:

1:1 = **Unison** (the root note, Fundamental or 1st partial)

2:1 = **Octave** [1] (2x the frequency of the fundamental, 2nd partial)

3:1 = 5th [1]

4:1 = **Octave** [2]

5:1 = Major 3rd [1]

6:1 = 5th [2]

7:1 = minor 7th [1]

8:1 = **Octave** [3]

9:1 = Major 2nd

10:1 = Major 3rd [2]

11:1 = 4th

12:1 = 5th [3]

13:1 = minor 6th

14:1 = minor 7th [2]

15:1 = Major 7th

16:1 = **Octave** [4]

Again, these overtones are resonant frequencies that naturally occur when just a single tone is played. So this whole-number harmonic structure is intrinsic to the fundamental physics of all sound, and therefore by extension in our working premise, all form in the cosmos. The same overtone ratios have been observed in highly resonant coherent laser light as well,[80] demonstrating the commonality of the harmonic structure of music in both acoustic and electromagnetic dynamics. This makes sense because we're talking about a quantized universe, which is inherently based upon whole-number quanta — just like we find in music.

5-LEVELS OF FRACTAL RECURSION

In Merrick's study of the interference pattern of a sonic standing wave he determined that **the same harmonic structure that's found within a single tone is actually present at five levels of pitch space — one-twelfth of a tone, a single tone, a semitone (two tones a half step apart), an octave, and twelve octaves.** This fractal powers-of-twelve hierarchy allows the same harmonic resonance to dynamically transfer energy up and down the entire sonic landscape from one-twelfth of a tone to twelve octaves while maintaining alignment of octave intervals throughout. According to Merrick,

> *"Since the square of twelve (144) defines the octave in the INTERFERENCE function,[81] we should expect that the harmonic series would also cycle its interference pattern recursively based on other powers of twelve. To support itself, such a hierarchy would have to start with the interference pattern inside a single tone and repeat itself recursively outward through pitch space in orders of magnitude. Furthermore, for an octave to align and resonate according to a power of twelve, harmonic standing waves must align at five specific levels of magnitude – one-twelfth of a tone, one tone, a semitone, an octave and twelve octaves. Mathematically, pitch space would then be organized as a 5-level 12th-power recursive Harmonic Hierarchy…*
>
> *As a unified musical framework for pitch space, we might even describe the alignment pattern of standing waves as a 5-layer harmonic projection screen. With a model such as this, music theory becomes far more than a bag of rules handed down by tradition – it becomes the study of geometrical shapes and how they fit together at different resolutions within a spatial harmonic landscape."[82]*

A spatial harmonic landscape… a fitting description of our cosmos whose space and form is composed of oscillating waves of sound and light fractally embedding geometric shapes of harmonic resonance throughout its hologramic whole.

We'll explore more of Merrick's findings for why this is so, but first let's return once again to the place where it all begins and ends — zero.

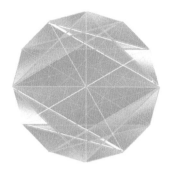

CHAPTER 37
THE ZEROPHASE OF MUSIC
(A.K.A. SILENCE)

We've just seen that within the full spectrum of auditory pitch space is a 5-level fractal hierarchy based upon a 12-tone system of harmonic relationships intrinsic to standing wave interference patterns of sound — the totality of which we call Music. Our observable, experiential universe is a cosmic sea of interacting waves creating dynamically evolving interference patterns of energy-matter-information — the totality of which we call The Cosmic Hologram. As Jude Currivan states in her book by that title,

> *"It's ultimately through the localized and universal fields of waveform energies and their interactions that the appearance of the physical world arises."* [83]

It stands to reason, then, that the harmonic structure of sound (which is convertible to electromagnetism, and vice versa) would in➜form the atomic-to-universal waveforms of the physical universe. After all, sound/electromagnetism *is* the universe, not something apart from it. The 12-tone system of music provides an inherent framework of harmonic relationships upon which the form and flow of energy-matter-information becomes manifest. If this is the case, can we find evidence that the 12-tone system of music can be correlated to the cosmometry of the universe as we did with unified physics? Is it present at the very foundation of cosmic dynamics — the zerophase at the center of all vibratory oscillation?

To answer this, we must reiterate that what we're exploring here is music as a *system.* Given that its harmonic ratios and interval relationships are fractally recursive across all scales, we can set aside the specific frequency interactions for a moment and consider just *the system of music itself* (as described in the previous chapter) that is naturally present in those interactions. When we do this, we quickly realize that the 12-fold, octave-scaling system of music is perfectly correlated to the zerophase cosmometry we started our journey with — the Vector Equilibrium (VE) — which is also a 12-fold, octave scaling system. Is this simply a (rather remarkable if so) cosmic coincidence?

As we saw in Chapter 7, the VE is a 12-around-1 geometric array that is defined when twelve spheres of equal size are close-packed around one central sphere. Connecting the centers of adjacent spheres derives the balanced geometry of the VE, as seen on the next page.

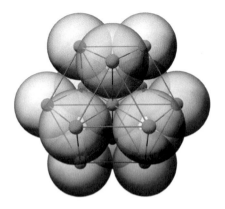 

While it's obvious, then, that a twelve-tone system of music can be correlated to this 12-fold geometry, there's a deeper understanding of the correlation that indicates just how compatible the VE-music system is. To illustrate this, we'll start with mapping music to a two-dimensional matrix, the kind of matrix we mentioned in the Introduction of the book.

Here you can see the 12-step Chromatic scale arrayed clockwise around a flat 12-around-1 matrix:

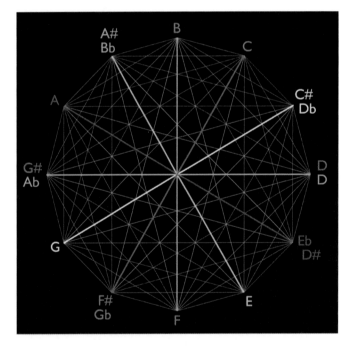

While all of the basic interval relationships can be mapped in this matrix, in this case the six colored lines are highlighting the Tritone intervals — the six pairs of opposite notes shown in the previous chapter (A/D# A#/E B/F C/F# C#/G D/G#). Splitting the octave in half, it could be said that the tritone introduces duality into the inherently unified (i.e. unison/octave) system of music. According to Richard Merrick, in fact, it is the tritone wave partials within the harmonic overtone series that "**physically** *divide the fundamental into twelve recognizable fringes. This is not a special case or abstract mathematics — it is a very real physical property of harmonics that occurs in any resonating medium.*" [84]

Returning now to the VE, we see that there are twelve vectors radiating from its center point. Buckminster Fuller describes these as six pairs of equal and opposite vectors. Sound familiar? He also specifies that the VE is not a structure, but rather it is a *system of relationships* in zerophase equilibrium. When considering music simply as a system of relationships, the six pairs of tritones comprising a 12-tone unity fit perfectly within the VE's systemic geometry. As we can see here, transforming the 2-D chromatic matrix to a 3-D VE shows that the tritone relationships in music align with the six pairs of the VE's radial vectors.

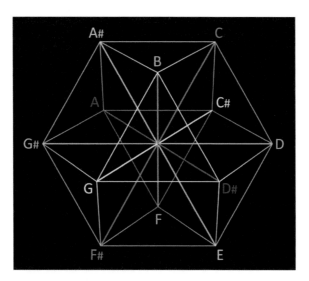

Even the clockwise chromatic sequence is visually maintained in this arrangement (though in the VE there is no clockwise or counterclockwise attribute).

And as we saw earlier, within the universal Isotropic Vector Matrix, the VE scales by doubling/halving just as the octave structure of music does. Here we can see three octaves of the music system within the VE-IVM matrix:

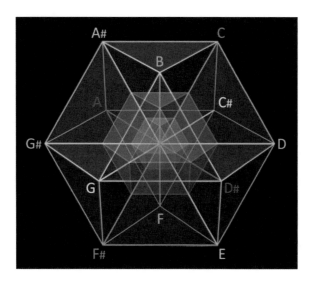

Each smaller scale of the VE is equivalent to an octave higher in frequency, showing that the zerophase of music is present at every octave in the spectra of sound and light. We could say that the VE is music when in a state of silence, "ready to accommodate any act and any audience." Additionally, the IVM inherently contains the Harmonic Series ratios of 1:1, 2:1, 3:1, 4:1, 5:1, etc.

 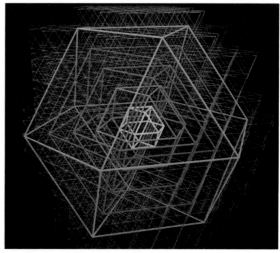

CIRCLE OF 5THS AND THE TRITONE DUAL TORUS OF MUSIC

In music theory there is a popular representation of the 12-tone system as what's called the Circle of 5ths. In this sequence, each consecutive note is an interval of a fifth (a Fibonacci 3:2 relationship, by the way) from the preceding one when moving clockwise around the circle. When we map the notes onto the 2-D matrix an obvious relationship emerges.

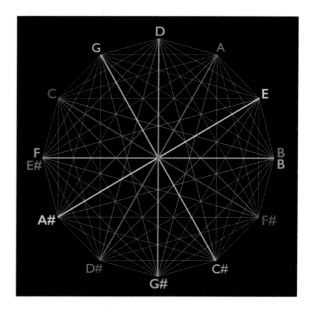

In this arrangement we can see the green line bisecting the middle with tritone notes F and B. Above and below this line are five other notes in each half of the matrix. The top group are the notes for the diatonic scale in the key of C (including the F and B — C D E F G A B) and the bottom group are the diatonic scale in the key of F# (also including the tritone notes B and F (called E# in this case) — F# G# A# B C# D# E#). The root notes of C and F# are a tritone pair, so we have two opposing keys each occupying half of the matrix and sharing the same bisecting (or intersecting, as the case may be) tritone notes (the F/E# and B, which swap roles as the 4th and 7th in each of the root keys).

When we consider that each key is a whole unto itself and map their seven basic triads (major and minor three note chords) with triangles, we can see that there is a beautiful symmetry of geometry and the implication of a dual torus dynamic.

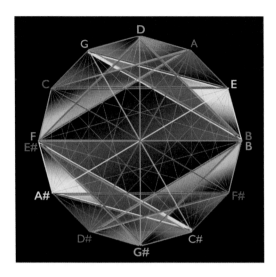 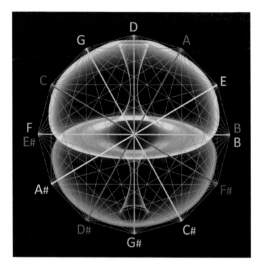

The 12-tone music system is revealed to be a tritone duality of opposing keys that intersect each other via their shared tritone notes. Each key is whole unto itself (a 7-note diatonic scale, single torus), and together they combine into a larger wholeness (the 12-note system of music, dual torus).

There is yet another fascinating aspect of the harmonic structure of sound that is present in this arrangement as well — Harmonic Symmetry.

CHAPTER 38
HARMONIC SYMMETRY

Symmetry is found throughout all of nature. Every animal, leaf, fish, insect, bird — even we humans — has symmetry of physical form and design (design meaning the actual body shapes and pattern colorations of fur, scales, feathers, etc.). Our DNA has symmetry. Crystals, molecules and atoms have symmetry. The Platonic Forms are symmetrical. With all this innate symmetry in the cosmos, it would stand to reason that there might be evidence of symmetry within the harmonic structure of music. In conventional music theory (other than related to music composition) the notion of symmetry is completely absent regarding the basic structure of music.

Richard Merrick (and others) has shown that, in fact, there is an obvious and important symmetry in music, and that the actual harmonic interference pattern of a tone "orbits" symmetrically around a single Harmonic Center. Merrick's analysis of this is in depth, but for our purpose we just need a simple understanding of this symmetry in music.

The basic 7-note diatonic scale is made up of a sequence of Whole and Half step intervals, as seen here in the key of C:

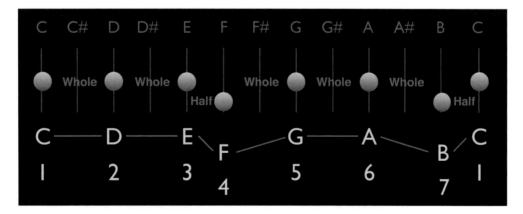

This is the Do-Re-Mi-Fa-Sol-La-Ti-Do scale taught in a beginner's music class. The C note is the root (determining the key of the scale) and the rest of the notes are intervals as marked by the numbers. Looking at this sequence we see no obvious symmetry or a specific note that stands out as a point of harmonic center.

When we extend the scale below the first C note, though, the interval structure does exhibit symmetry:

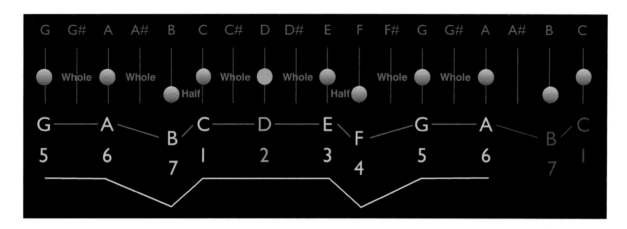

We can now see that there is a Harmonic Center to the structure of diatonic music, though it's not where we likely expected to find it in the scale — it's the 2ⁿᵈ note rather than the 1ˢᵗ or root note. In music theory, the root note is called the Tonic and the 2ⁿᵈ note is called the SuperTonic (above the Tonic). In Merrick's analysis of the interference pattern of the harmonic overtone series of a tone, he determined that *"Partial 9* [the location in the series of the harmonic associated with the SuperTonic] *acts as a resonant point of symmetry or Harmonic Center in the harmonic series which other harmonics orbit like a miniature solar system. Corresponding to this, the SuperTonic acts as a Harmonic Center in a diatonic scale to create a sense of stability and consonant tonality in music."* [85]

Looking again at our matrix of the Circle of 5ᵗʰˢ, this Harmonic Center symmetry becomes clearly apparent:

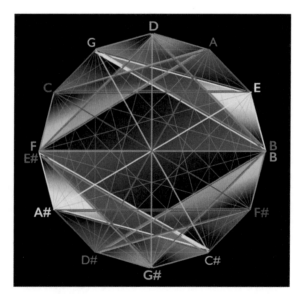

The top half of the matrix shows the seven notes in the key of C — C, D, E, F, G, A, B. At the very top we find the SuperTonic, D. We then see the symmetry of notes on either side of it (G, A, C, E).

All combined, these five notes comprise the Pentatonic scale. Lastly, at the horizontal midpoint of the matrix we see the Tritone (F, B). While arrayed differently, this symmetry matches perfectly with that which we saw above in the linear diatonic scale.

The same symmetry is mirrored in the bottom half of the matrix where the opposite key of F♯ is mapped in the same manner. We now see that there's a dual axis of symmetry that provides harmonic structure to the whole of the music system — the vertical Harmonic Center axis and the horizontal Tritone axis.

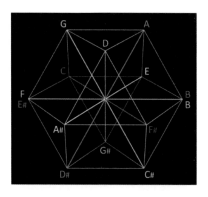

Extending this further into three-dimensional space we can see that this same Circle of 5ᵗʰˢ arrangement can be mapped to a Vector Equilibrium (as we did the chromatic scale in the previous chapter). Here we can see the same dual axis of symmetry within the overall harmonic space. But the VE is undifferentiated equilibrium, the zerophase at the center of all vibratory phenomena. Remember though, the VE oscillates — Fuller's Jitterbug motion, which produces all of the Platonic Forms. So if this map of music is the zerophase, what happens when we jitterbug it into other forms?

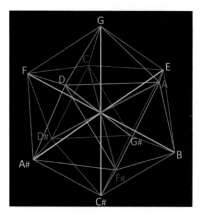

As we saw in Section 5, when the VE collapses, the first phase of symmetry it finds is that of an Icosahedron, which has 12 vertices. To the right is the same music system mapped to an icosahedron. The symmetrical dual of the icosahedron is the dodecahedron, which has 12 faces upon which we can also map the twelve notes of the music system (bottom). In each of these cases we can see that both the green Tritone axis and the 7-tone diatonic duality on either side of it are maintained in these geometries.

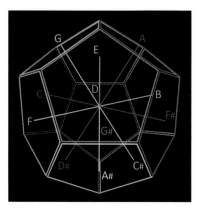

Is there any actual physical relevance to this geometric exploration of music? According to Merrick's research of harmonic overtones in a standing wave, the tritone interval (partials 5 and 7 for those more technically inclined) not only *"physically divide the fundamental into twelve recognizable fringes"* but do so in correlation to **Golden Ratio damping along the Harmonic Axis that splits the twelve tones into two groups with exact proportions of a regular dodecahedron.** Rather than being a purely conceptual spatial model of music, this fundamental harmonic arrangement literally informs the geometry of structures across all scales. The gravitational tensegrity of protons, atoms, molecules, crystals, cells, planets, stars, etc. has a physical basis of harmonic resonance and phi ratio damping that defines a spherical geodesic form and associated geometric structures.

Let's explore evidence indicating that the 12-tone harmonic resonance system of Music does indeed in→form our physical universe.

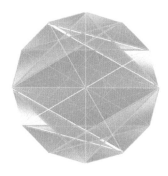

CHAPTER 39
HARMONIC IN→FORMATION

A 2003 paper entitled *Dodecahedral space topology as an explanation for weak wide-angle temperature correlations in the cosmic microwave background* [86] proposes spherical dodecahedral geometry at the largest scale of our universe as a whole. Referencing the analogy of musical harmonics in describing the spherical harmonics of temperature fluctuations in the microwave background energy of the cosmos, the authors write,

> *"Temperature fluctuations on the microwave sky may be expressed as a sum of spherical harmonics, just as music and other sounds may be expressed as a sum of ordinary harmonics. A musical note is the sum of a fundamental, a second harmonic, a third harmonic, and so on. The relative strengths of the harmonics — the note's spectrum — determines the tone quality, distinguishing, say, a sustained middle C played on a flute from the same note played on a clarinet. Analogously, the temperature map on the microwave sky is the sum of spherical harmonics. **The relative strengths of the harmonics — the power spectrum — is a signature of the physics and geometry of the universe.** [Emphasis added] Indeed the power spectrum is the primary tool researchers use to test their models' predictions against observed reality… The density fluctuations across space split into a sum of 3-dimensional harmonics — in effect the vibrational overtones of space itself — just as temperature fluctuations on the sky split into a sum of 2-dimensional spherical harmonics and a musical note splits into a sum of 1-dimensional harmonics… While most potential spatial topologies fail to fit the WMAP results, **the Poincaré dodecahedral space fits them strikingly well."***

Given that all energy dynamics are frequency oscillations with harmonic overtones just as is sound, it stands to reason that the correlation to music is not an analogy but rather the actual underlying system of Phi damping and resonance relationships that in→forms our fractal-hologramic universe. The 12-tone, 5-level music space described by Merrick innately matches the 12-fold pentagonal geometry of the dodecahedron and icosahcdron. As we know, pentagonal geometry *is* Phi ratio geometry, and as we also saw in the previous section, both the icosahedron and dodecahedron contain within their geometric topology the symmetry of three Golden Rectangles in 90° XYZ coordinate relationship. Could it be that Phi damping and resonance of an acoustical interference pattern, which according to Merrick defines the 12-tone musical system, is the actual basis of our 3-D perceptual and measurable electromagnetic cosmos? And could the ubiquitous symmetry we see in nature be present as an inevitable consequence of Harmonic Symmetry, not only found in music but within all oscillating systems (which is of course everything)? As Merrick puts it,

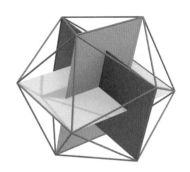

> *"…the Reflective Interference resonance model expresses the simplicity and symmetry of harmonic behavior in the most organic way. It explains in the broadest terms the balance of harmonic and damping forces that must be at the bottom of all things. In the standing waves of quantum structure, atomic binding, molecular lattices, plant/animal physiology and planetary activity, the same musical forces manifest all around us. Statistical models based on the Gaussian distribution predict the frequency of human intelligence, social trends, market fluctuations and other human behavior as a variance against the coherent harmonic series. And though it is seldom mentioned in either scientific or musical circles, wherever we find harmonic activity we will always find the golden ratio and the Fibonacci series to establish coherence. One does not exist without the other."*

Another pioneering researcher of cycles and standing waves across all scales, Ray Tomes, expresses this idea of fractal harmonic recursion very simply in his "single axiom of Harmonic theory":

> *"The Universe consists of a standing wave which develops harmonically related standing waves and each of these does the same."*[87]

In his theory, the electromagnetic wavelength at the size of the universe is the fundamental tone, which contains whole-number ratio harmonic overtones exactly as does a musical tone. These overtones then also develop harmonics in whole number ratios, and this trend continues in a fractal progression throughout all scales from universal to atomic.

In his study of harmonics of numbers and their multiples, Tomes discovered patterns of resonance that accurately equate to both music and spatial harmonics across a vast range of scale. The basis of his theory is simple; find which numbers have the most ways they can be derived through multiples of other numbers, as shown in this chart:

	1	2	3	4	5	6	7	8	9	10	11	12	13	14	15	16 etc...
2 →		2		4		6		8		10		12		14		16
3 →						6			9			12			15	
4 →								8				12				16
5 →										10					15	
6 →												12				
7 →														14		
8 →																16

...etc.

The more instances a number has, the stronger is its harmonic energy (in the sense of actual physical wave forms combining to increase overall energy). Notice that in the first sixteen numbers, 12 is the strongest, followed by 16. When we look at a chart of the relative strength of the first 100 numbers, it becomes obvious that multiples of 12 are clearly the most resonant numbers:

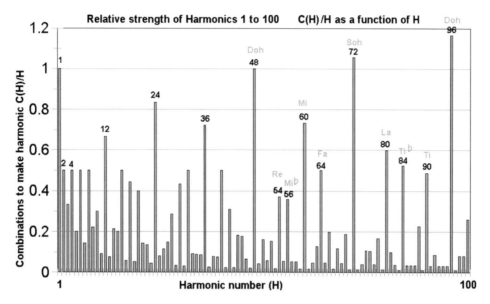

In this chart Tomes also shows that within this spread of whole-number harmonics can be found specific musical ratios, labeled accordingly as Doh, Re, Mi, Fa, Soh, La, Ti, Doh. He writes, *"looking at the interval from H=48 to H=96 the very strongest harmonics are 48-60-72-96 which is a major chord in music (usually known as the ratios 4:5:6:8 resulting when cancelled by factors of 12). In addition, the notes of the just intonation music scale are exactly represented in the harmonics 48-54-60-64-72-80-90-96."*[88]

Using computers, Tomes calculated these harmonics out to very large numbers, finding one in particular that appears regularly within the harmonic spacing of physical objects in the universe — 34,560. Calculating the average distances between these objects he found a consistent ratio based upon powers of 34,560.

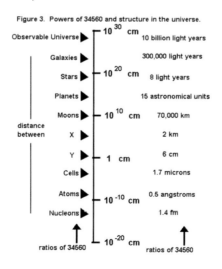

Figure 3. Powers of 34560 and structure in the universe.

251

He also points out that, as presented in a study published in *New Scientist* in March of 1990, superclusters of galaxies are formed in regularly spaced intervals, as shown in this graph from Tomes:

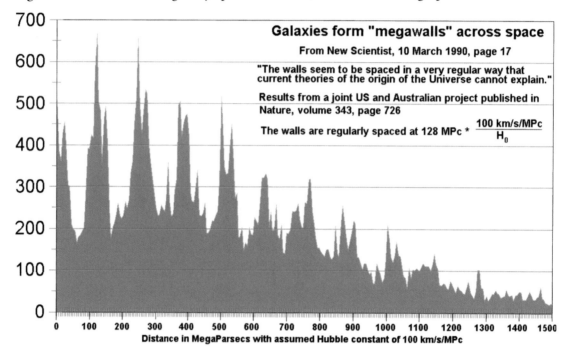

This phenomenon is readily predicted by both his harmonic number theory and the fundamentals of musical harmony.

Back in Section 2 we saw that this periodic spacing of galactic superclusters is in fact organized in a fractal octahedral arrangement (left illustration) and proposed that this arrangement is itself a conse-

quence of harmonic resonance with the underlying cosmometry of space — the Isotropic Vector Matrix. With the IVM's intrinsic 12-fold Vector Equilibrium and Octave-scaling symmetry, which as we've seen is an appropriate model for the basic music system, is it any wonder that musical harmonic proportions would in→form the resonance dynamics of energy-matter-information as it oscillates "on either side of zero" across all scales?

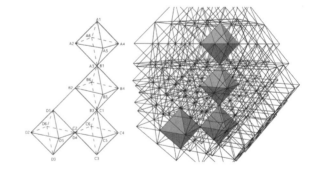

"The universe is a musical instrument and everything in it is vibrating in tune with the larger things that contain it. I believe that there are no other laws in the universe than this. All the other laws of physics appear to be the result of the wave structure that leads to the Harmonic law." – Ray Tomes

Perhaps one of the most essential findings relating music's harmonic resonance system to emergent properties in the cosmos is presented in the research of Dirk Meijer and Hans Geesink from the

Netherlands. Through meta-analysis of over 500 scientific papers dating from the 1950's to the present, Meijer and Geesink came to identify what they call **an "algorithm for coherent life processes" that produces a set of frequencies spanning 127 octaves of electromagnetic and acoustic waves that are found to be "life-sustaining"** — that is, they support healthy cellular functioning. From their paper entitled *Quantum Wave Information of Life Revealed: An Algorithm for Electromagnetic Frequencies that Create Stability of Biological Order, with Implications for Brain Function and Consciousness*,[89] the authors state:

> *"An algorithm of multiple scales is proposed based upon a tempered Pythagorean scale and composed only by connecting approximated stacks of fifth's (frequency ratio of 2:3), and octaves (ratio of 1:2), while **12 discrete frequencies fit within each octave**. [Emphasis added] By making use of scales of fifths and octaves there is an algorithmic relation between the basic frequencies, the overtones and harmonic frequencies... If a frequency of one cycle per second is used, which is 1 Hertz, than all frequencies in all scales can be calculated. Under these conditions preferred coherent frequencies... of a so-called 'reference scale' can be calculated: 256.0, 269.9, 288.0, 303.1, 324.0, 341.15, 364.7, 384.0, 404.5, 432.0, 455.1, 486.0 Hz.*
>
> *This particular scale is called a 'tempered Pythagorean scale' and its patterns of harmonic and coherent waves can be extended to all frequency scales: all lower and higher preferred frequencies are entangled by this scale and can be simply calculated by multiplying or dividing each preferred frequency of this reference scale by powers of 2. In this manner about 127 scales having coherent algorithm frequencies can be derived from 0.001-Hertz till the highest possible frequency of ≈6.2x10^34 Hz. The latter is related to the smallest theorized unit of distance of the Planck length, as represented in a mathematical algorithm of coherent frequencies."*

Here's a chart showing data points of 315 beneficial frequencies (green) and 171 detrimental frequencies (red) that fall in between the life-sustaining bands (normalized to the twelve-frequency reference scale described above):

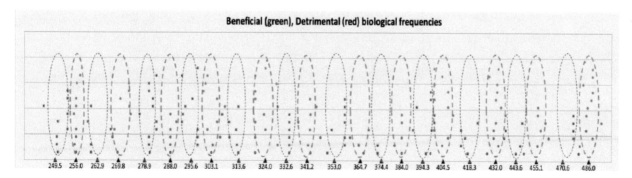

Beneficial (green), Detrimental (red) biological frequencies

249.5 256.0 262.9 269.8   278.9   288.0 295.6 303.1   313.6   324.0 332.6 341.2   353.0   364.7 374.4 384.0 394.3 404.5   418.3   432.0 443.6 455.1   470.6   486.0

According to their findings, there is inherent in nature an algorithm of frequencies that *"may indicate that we identified the involvement of a universal electromagnetic principle that underlies the observed life sustaining effects and also may have been instrumental in the creation of biological order in first life and quantum consciousness."* [90]

> *The prime attribute of both Music and the Quantized Universe is one and the same: whole-number harmonic ratios that organize into coherent geometric relationships and resonant structures across all scales.*

Again, we find a 12-tone fractal harmonic resonance system being indicated as fundamental to the organization and healthy functioning of biological life, as well as potentially active in the interaction of our brains with the universal field of information and consciousness (as we'll see in Section 7). Notably, Meijer and Geesink's life-sustaining frequency system uses an octave doubling algorithm that spans from Cosmological to Planck scales — exactly what we find in the 12-around-1 VE/IVM geometry, which is of course viewed in our cosmometry model as the zerophase reference of the system of Music and all harmonic resonance it expresses. (As we'll see in Section 7, they also refer to a non-visible 4-dimensional informational framework related to the brain and consciousness, which the 4D cosmometry of the IVM may correspond to as well.)

Also notable is that the reference scale identified is directly correlated to the Binary number system in that it contains the note C at 256 Hz (the first frequency in their reference scale), which is of course found in the Binary 1 2 4 8 16 32 64 128 256... sequence. When 256 Hz is assigned to the note C in the music system, the note A has the frequency of 432 Hz, which is also one of the beneficial frequencies in their algorithm. So, for all those who are discussing the merits of tuning your instruments to a reference of A=432 Hz, the findings above indicate that this is, indeed, a beneficial and life-sustaining choice! (It is highly compelling to note that when the Planck distance is measured in Imperial units rather than Metric, its value is 1×10^{-38} miles, thus defining a reference value of 1 upon which we can measure other attributes of the universe in whole number ratios, suggesting that the frequency harmonics that are life-sustaining are heterodyning from the Planck scale up into the biological scale.)

The prime attribute of both Music and the Quantized Universe is one and the same: whole-number harmonic ratios that organize into coherent geometric relationships and resonant structures across all scales. Music IS the quantized universe expressed in our audible perceptual dimension of scale, just as visible light is the quantized universe expressed in our visual perceptual dimension of scale. With the 12-fold system of music in the mix, we now have three basic number systems working in mutually co-operative integrity — Binary, Phinary, and now, 12-fold Dodecanary.

CHAPTER 40
THREE AS ONE (AND THEN SOME)

It is a common metaphysical aphorism that "unity comes in threes." Similarly, Buckminster Fuller stated, "Unity is plural and at minimum two." With two being prime duality, three arises as prime structure — the triangle. The triune as Unity is what makes our manifest cosmos possible. Two points on either side of a zero-reference point create a triangulated relationship by which all physical phenomena emerge. It is no surprise, then, to learn from Ray Tomes's study of number harmonics that 2 and 3 are the most common root powers (obviously, since they're the lowest common denominator, they'll be the most common). These are then combined with 5 and 7 to derive families of number harmonics across large quantities (note correlation to Pentatonic/5 and Diatonic/7 music scales). These attributes of number harmonics are at the foundation of our now three Basic Number Systems. Let's see how…

Throughout our exploration we've referenced the first two number systems — the Octave-doubling Binary and Fibonacci-scaling Phinary.

Binary

1   2   4   8   16   32   64   128   256   512   1024 …

Phinary

0   1   1   2   3   5   8   13   21   34   55   89   144   233   377   610   987 …

The Binary is intrinsic to the cosmometry of the zerophase Vector Equilibrium as it scales throughout the Isotropic Vector Matrix in doubling ratios. It is, of course, the foundational ratio of music as well — the octave. And it is the system with which cell division initially occurs in multicellular organisms, which is essentially the same thing as octave division; doubling the frequency (number of cells) while halving the wavelength (size of cells) in the first phases of mitosis.

The Binary system is also fundamental to time and rhythm in music, with the division from Whole notes, to Half, Quarter, Eighth, Sixteen, Thirty-second and Sixty-fourth notes.

The Phinary is intrinsic to the dynamics of form and flow throughout the cosmos, found from atomic to galactic scales as spirals, angles, quantities, and proportions that arise from the Fibonacci sequence's self-similar recursion. As Richard Merrick has shown us, it is this aspect of the quantized cosmos that provides the damping necessary to enable stable and coherent whole-number resonance within all vibratory systems — the sum total of which we call Universe. Its function is to define the spatial limits within which harmonic resonance manifests both form and flow, be it in music, water, plants, hurricanes, planetary size and spacing, galactic spirals… and in our body's skeletal structure, cellular microtubules, DNA, and inward still to molecular geometries and atomic symmetries.[91] It does this by damping all non-whole number harmonics (enharmonic frequencies) down little (and sometimes very big!) golden ratio vortices, essentially capturing them and stepping them down in ever-increasing magnitudes of Fibonacci number frequencies (i.e. smaller wavelengths) that approach the ultimate destination — the Planck scale zerophase equilibrium, a.k.a audible silence and spatial stillness. It is also the irrationality of pure mathematical Phi (1.6180399…) that provides the "wiggle room" necessary for resonating structures to oscillate without destructively interacting with each other, such as within a musical tone's standing wave.

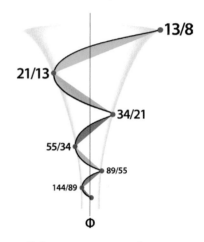

"There is no distinction between Phi, Fibonacci or harmonics as a single integral and emergent process from perfect damping."

– Richard Merrick

The Binary/Octave and Phinary/Fibonacci systems combine through standing wave interactions to define the 12-tone music system — our third, Dodecanary, number system. It could be said that the Dodecanary system is a synergetic outcome of the combination of these two fundamental number systems, being that **the 12-tone system resides *within* the octave scaling system and is *defined by* the division of the octave through Fibonacci damping.** As we've seen, powers of 12 exhibit strong resonance in Ray Tomes' number harmonics analysis, indicating the ubiquitous presence of the Dodecanary system within frequency cycles across all scales. And as we know, the Vector Equilibrium itself is a 12-around-1 system.

The Dodecanary system has an additional correlation with the Binary and Phinary. We've seen from the study of the music system that within the 12-tone chromatic octave is the 7-tone diatonic scale, with the eighth note being the octave. When we look at all three systems together using the diatonic music scale as our reference, we can see that they share one number in common (other than 1 and 2) — the octave, 8.

Binary

1   2   4   [8]   16   32   64   128   256   512   1024 …

Phinary

0 1 1 2 3 5 [8] 13 21 34 55 89 144 233 377 610 987 ...

Dodecanary (as diatonic scale)

1 2 3 4 5 6 7 [8] (diatonic octave; chromatic octave is 13)

So, all three number systems are unified in the octave ratio, a strong indication that we're fundamentally considering one system here.

This can actually be seen in the cosmometry of the **Octa**hedron (8 faces) within the VE's jitterbug dynamic. As we saw before, an octahedron symmetrically encloses the open VE (left image below). It is also formed when the VE contracts to the point of its edges coming together (middle image). The sizes of these two octahedra are in a 2:1 ratio, an Octave. And as we also saw, when we divide the edges of an octahedron by the golden ratio, we get the exact symmetry of an icosahedron (right image). The Phinary (golden ratio division) divides the Binary (octahedrons in octave ratio) to create the Dodecanary (12 points of icosahedron within octahedron) — a geometric model for exactly what was described above.

A piano keyboard also illuminates the unification of these three systems. The white keys are the basic notes of a major diatonic scale, C D E F G A B C, and the black keys are the sharps and flats of those notes. Here we can see an obvious Fibonacci number correlation, wherein there are groups of 2 and 3 black keys, which combine into 5 notes of a pentatonic scale. We then have the 8 white keys of a diatonic scale octave. When we combine the 5 black notes with the 8 white notes we get the 13 notes of the chromatic scale octave. Of course, the same pattern repeats by octaves up and down the frequency spectrum.

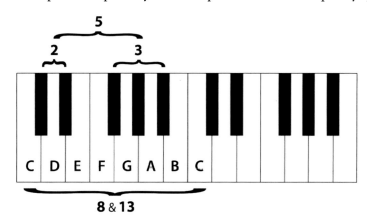

Other indications of a unified system include:

- The presence of 64 in the Binary, which is 8 x 8 or eight octaves and the prime geometric arrangement of the polarized Isotropic Vector Matrix, the 64 Tetrahedron Matrix. (In cell division, it is at the 64-cell stage that the internal and external cells branch into separate developmental lineages.[92] And as well, the DNA inside every cell is composed of a set of 64 codons.)

- The presence of 144 in the Phinary, which is 12 x 12 or twelve chromatic octaves. (It's also the twelfth number in the Fibonacci sequence.)

- Half of 144 is 72 (a Binary conversion), which is the number of degrees that divides a circle into a pentagon, bridging the 5-fold Phinary and 12-fold Dodecanary systems. Additionally, the ratio of the span of the pentagon's vertices is Phi (left image). And all of its internal angles are multiples of twelve as well (3, 6 and 9 x 12 — right image).

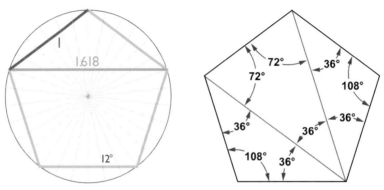

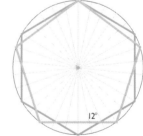

When a circle is divided by 12° increments as above, the symmetry of a hexagon is also accommodated. When we overlay both the pentagon and hexagon together, a specific correlation becomes evident that exactly matches a fundamental attribute of the dynamics of music that Richard Merrick illustrates in what he calls the **Tritone Function on the Chromatic Ring Model**, as part of his Harmonic Interference Theory.

If you're not a musician this will be somewhat abstract, but there's an easy way to know what is being described. You've probably heard the fulfilling resolution at the end of a religious hymn when the final "Aaaa-men" is sung. This movement, from "Aaaa" to "men", provides a strong feeling of shifting from being suspended in the air and unresolved to landing solidly on the ground again, returning "back home" to a resolved state. In music theory this movement is called the Tritone Function and is quite simply when the two tritone notes in a given 7-tone scale sound together ("Aaaa"), then move towards each other to their immediate neighbors ("men"). The resulting (resolved) interval is a Major Third, which is the "home" interval of the key the song is in. This Tritone Function is what introduces tension and resolution in all kinds of music.

Merrick shows this in his Chromatic Ring Model, as seen in this illustration:

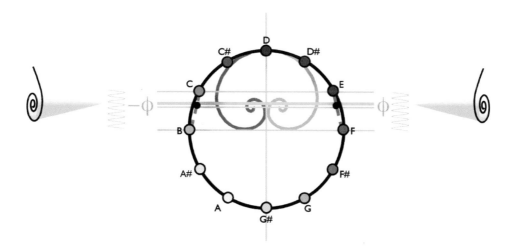

The two axes of the Tritone (horizontal, B-F) and the Harmonic Center (vertical, D) are the same as we've seen before. Just above the Tritone axis are the notes C and E. This is the Major Third interval in the key of C. In between those notes and the Tritone notes we can see two Phi damping vortices that define the bridge of energetic motion that must be crossed when the Tritone shifts to the Major Third. This is not a metaphorical crossing, it is a real and physical exchange of energy within a sound's standing wave dynamics. "Aaaa-men"… we can actually feel it!

Well, from our study of the geometry of a circle based upon a Dodecanary (12°) division, we can see that the pentagon aligns exactly at the Phi point, and that the hexagon aligns with the resolved Major Third, as seen here:

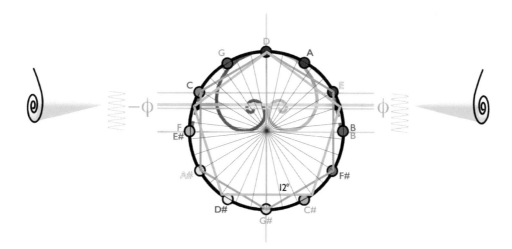

The 5-fold pentagon (Phinary system) resolves to the 6-fold hexagon (Dodecanary system) by means of the Tritone Function (Binary system, since the tritone splits the octave exactly in half).

It is compelling to note that the 5-fold pentagonal and 6-fold hexagonal symmetries are found in the "source code" of our very physiology — the structure of DNA, as can be seen in this illustration of its chemical structure. It is, as well, common in many chemical bond structures.

Whew! As simple as this 3-in-1 system actually is, it can seem rather heady to describe it all. How about a relaxing "Aaaa-men" from the angelic choir about now!

Two more points to highlight in this Basic Number System exploration…

As mentioned in Section 1 on this topic, the Binary and Phinary systems share a very close similarity when viewed in relationship to the Phi ratio of 1.618. Multiplication and division of this number by a factor of 2 (Binary doubling and halving) yields decimal values that closely equate to the Binary values:

Illustration by Madeleine Price Ball

Phinary =	Binary		
Phi/16 =	.10112	=	1
Phi /8 =	.20225	=	2
Phi /4 =	.40450	=	4
Phi /2 =	.80901	=	8
Phi =	**1.61803**	=	16
2x Phi =	**3.23606**	=	32
4x Phi =	**6.47213**	=	64

The decimal values that make up the difference can be attributed to the "wiggle room" provided by the Phi ratio's damping function that allows for the whole-number resonance of octave harmonics to occur in the Binary. **Harmonic coherence is the result of these two fundamentally similar systems interacting and weaving a Dodecanary musical space that permeates the entire cosmos.**

It is also noteworthy that the Phinary/Binary values are offset by a factor of 10, exhibiting an inherent correlation to the base-10 number system within which these systems reside (which is itself the result of Binary doubling of the Phinary (2 x 5)).

So, looking at our three octave-scaling Number Systems we see every single-digit number represented from 0 to 9… except 9:

Binary	**1**	**2**	**4**	**8**	**16...**			
Phinary	**0**	**1**	**1**	**2**	**3**	**5**	**8**	**13...**
Dodecanary	**1**	**2**	**3**	**4**	**5**	**6**	**7**	**8** (diatonic octave)

Ahhh 9. Too much to say about 9 for this book, but here are four things to consider, stated as simply as possible for the sake of keeping our brains from becoming numbed (as in excessively numb-er-ed).

9… is the Harmonic Center note in the overtone series and diatonic scale. So essentially, all of the above revolves around 9. (The harmonic center is the 2nd note in the diatonic scale, which is the same note just above the octave/8, therefore it's called the 9th.)

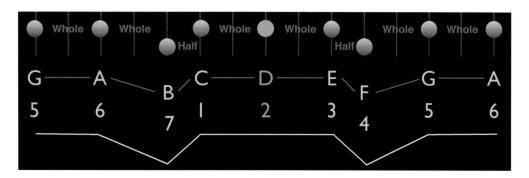

9… plays the same role as zero. "What???" you might rightly say. Here's why… In the study of numbers resolved to their digital roots, we find:

10 = **1** (1+0)
11 = 2 (1+1)
12 = 3
13 = 4
14 = 5
15 = 6
16 = 7
17 = **8** (octave)
18 = **9** (= 0)
19 = 10 = **1**
20 = 2… etc.

In an Octave-scaling universe, **9** resides between **8** and the next **1**, playing the role of zero. The fractal division of space and time as an interplay of harmonic resonance and Phi damping within wave form interference patterns of sound and light revolves around 9 as the still point Harmonic Center. Buckminster Fuller puts it this way:

> "There is an octave pattern in every system and every time we come to nine — whether it be 3+6, 2+7, or 8+1 — it is zero. Waves are octave and one reason they do not interfere with each other is because of the zero."

Both Buckminster Fuller and Walter Russell view wave dynamics as octaves centered by zero-nine, with a +4 / -4 cycle of wave propagation.

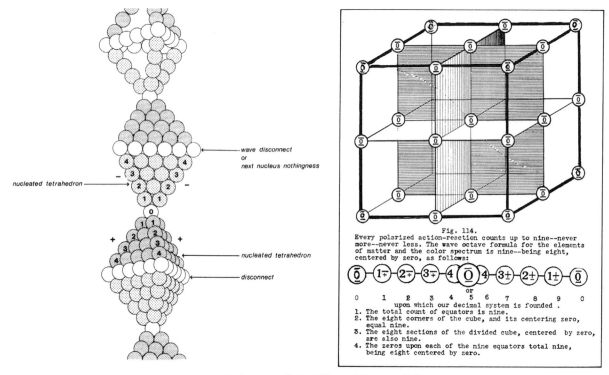

Buckminster Fuller's "bow-tie" waves (left);
Walter Russell's cubic zero-point space model in which wave dynamics occur in octaves (right)

Remarkably, by applying his octave wave model to the periodic table of elements, Russell was able to successfully predict the existence of a number of elements that had not yet been discovered experimentally.[93]

9... is "the Primal Point of Unity" in the relatively new field of number study called Vortex-Based Mathematics (VBM). Originated by Marko Rodin, VBM uses the same digital root conversion process as seen above, this time applied to a doubling sequence — the Binary system. **1, 2, 4, 8**, 16 (=**7**), 32 (=**5**), 64 (=10=**1**). As it turns out, this doubling sequence (or circuit, as it's called) repeats with all subsequent doubling (or halving). **1, 2, 4, 8, 7, 5,** 1 2, 4, 8, 7, 5, **1, 2, 4, 8, 7, 5**... It is typically illustrated in the simple diagram to the right.

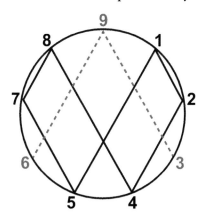

Noticeably absent from this sequence are the numbers, 3, 6 and 9. The theory in VBM is that this sequence oscillates between the 3 and 6 as a basic polarity, due to the doubling of these numbers alternating between them in their digital roots (e.g. **3, 6**, 12=**3**, 24=**6**, 48=12=**3**, 96=15=**6** etc.). Nine is unique, though, in that doubling it always resolves to itself — **9**, 18=**9**, 36=**9**, 72=**9**, 144=**9**... In this way, nine is seen as the pivot point around which the entire circuit moves in balanced polarity. Sound familiar? The Harmonic Center of an oscillating system of eight numbers derived from an octave scaling structure? It's tempting to say it's "music to our ears," but we won't go there.

Why is this considered "vortex" based mathematics? It happens to be that the repeating pattern of VBM maps readily to a torus topology, as seen in this illustration:

In this it is theorized that VBM offers a fundamental mathematical tool with which to explore the flow of energy in toroidal dynamics within all kinds of physical processes, as well as a basis for technological application across many fields. While the science of VBM is young, the model does correspond well with our exploration of the number systems, music and toroidal dynamics.

To top off all of the above…

9… is the digital root of the sum of angles in all of the Platonic Forms. As seen in this illustration, when the face angles are tallied for each form and the total number is reduced to its digital root, the result is always 9 (as is true for all of the polygons at the bottom as well):

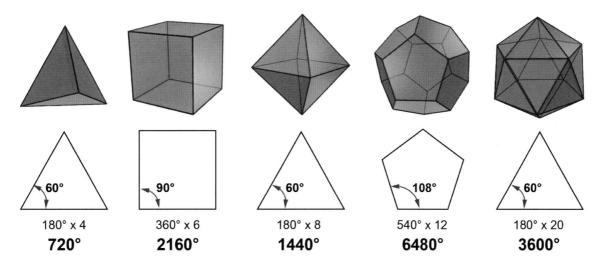

The same also holds true for the Archimedean and Catalan solids — the sum of their angles all resolve to a digital root of 9. It suggests to me that the symmetrical balance (Harmonic Symmetry – 9) of these basic geometric forms complete their wholeness and equilibrium by adding up to zero, which in this case is represented by 9.

So as you can see, 9 holds a special place in the pantheon of numbers.

As one more indication of the integrated nature of the Binary, Phinary and Dodecanary number systems, when the digits of the Fibonacci Sequence are resolved to their digital roots, a pattern emerges that repeats every twenty-four numbers, like this:

1, 1, 2, 3, 5, 8, 4, 3, 7, 1, 8, 9, 8, 8, 7, 6, 4, 1, 5, 6, 2, 8, 1, 9, 1, 1, 2, 3, 5, 8, 4, 3, 7, 1, 8, 9, 8, 8, 7, 6, 4, 1, 5, 6, 2, 8, 1, 9, 1, 1, 2, 3, 5, 8, 4, 3...

Mathemetician, Jain108,[94] discovered that the repeating sequence can be further reduced to two twelve-number systems that when correlated by pairs of each number in the sequence and summed to digital roots, all add up to 9.

1, 1, 2, 3, 5, 8, 4, 3, 7, 1, 8, 9, 8, 8, 7, 6, 4, 1, 5, 6, 2, 8, 1, 9

1, 1, 2, 3, 5, 8, 4, 3, 7, 1, 8, 9

+

8, 8, 7, 6, 4, 1, 5, 6, 2, 8, 1, 9

=

9, 9, 9, 9, 9, 9, 9, 9, 9, 9, 9, 18 (1+8=9)

So, the Fibonacci digital root pattern (Phinary) repeats in two (Binary) sets of twelve (Dodecanary) numbers. A clearly integrated pattern is revealed that, once again, resolves to 9 — the zero-point center.

UNIFIED MATHEMATICS

The three number systems — Binary, Phinary and Dodecanary — are components of a single unified system. Together they inform the dynamics of periodic waveforms that underlie all physical phenomena (the frequencies of sound and light), with octave doubling being the container within which Fibonacci spirals define a 12-fold system of resonance in harmonic ratios. These number systems represent intrinsic qualities of the quantized nature of the cosmos, providing a whole-number rational basis of order that in→forms the geometry and flow of matter and energy. Numbers, periodic waveforms, geometry and music are, in fact, one and the same thing.

Unified Mathematics pioneer, Robert E. Grant,[95] is exploring this singular relationship in great depth, proposing that the physical constants (such as Pi, Phi, Euler, Fine Structure Constant,

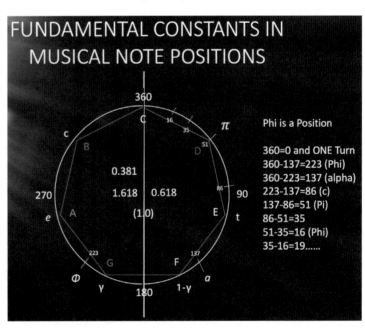

FUNDAMENTAL CONSTANTS IN MUSICAL NOTE POSITIONS

Phi is a Position

360=0 and ONE Turn
360-137=223 (Phi)
360-223=137 (alpha)
223-137=86 (c)
137-86=51 (Pi)
86-51=35
51-35=16 (Phi)
35-16=19......

Speed of Light, etc.) are specific attributes of the angles and geometries created by spiraling waveform interference patterns within the cosmic sea of frequencies and musical harmonic ratios. For example, the Phi Rotation Angle of 137.5° (seen in Chapter 25) is intrinsic to the growth pattern of leaves in many plants, providing for maximum exposure to sunlight throughout the foliage. Grant's hypothesis is that this angle is directly correlated to the ratio of the Fine Structure Constant — approximately 1/137 — that is the "coupling constant" or measure of the strength of the electromagnetic force that governs how electrically charged elementary particles (e.g., electrons, muons) and light (photons) interact (as Grant puts it, the properties of reflection and absorption of light energy in atomic structures). Perhaps the Fine Structure Constant is an attribute of Phi ratio resonance and damping within atomic geometries and frequencies that defines angular interaction with light inherent in the electrochemical processes of plant photosynthesis, and also in→forms their physical growth pattern at the macro scale? Grant's research is potentially opening up new vistas in our understanding of known physical constants and the possibility for discovery of many new ones.

In direct correlation with the Fibonacci Sequence's repeating pattern of twenty-four numbers, Grant has also discovered a relationship of prime numbers (including a new classification that he calls "quasi-primes") that maps into a 24-modulus wheel diagram (seen below) and for the first time reveals a predictable pattern of prime number determinacy to infinity[96] (in the process inadvertently compromising essential data encryption algorithms used in digital transaction systems that are based on prime number *in*determinacy!). As well, his Wave Theory of Numbers[97] illustrates a repeating 6-, 12- and 24-fold pattern of numbers and their correlations to sound frequencies, musical ratios, the light spectrum, geometries, physical constants, and atomic elements.

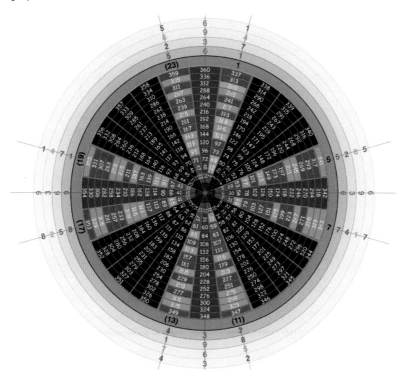

It is evident through the analysis of Grant, Merrick, Geesink & Meijer, Tomes and others, that the 12-fold system of harmonic resonance we call Music is, indeed, a Master Code for understanding an implicate order and organization found at all scales throughout the cosmos.

HARMONIC WHOLENESS

Let's take stock of where we've come to in our journey…

It's easiest to do so by circling back around to our Unified Model of Cosmometry, adding in the musical notes as a reference to the harmonic system it portrays. What we see now is a model of the harmonic potential of any and all oscillating events in the cosmos, represented as the zerophase state of equilibrium (VE, silence, stillness) with the dynamic motion of the torus and double spiral (sound, light, waves).

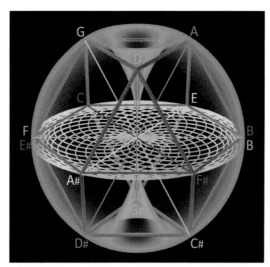

The Dodecanary system becomes musical harmony when the string is plucked, causing the innate 12-fold cosmometry to oscillate around a neutral axis (the Harmonic Center), introducing tension/compression dynamics that literally carve a 7-fold Diatonic scale in time and space, forming specific standing wave tensegrity structures (geometric forms) that we call music, and atoms, and molecules. These then aggregate in resonant harmonic proportions to form organs and organisms, with ears to hear and eyes to see, perfectly attuned to the octave-scaling Binary/Phinary/Dodecanary symphony of life here on Earth and beyond.

This is the inevitable manifestation of a quantized uni-verse — the cosmic dance of the One Song being sung at every point in the cosmos. Every acoustic and electromagnetic quanta is a pluck of the Great Instrument, an action set in motion by the in-tension of you, me and every other entity large and small in the cosmic orchestra. A play of Light and Sound so beautifully synchronized it brings tears to your eyes when you catch a glimpse of its perfection (with a little wiggle room :Φ). At this point there's only one thing left to say…

It's about Time.

CHAPTER 41
IT'S ABOUT TIME

"Everything in the Universe has rhythm. Everything dances."
– Maya Angelou

OK, next chapter! Maya Angelou has summed it up nicely.

But of course, there's more we can say about this, especially as it pertains to the basic concept of a quantized universe. In fact, the origin of the word 'quantum' in quantum theory is in reference to a packet of energy in motion — a quantum of action. As previously mentioned, it originates from the discovery by Max Planck that the energy emitted from every kind of electromagnetic radiation (visible light, x-rays, infrared, radio waves, etc.) comes in discrete packets, or quanta, of action. The operative word here is action. It is movement, and movement requires the dimensions of space and time. Time is an essential component of the quantized structure of the cosmos in this context, at least as it pertains to action and energy.

In quantum mechanical physics, the **quantum of action** became formalized as a physical constant, appropriately named the Planck Constant. (That guy was truly a cosmic thinker!) Here is the value for it:

$$h = 6.626070040… \text{ x } 10^{-34} \text{ Joules/second}$$

The symbol h is used to specify the Planck Constant in physics equations. A Joule is a standard unit of energy equal to the work done on an object when a force of one newton acts on that object in the direction of its motion through a distance of one meter. Because it occurs across one second of time, the Planck Constant is a value of action and movement. As you can see, it is a very small value (10^{-34}). It is correlated with the frequency of an electromagnetic wave (such as a color in the visible light spectrum) to derive the energy value of that frequency using the equation $E=hf$ (E (energy) = h (Planck Constant) x f (the frequency)). In simple terms, every frequency across the electromagnetic spectrum has a discrete value or quantum of energy associated with it. It is this realization of the quantized nature of the energetic cosmos that kicked off the field of quantum mechanics and led to Einstein's coining the name 'photon' for the quantum energy event.

So, what does this have to do with Maya Angelou's statement and music? Quite simply that the very foundation of the universe — the so-called quantum field — is rhythmic as quanta of action. The frequency of an electromagnetic (EM) wave is determined by how many pulses or oscillations of the wave occur in one second of time — known as cycles-per-second and given the name Hertz (Hz). For example, the frequency value of green light is in the range of 526–606 THz (terahertz, e.g. 526 x 10^{12} cycles/second). There are a very large number of EM wave oscillations in one second of time that we see as green light! If we were to convert this to sonic impulses, it would be vastly beyond the range of human hearing. Nonetheless, the pulsations of energy that is green light are exactly the same as those of sound and rhythm. In sound we hear it as tone, in rhythm we hear it as tempo (described below), and in light we see it as color. Richard Merrick highlights the actuality of this correlation by applying the same 12-step octave division of sound to the octave of visible light (370-740 THz), seen in his diagram below.[98] The correspondence of the music system to the primary, secondary and tertiary color relationships is further evidence of a unified harmonic system across the vast range of electromagnetic and acoustic frequencies.

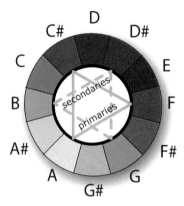

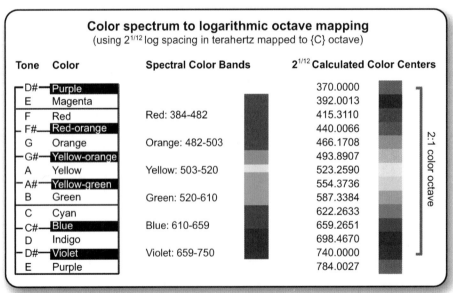

Color spectrum to logarithmic octave mapping
(using 2$^{1/12}$ log spacing in terahertz mapped to {C} octave)

Tone	Color	Spectral Color Bands	2$^{1/12}$ Calculated Color Centers	
D#	Purple		370.0000	
E	Magenta		392.0013	
F	Red	Red: 384-482	415.3110	
F#	Red-orange		440.0066	
G	Orange	Orange: 482-503	466.1708	
G#	Yellow-orange		493.8907	
A	Yellow	Yellow: 503-520	523.2590	
A#	Yellow-green		554.3736	
B	Green	Green: 520-610	587.3384	
C	Cyan		622.2633	
C#	Blue	Blue: 610-659	659.2651	
D	Indigo		698.4670	
D#	Violet	Violet: 659-750	740.0000	
E	Purple		784.0027	

Let's continue to step this down into the realms of sound and rhythm.

The frequency range of human hearing is considered to span from 20 Hz (twenty cycles/second, very low tones) to 20 kHz (twenty-thousand cycles/second, very high tones). It is in this range of frequency oscillation that all music is experienced (and all other sound for us humans, of course). Being many orders of magnitude slower in frequency than visible light, if we convert these acoustical sound waves into electromagnetic waves through a microphone, we would not be able to see these frequencies with our eyes (though we can make them visible on an oscilloscope). And yet, it's still the same pulsation-of-energy-per-second phenomenon.

Now let's bring it into the range that we experience as rhythm. In music, the most fundamental basis of rhythm is the tempo. Whereas with light and sound the pulsa-

The extremely high frequency of the Planck-scale oscillators (the PSUs, at 10^{44} cycles per second) is just as relevant to music as are the tones of sound and tempos of rhythm.

tions are counted in a *second* of time, tempo is counted in a *minute* of time, referred to as *beats per minute* or BPM. So, for example, a tempo of 60 BPM has a pulsation every 1 second, which is equivalent to 1 Hz (one cycle per second). Doubling the tempo to 120 BPM is equal to tapping your finger twice every second. Doubling it again to 240 BPM is tapping four times every second. You can try that now — just count "one-mississippi, two-mississippi, three-mississippi, etc...." and tap once each time. Then tap twice for each count, then four times. You are experiencing tempo! Try doubling again to 480 BPM (eight times per second) and you'll see that it doesn't take long to reach an upper limit of useful tempo rates. So, just as with the limited ranges of visible light and audible sound, there's a limited range of tempo, and therefore rhythm, that we can play music within and dance to. Too fast and we'll jumble everything together into an incoherent frenzy; too slow and we'll just be sitting still, waiting for the next pulsation to move to.

The dynamic pulsation of energy at all scales of time and space is fundamentally the same from a rhythmic perspective. The frequency "tempo" of the visible world is extremely fast, and yet the music of light is seen by our eyes. The frequency "tempo" of audible sound is also fast, and yet it is the exact right range that manifests the ineffable magnificence of tones we combine as music. When we combine these tones with the much slower tempos of rhythm, we can dance! So, from this broad perspective... *"Everything in the Universe has rhythm. Everything dances."*

There's an important distinction to be made about the nature of time at this point. **Time in the context of light, sound, rhythm and music is that of cycles rather than the linear concept of Time that we call the 4th dimension.** This cyclical time is measured *in reference to* the linear time of seconds and minutes, and yet as a phenomenon that is intrinsic to the cosmos, it is not dependent upon linear time. It simply is present as a spectrum of tempo and rhythm across a vast range of cycles of pulsation from Planck to Universal scales. The extremely high frequency of the Planck-scale oscillators (the PSUs, at 10^{44} cycles per second) is just as relevant to music as are the tones of sound and tempos of rhythm. So too are the cycles of galaxies, stars, planets and life here on Earth, and inward to those of cells, molecules and atoms. Our modern calendar system is in a 7-beat cycle of days that make up a week; with 52 weeks defining a larger musical phrase we call a year. The Solstice and Equinox points in the Sun-Earth cycle occur in a tempo of 4 beats per year — a very slow tempo. Yet it's one that we can still relate to (and even dance to if we're paying attention).

We ourselves are an aggregation of tempos and cyclical rhythms. Our heartbeat is the most obvious (and perhaps vital) one, with an average pulse rate of 60-100 BPM when at rest. These are tempos that we can play music and dance to. And in a study published in the journal *Circulation*, researchers determined that listening to music "can directly trigger physiological changes that modulate blood pressure, heart rate and respiration."[99] The rhythms of our human physiology are numerous and occur at many cyclical scales, as described by Deepak Chopra and physicist Menas Kafatos from their book *You Are the Universe: Discovering Your Cosmic Self and Why It Matters*:

> *"The human nervous system is constructed of tiny clocks that regulate other tiny clocks all around the body. Besides the really big rhythms the body follows (sleeping and waking, eating, digesting, and excreting wastes), there are medium rhythms (breathing), short rhythms (heartbeat), and very short rhythms (chemical reactions inside our cells)."* [100]

Anirban Bandyopadhyay, senior scientist in the National Institute for Material Science in Tsukuba Japan, calls this the Nested Rhythm Network in the Living System. Based upon experiments to study a single resonating protein,[101,102] he proposes that the system of time cycles in the body (or clocks), from quantum mechanical processes in proteins to cell replacement cycles in organs, is a fractal network with all time-scales (i.e. frequencies) transferring information up and down the micro-macro biological system. The clock inside a clock inside a clock inside a clock is continuous, with no discontinuities. He proposes a new Fractal Information Theory (FIT) and Geometric Musical Language (GML) for this purpose.[103] The classical music played by proteins, like an Indian Raga, does not get diluted but is played out within the protein complex. The music of biology morphs life following a new more advanced form of mechanics called Fractal Mechanics.[104] In this image of vibratory states of a protein, Bandyopadhyay shows just how similar these quantum mechanical harmonics are to those of a classically vibrating guitar string (compared here with an overtone series diagram):

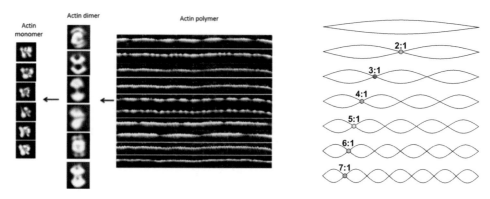

There are many cyclical divisions of time occurring simultaneously throughout our bodies, in some cases synchronizing with external rhythmic cycles such as day and night, and in others synchronizing with deeply internal cycles of cellular and chemical activity. In music, this is called polyrhythm — a number of rhythms playing simultaneously, overlapping, interacting and creating a combined "groove" that works together as a whole. When we're healthy this body groove is orchestrated quite coherently, akin to that of a well-timed rhythm section, albeit far more polyrhythmic!

These cycles each have repeating patterns just as we find in music. A simple vibration may be back-and-forth — one-two • one-two • one-two… Or it can become more complex; one-two-three • one-two-three • one-two-three… one-two-three-four • one-two-three-four… one-two-three-four-five • one-two-three-four-five…

These cycling rhythms are not only occurring in time but in space as well. The periodicity in atomic and molecular structures is an oscillating sequence that forms triangles (3 beats), squares (4 beats), pentagons (5-beats), hexagons (6-beats)… and these rhythms literally in→form the structures they create.

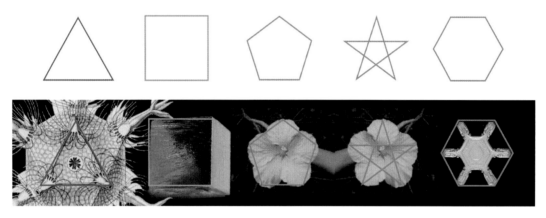

Trace your finger repeatedly around each of the polygons above and count a number for each corner; you'll experience rhythms used in music and throughout the entire vibratory cosmos. We know, as well, that these cyclic rhythms can be extremely accurate and consistent in timing, such as with the resonant vibration of molecules in a quartz crystal used for keeping time in clocks and watches. The most accurate timekeeper is an atom whose electrons emit microwave frequencies as they change energy levels with an astounding degree of regularity, which is the basis for atomic clocks. According to Nobel Laureate physicist, Frank Wilczek,

> "In modern Quantum Mechanics, atoms are not little balls revolving around other little balls, they are patterns of vibrations; they are wave functions… And patterns of vibration are what you have in musical instruments. So the atom can be thought of as a kind of musical instrument. And the way those patterns manifest themselves in things we can observe are that the frequencies of vibration of the atom turn into the frequencies — or effectively, the colors — of the light they emit. So each atom has a kind of

tonal palette, which shows up as the kind of light that it prefers to emit or absorb. And the equations that tell you from the shape of an atom and the forces that act on it, how you get to the tones — that is, the frequencies of the light — are really... it's hard to exaggerate how close they are... they're almost literally the kinds of equations that describe how you design musical instruments. You want to know if you put the sounding board here and weight it this way, what kinds of tones will come out. You solve the same kind of equations. There are many differences, but perhaps the most striking thing is that the atoms are much more perfect musical instruments than man-made instruments. There's no friction. Every atom of the same element is the same." [105]

As Jude Currivan says in her book, *The Cosmic Hologram*:

> *"The different attributes of all elementary particles are vital for the existence and evolution of our perfect Universe and are now being understood in terms of their harmonic, resonant, and coherent behaviors— all signs of the cosmic hologram."*

Shifting from atoms to the scale of our solar system, it is widely known that planetary spacing and orbital cycles also have harmonic proportions. Most popularly presented is the apparent path of Venus relative to us here on Earth. With an orbital ratio of 13:8 — a Fibonacci number pair — Venus traces a pentagram pattern in the night sky every eight years.

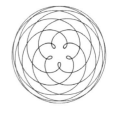

In applying his Harmonic Interference Theory to the size and orbital spacing of planets in our solar system, Richard Merrick has revealed that the entire system follows the same harmonic resonance and Phi damping as found in music. He writes, *"...unlike Newton's gravity equation that requires a complex mass variable or Gauss's gravity constant that demands knowledge of the days in an Earth year and distance from the Sun, this musical solar system model estimates both the gravity constant and planetary spacing geometrically based on a consistent distribution around a recursive Φ–spaced ring pattern. No physical knowledge of the solar system is required since the entire solar system can be modeled as a giant vibrating string..."* [106]

He illustrates the musical correlation in this diagram, upon which I've also overlaid a Phi vortex pattern to show how the Phi Boundary Condition comes into play in this context (the red circle around the inner orbit for Mercury), and lays out the octave tone and color mapping of planets relative to the harmonic series (next page).

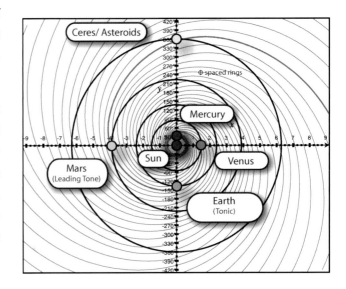

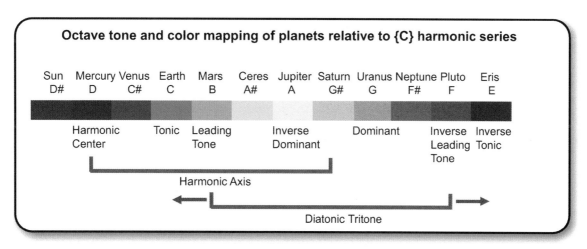

Octave tone and color mapping of planets relative to {C} harmonic series

Sun	Mercury	Venus	Earth	Mars	Ceres	Jupiter	Saturn	Uranus	Neptune	Pluto	Eris
D#	D	C#	C	B	A#	A	G#	G	F#	F	E

Harmonic Center — Tonic — Leading Tone — Inverse Dominant — Dominant — Inverse Leading Tone — Inverse Tonic

Harmonic Axis

Diatonic Tritone

As further evidence of harmonic resonance defining solar system dynamics, a January 2018 paper entitled *The K2-138 System: A Near-resonant Chain of Five Sub-Neptune Planets Discovered by Citizen Scientists*, published in The Astrophysical Journal, describes a star that "hosts five small… transiting planets in a compact architecture. The periods of the five planets are 2.35, 3.56, 5.40, 8.26, and 12.76 days, forming an unbroken chain of near 3:2 resonances."[107] All of these planets have orbital periods that are in near Perfect 5th ratio with each other.

Merrick goes on to say,

"As the golden spirals [of the Sun's heliospheric current sheet] *damped down the harmonic resonance between planets — performing the same function the Fibonacci series and Φ-damping locations do in a musical octave — the planets resonated into spherical nodes. And as they did so, their relative sizes were determined by the same physics that determines resonant gap size as two tones diverge over a musical octave…*

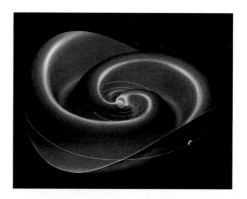

Given the starting conditions of the solar system, the planets had no alternative but to space along a golden spiral. They had no "choice" in sizing themselves according to their resonant velocity locations. And no choice in attaining orbital speeds that perfectly balanced their size and distance from the Sun. They were simply following the physics of gravitational harmonics that crystallize light energy into form inside a geometrically structured and polarized space." [108]

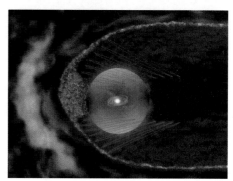

The solar system is a cyclically tuned system of harmonic resonance and Phi damping within the spherical container of the Termination Shock in the Sun's heliosphere (the termination shock is the spherical "bubble" in the bottom illustration on the previous page, with the white dot being the Sun). This spherical container provides the necessary reflectivity (or feedback loop) for a harmonically coherent standing wave pattern to form, just as is the case with the harmonic overtone structure of sound, which, as Merrick says, *"is a physical interference pattern that occurs as a result of coherent interference in any round or spherical container."* The Sun's termination shock is the point at which the pressure (i.e. acoustic waves) from the solar wind plasma, traveling at supersonic speeds, interacts with the local interstellar medium and slows to subsonic speeds.

The circular, cyclical characteristic of Time as energy in motion in both electromagnetic and acoustical dynamics in→forms the manifestation of harmonic structures in Space always-and-only in consort with the Golden Ratio's coherence-engendering heterodyning and damping attributes.

Interestingly, a common analogy for a termination shock is the turbulent ring around water as it hits (for example) a chopping block in a sink, just as we saw in Section 4. Within this area we saw that there's a Phi double spiral pattern (like the heliospheric current sheet) defining a coherent flow that's emanating from the vertical axis of the water, the point of impact of which would represent the Sun in the solar model with the double spiral on the chopping block representing the celestial equator (or solar accretion disc) of planets in orbit. This suggests that in both of these cases the termination shock represents a Phi Boundary Condition, and within this circular/spherical space is a harmonically coherent spatial and temporal geometry resulting from the same reflective pressure wave interference dynamics occurring at different scales. We can also see the same pattern in a sunflower.

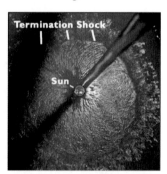

The circular, cyclical characteristic of Time as energy in motion in both electromagnetic and acoustical dynamics in→forms the manifestation of harmonic structures in Space always-and-only in consort with the Golden Ratio's coherence-engendering heterodyning and damping attributes. Atoms and molecules are literally musical instruments that transfer their harmonic information up the cosmic ladder of scale, becoming visible as the rainbow octave of light and audible as the musical octaves of sound, both of which are perceptible to us due this very same harmonic transfer in→forming our physiological design and proportions.

As Merrick states,

> *"Stop and ask yourself if it seems reasonable that all biological processes — bones, organs, muscles, nervous system, blood, brain and senses — would grow coherently out of carbon-12* [which accounts for 98.89% of all forms of carbon] *according to the same balance of resonance and damping in a 12-step octave. Does it make sense that life would grow in conformance with the coherent geometry found in the standing waves of light, sound, electromagnetism, gravity, the solar system and everywhere else in the cosmos? If so, then you would probably conclude that harmonic science is the one and only unifying natural philosophy for all natural science — a complete and comprehensive system of thought — capable of "breaking open the head" and replacing the countless artificial theories currently in vogue."* [109]

Time will tell if Merrick's proclamation is proven true when mainstream academia opens its mind to considering the premise of Harmonic Interference Theory. Given how integrally compatible it is with the 12-fold, Octave and Phi proportioned cosmometry of unified physics and our fractal-hologramic model of wholeness, it's clear that it deserves thorough consideration as a fundamental system of harmonic science that can inform all other natural sciences.

To round out this picture of Music as harmonic cosmometry, we'll complete this part of our exploration with a simple introduction into the emerging field of Cymatics — the art and science of making visible the flows of sound as they create remarkably beautiful patterns in water… and in life.

> *"Electromagnetically seen, we may be living in a "diluted plasma" with natural coherent quantum resonances, that can be approached by equations for standing waves as present in strings, at 1:2 ratios* [Octaves] *and approximated 2:3 frequency ratios* [Circle of Fifths] *according to an algorithm of scalars. We propose that a natural quantum field makes use of, invariable, 12 typical basic quantum resonances."* [Correlations added by author.]

> – Hans J. H. Geesink and Dirk K. F. Meijer, *Quantum Wave Information of Life Revealed: An Algorithm for Electromagnetic Frequencies that Create Stability of Biological Order, with Implications for Brain Function and Consciousness*

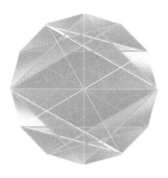

CHAPTER 42
CYMATICS

The word cymatic was coined by Hans Jenny (1904-1972), after the Greek word for "wave". Jenny (and Ernst Chladni before him in the eighteenth century) was a pioneer in making visible the standing wave patterns of sound in a vibrating medium. Using a sound-generating oscillator, Jenny studied how sand, powders and liquid were affected by different frequencies, often causing them to organize into coherent geometrical patterns. While the field of cymatics has been emerging for a few decades, the science of it is still quite nascent. To analyze, catalog and demonstrate repeatable patterns with rigorous scientific integrity requires a high-degree of parameter control for such variables as sound source, frequency, amplitude, phase/timbre, size/depth/density of the container, density or viscosity of the vibrating medium, temperature, atmospheric pressure… etc. It is therefore not our purpose in this exploration to address the science of cymatics but rather to see how the resulting patterns may correspond to the idea that acoustical pressure waves in→form the same kind of geometric patterns we find in nature; to see if indeed "Music is liquid architecture; Architecture is frozen music," as Johann Wolfgang von Goethe said.

While Hans Jenny used large surfaces to make cymatic patterns visible, today's technology is vastly more refined — and small. Imagine a round cup a mere half-inch in diameter and depth. Inside this cup is water, and underneath it is an audio speaker. Above the cup is a ring of LED lights. As the sound passes through the water it creates a standing wave pattern, which is made visible on the surface of the water by the reflection of the LED lights. Mounted directly overhead is a high-resolution digital camera with a macro lens that captures images like this:

Magnifying the image to one small section reveals a remarkable degree of detail in the patterns of dynamic flow captured in one moment of time:

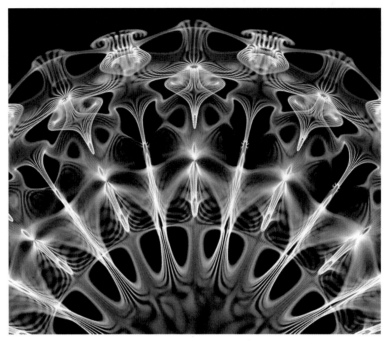

Even in this still 2D image we can see a 3D layering of swirls and currents. Considering what a small portion of our half-inch cup this represents, the amount of pattern information is quite astonishing!

Let's look at a few more examples and see how they correlate to natural phenomena. Bear in mind, these are simple snapshots of a moment of time in what's otherwise a dynamic flow of energy. The importance of this is realizing that all form in the universe is doing exactly the same thing — manifesting standing wave patterns into "temporarily stable abstractions" (as Bohm would say) of physical matter, form and flow. Note that all of these cymatic images are original unedited images. (Above image by cadboy_hk; all others courtesy of Erik Larson, Aqueous Technologies.)

Here are a couple of cymatic patterns exhibiting pentagonal symmetry within the overall dynamic flow:

Pentagonal symmetry is often found in flowers, and as we know it's Phi proportioned, so it's easy to see the Fibonacci damping in these patterns.

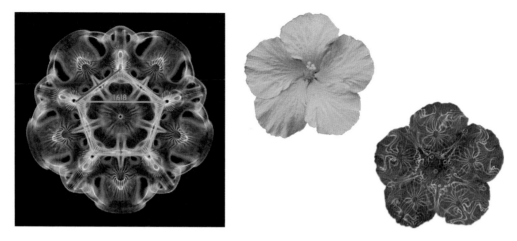

We can even see tendencies towards dodecahedral symmetry in this pattern, which may in fact be underlying the 3-dimensional waveforms.

Next we see hexagonal symmetry in this cymatic pattern, along with an overlay of a snowflake's hexagonal crystalline symmetry (note same proportions of inner hexagon of cymatic and snowflake):

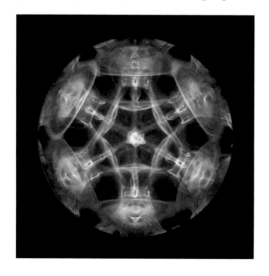 

Here we see 3-fold symmetry, which is often found in tomatoes and other fruit:

  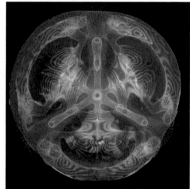

The tomato is cut horizontally through the middle to reveal its 3-fold cross-section. When a tomato is cut vertically through the middle it reveals another of our fundamental patterns, the Phi spiral, in this case as two offset vortices. We can begin to see how both Phi damping and harmonic symmetry are simultaneously at play within the toroidal wholeness of a humble (if not some-what toothy grinning) tomato.

In this next example, the image on the left is a still frame from a cymatics video. The specks you see are small flakes of glitter put into the water so as to make the flow patterns visible. When looking at this, imagine the three glitter-filled sections convoluting in torus flows. This is the energetic resonance in the flow pattern. In between them are spaces without glitter. These are the areas of damping between the reso-nance zones, which as you can see are defining the 3-fold geometry. Notice the similarity to the 3-fold lines and swirls in a watermelon.

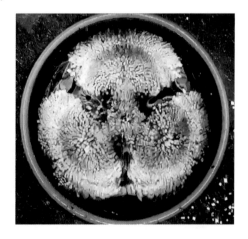 

Another 3-fold cymatic symmetry bears resemblance to the face of a Praying Mantis:

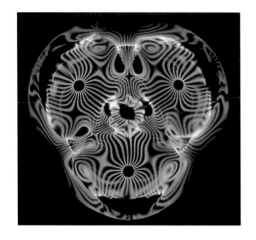 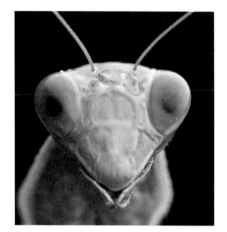

And then there's this one…

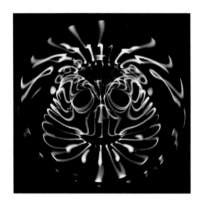 

Remember, it's just a snapshot of light reflected off of the surface of water that's being vibrated by sound in a cup about ½ inch in diameter. This image was not modified. Sometimes ya just don't have to make this $&#@ up!

Sure, it's a bit of a reach from sound waves that look like a face to an actual face… or is it? That's the inquiry here. Cymatics provides a potential means to make visible the cosmometry of standing wave patterns that harmonic resonance within the energetic cosmos is invisibly — or implicitly, as per Bohm's Implicate/Explicate order — using to in→form said energetic cosmos. These very simple, even simplistic, examples of cymatics correlated to natural forms are presented solely with the intention of being a catalyst for inspiring deeper inquiry. A true science of cymatics is warranted when we consider the possibility that the acoustical component of energy-matter-information is literally the compressing of electromagnetic aether into form and flow at all scales as a direct consequence of quantum and cosmological gravitational tensegrity, doing so as a unified whole-number harmonic system called Music. Cosmometry, Unified Physics, Music — one thing.

To wrap up this Section of the book I want to share one more cymatic example and how it relates to our friend the Tabla drum that played a role awhile back as we explored Tuning the Universe. In a simple yet profound way, this brings together all that has been said about the harmonic system of music and its correlation to physics and cosmometry.

To the right is a cymatic pattern with 8-fold symmetry, which we can overlay onto the head of the tabla drum. The straps that put tension into the head are essentially in pairs since two straps cross each of the eight tuning blocks (the brown wooden cylinders). So this cymatic may offer a fairly good representation of the tensegrity pattern within the drumhead.

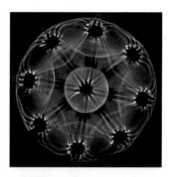

In Section 5 we talked about tuning the tabla, using a hammer to increase or decrease tension all around the rim of the drumhead to balance out the overall tension. Doing so ultimately arrives at a nice sounding resonant tone when the drum is struck with a finger. Having done this tuning exercise many times, I've come to realize that there's a most interesting correlation to what Richard Merrick has brought to light in Harmonic Interference Theory.

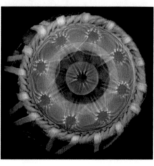

In the quote near the end of the previous chapter, Merrick refers to carbon-12, which is the most common form of atomic carbon (about 99%). The goatskin drumhead, for example, would be primarily made of these carbon atoms. Carbon-12 is also used as the standard reference for calculating the atomic mass of all other elements, with 6 protons and 6 neutrons in its nucleus, and 6 electrons. Merrick proposes that the atomic structure of carbon-12 can be correlated to the harmonic dynamics of music, illustrating the concept in this diagram:

The Chromatic Dual Rings as archetype for carbon-12

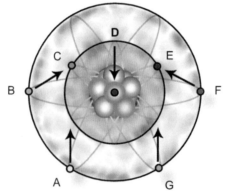

$$^{12}C = 6 \text{ neutrons} + 6 \text{ protons} + 6 \text{ electrons}$$

Here we can see that the Harmonic Center (D, the SuperTonic 9th) is located in the nucleus, with the other six notes associated with the dynamic oscillations of the six electrons — two in the first orbital correlated with the 1st and 3rd notes (C, E — the root and major 3rd) and four in the second orbital correlated with the other four notes. Across the middle is the Tritone Axis (B, F), which shifts from an excited state to a stable state through the Tritone Function "Aaa-men", as we saw earlier (the arrows show this here).

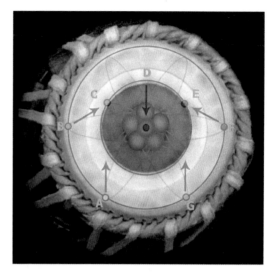

As Merrick says, it is a reasonable consideration that biological processes that form organs, tissues, bones — goatskin — would *"grow coherently out of carbon-12 according to the same balance of resonance and damping in a 12-step octave."* Well, if this is any evidence of this being so, the harmonic resonance of a tabla drumhead exhibits a close match to this carbon-12 harmonic model. The image to the right shows an overlay of the carbon harmonic model on the drum.

When tuning a tabla drum, one does not tune to the open note in the middle of the drum, but rather it is tuned to a harmonic overtone that rings out when the open head is slightly damped with one finger while another taps it between the middle and rim. It is this overtone that is the note that determines the key the drum is tuned to. So for example, when tuning the drum to C, the drumhead would have this arrangement of tones:

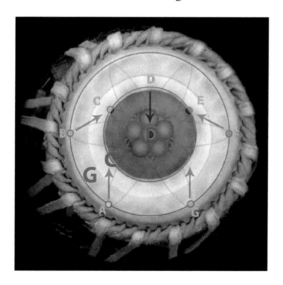

In the middle of the drumhead is D (the SuperTonic 9th), which rings out when the drum is struck open, without damping. Between the middle and the rim is C, the root note of the key being tuned to, which rings out when the head is slightly damped while striking it. Striking the drum toward the very outer rim while slightly damping will produce another overtone, in this case G (the fifth note in the key of C). Comparing these tones to the carbon-12 harmonic model, we can see that they match in their positions relative to the center and rim. The note D in the middle, the open tone, is the Harmonic

Center in the key of C. It is literally seen here as the harmonic center of the drumhead, around which the other notes are orbiting. The root note C is located in the "first orbital" of the carbon-12 harmonic model, and G is in the "second orbital". So Merrick's Chromatic Dual Ring model finds an audible correspondence in the tonal relationships of a tabla drum. And given that a drumhead is a physical example of a tensegrity field — such as found in atoms, molecules, organs, tissues, solar systems, galaxies — it just may well be ringing out the actual "music of the spheres" harmonic structure.

Again, there is much to be researched in all this, yet there is compelling observational evidence to suggest it is a worthy and viable pursuit. Music as a system of harmonic relationships in the dynamics of oscillating energetic structures may well inform the physics of tomorrow in academic and research institutions, readily made visible through cosmic geometry correlations.

For now, though, it's time to "tune in" to that which makes everything we're exploring even possible to explore — Consciousness and the Human Experience. In other words, it's time to face the music...

*"Don't worry about saving these songs.
And if one of our instruments breaks,
it doesn't matter.
We have fallen into the place
where everything is music..."*

- Rumi

Section 6 Endnotes

78 "interference pattern". *The American Heritage® Science Dictionary*. Houghton Mifflin Company. 28 Mar. 2017.
http://www.dictionary.com/browse/interference-pattern

79 Bobby McFerrin Demonstrates the Power of the Pentatonic Scale, World Science Festival, 2009.
https://www.youtube.com/watch?v=ne6tB2KiZuk

80 Merrick, Richard, *INTERFERENCE: A Grand Scientific Musical Theory*, p. 235.
http://www.interferencetheory.com/Books/BooksInterference/Summary.html

81 IBID, p. 116

82 IBID, p. 163-4

83 Currivan, Jude (2017-02-16). *The Cosmic Hologram: In-formation at the Center of Creation*, Inner Traditions/
Bear & Company.

84 Merrick, Richard, *INTERFERENCE: A Grand Scientific Musical Theory*, p. 169.

85 IBID, p. 154

86 Luminet, Jean-Pierre, Weeks, Jeffrey R., Riazuelo, Alain, Lehoucq, Roland and Uzan, Jean-Philippe,
*Dodecahedral space topology as an explanation for weak wide-angle temperature correlations in the cosmic
microwave background*, Nature, volume 425, pages 593–595 (2003).
https://www.nature.com/articles/nature01944

87 http://ray.tomes.biz/

88 http://ray.tomes.biz/maths.html

89 Geesink, Hans J. H. and Meijer, Dirk K. F., *Quantum Wave Information of Life Revealed: An Algorithm for
Electromagnetic Frequencies that Create Stability of Biological Order, with Implications for Brain Function and
Consciousness*, *NeuroQuantology*, Vol. 14, No. 1 (2016).
https://www.neuroquantology.com/index.php/journal/article/view/911/751

90 IBID

91 "Golden ratio discovered in quantum world: Hidden symmetry observed for the first time in solid state
matter", Helmholtz Association of German Research Centres, article in Science Daily, January 7, 2010.
https://www.sciencedaily.com/releases/2010/01/100107143909.htm

92 Early Embryonic Development: The Morula and Blastula, Study.com.
http://study.com/academy/lesson/early-embryonic-development-the-morula-and-blastula.html

93 PESwiki article on Walter Russel.
https://peswiki.com/powerpedia:walter-russell

94 Jain108 website.
https://jain108.com/discoveries/

95 Robert E. Grant website.
https://www.robertedwardgrant.com/about

96 Grant, Robert E, Ghannam, Talal. *Accurate and Infinite Prime Prediction from Novel Quasi-Prime Analytical
Methodology*, March 2019.
https://arxiv.org/abs/1903.08570

97 Grant, Robert E, Ghannam, Talal. *The Wave Theory of Numbers*, March 2019.
https://docs.wixstatic.com/ugd/39d6ce_56e9a30646e64df597dbcffa390acf8e.pdf

98 Merrick, Richard, *INTERFERENCE: A Grand Scientific Musical Theory*, p. 232.

99   "Heart Beat: Music May Help Keep Your Cardiovascular System in Tune", *Scientific American* article by Lynn Peeples, June 24, 2009.
https://www.scientificamerican.com/article/music-therapy-heart-cardiovascular/

100   Chopra, Deepak; Kafatos, Menas C. (2017-02-07). *You Are the Universe: Discovering Your Cosmic Self and Why It Matters* (p. 80). Potter/TenSpeed/Harmony. Kindle Edition.

101   S. Ghosh, S. Sahu, L. Agrawal, T. Shiga, A. Bandyopadhyay, *Inventing a co-axial atomic resolution patch clamp to study a single resonating protein complex and ultra-low power communication deep inside a living neuron cell*; J. Integrated Neuroscience,15(4), 403-433 (2016); DOI: 10.1142/S0219635216500321.

102   L. Agrawal, S. Sahu, S. Ghosh, T. Shiga, D. Fujita, A. Bandyopadhyay, *Inventing atomic resolution scanning dielectric microscopy to see a single protein complex operation live at resonance in a neuron without touching or adulterating the cell*; J. Integrated Neuroscience,15(4), 435-462 (2016); DOI: 10.1142/S0219635216500333 (Cover Article).

103   L. Agrawal, R. Chhajed, S. Ghosh, B. Ghosh, K. Ray, D. Fujita, A. Bandyopadhyay, *Fractal Information Theory (FIT) derived Geometric Musical Language (GML) for brain inspired hypercomputing*; Advances in Intelligent Systems and Soft Computing AISC, Series Ed.: Kacprzyk, Janusz; ISSN: 2194-5357 page 37-61 (2016) Proceedings of SocTA 2016, Springer.

104   L. Agrawal, S. Ghosh, B. Ghosh, K. Ray, S. Sahu, D. Fujita, A Bandyopadhyay; *Replacing Turing tape with a Fractal tape: a new information theory, associated mechanics and decision making without computing*, Consciousness: Integrating Indian and Western perspective. Chapter 6, 87-159 (2016). Paperback: 630 pages, Publisher: New Age Books; 1st edition (October 5, 2016), Language: English, ISBN-10: 8178224933, ISBN-13: 978-8178224930, India.

105   Frank Wilczek, transcribed from an interview on BBC Radio 3's program, Why Music?
http://www.bbc.co.uk/programmes/b06db6tx

106   Merrick, Richard, *INTERFERENCE: A Grand Scientific Musical Theory*, p. 323.

107   Christiansen, Jessie L., et al, *The K2-138 System: A Near-resonant Chain of Five Sub-Neptune Planets Discovered by Citizen Scientists,* 2018 January, The American Astronomical Society.
http://iopscience.iop.org/article/10.3847/1538-3881/aa9be0

108   Merrick, Richard, *INTERFERENCE: A Grand Scientific Musical Theory*, p. 324 & 331.

109   IBID, p. 338

SECTION 7
CONSCIOUSNESS AND THE HUMAN EXPERIENCE

SECTION 7
CONSCIOUSNESS AND THE HUMAN EXPERIENCE

Wholeness, Starting From Zero, Flow Process, Field Pattern, Structural Integrity, Music… the progression of our journey has traversed a variety of ways in which we can explore one unified phenomenon — the universal dynamic of energy-matter-information in→forming the cosmos at all scales. To round out this picture, we must put ourselves right smack in the middle of it. And in fact, we *are* pretty much right in the middle of it, with the size of the microtubules in our cells being at about the mid-point between the Planck and Universal scales.[110]

We humans, along with the rest of biological life here on Earth, appear to play a pivotal role at the cross-section between the tiniest origins of cosmic creativity and the totality of the Uni-Verse being continuously sung into existence. We have consciousness. And we're aware of it. We are self-aware beings having a human experience here on this small planet. We know our bodies are an integral part of the natural world around us, sharing the same fundamental biological systems and processes as found in other organisms. But what of our minds, our emotions, our intelligence and innovative creativity, are these equally as integral with the natural world, or are they an anomaly that just happened to emerge in us by some fluke of chance? Sometimes it's easy to think it's the latter (as contemporary scientific theories more commonly propose), given we appear to be unique in the degree of self-awareness and creative intelligence that we possess. In a holofractal model of the cosmos, though, this kind of anomaly doesn't make sense, suggesting instead that it's more likely these attributes have emerged from the very foundation of the cosmos itself — that our experience of consciousness and self-awareness is an inevitable evolutionary product of the same attributes being present throughout the entire universal structure.

The question of how consciousness emerges from a randomly evolving physical universe has been a challenging inquiry in physics for a long time. When the quantum, atomic and molecular realms that comprise the physical universe are viewed as being devoid of any attributes we might correlate with intelligence and consciousness, it certainly poses a rather irreconcilable problem. What if we were to allow ourselves to view these realms otherwise? What if we set aside the historical taboo of letting spiritual beliefs of a universal intelligence bleed into scientific models? Can we consider such a scientific model without incorporating religious ideology and still be open to the validity of this universal intelligence?

While the inquiry into these questions is far vaster in scope than what is intended for this book, it is nonetheless valuable to touch into it enough to bridge what has been presented thus far and explore how cosmic geometry, unified physics and music fit into our human experience, and how we can benefit from this knowledge.

In this section I'll share ideas, conjectures, observations, personal experiences and practices, and scientific theory. I am deliberately keeping it simple, knowing that attempting to go deeper into this far-reaching exploration will result in too many rabbit holes taking us off point within the context of this book. My intent is to round out the picture of all that has preceded this section with insights into how the universal field of energy-matter-information moves within, through and as us, just enough to be relevant to this exploration and no more. Going further would require a whole book unto itself. Additional musings and other resources will be shared on the cosmometry.com website related to this most intimate and mysterious topic — consciousness and the human experience.

So then, off we go, holding the big cosmic mirror up to ourselves… let's start by jumping right into the deep end.

CHAPTER 43
CONSCIOUSNESS

Consciousness is…

If only it were that easy. In fact, defining consciousness seems as yet to be the most vague and non-definitive pursuit of all that we're exploring here. Is it an emergent phenomenon of the brain, as is commonly held in contemporary scientific theory? Does anything other than us humans have an experience of consciousness as we know it (or otherwise)? Are there any indications that consciousness is a universal phenomenon that permeates the entire physical universe, in which our experience of it is but one relative aspect? Is it possible to consider a source of consciousness in the cosmic scheme?

The Latin origin of the word 'conscious' is *conscius*, from *com-* + *scire* — to know.[111] The taxonomic name for us modern-day humans is *Homo sapiens sapiens*, from the Latin homo (man) and sapiens (wise). So, we are deemed to be wise to the fact that we're wise. We know that we know. We have an awareness that recognizes itself distinct from the other "things" of the world, and we have awareness that we're doing so. In other words, we're conscious of the fact that we're conscious.

This is really quite remarkable! There is no doubt that our experience of that which we call consciousness is unique relative to what we observe in nature, given our extensive abilities to speak, write and read, to amass, store and retrieve vast amounts of information, to imagine, design and execute innovations, to paint artistic visions with colors and compose music with sounds, drive cars, create a global communication network, explore space… We are indeed quite awesome (when we're not being downright stupid, fighting with each other and squandering the bounty of all that is provided and the awesome opportunity we have to succeed as a species).

So here we are, exploring the nature of the very thing that allows us to explore the nature of itself — consciousness. What is it? Rather than rely on dictionary definitions, let's start with some attributes that we can say are at least partially descriptive of that which we call consciousness:
- Awareness
- Intelligence
- Perception of environment
- Reflection (as in self-reflection or subject/object relationship)
- Volition and Response (e.g. will, free will)

William Brown, researcher in biophysics at the Resonance Science Foundation, references these additional attributes as elements that engender awareness:[112]

- Diversity of Parts (functional complexity)
- Information Processing (sensitivity to states)
- Memory (recording of information, state hysteresis)
- Communicability (reception and transmission of information/energy)
- Integration (emergence of system as entity)

Integrated systems composed of a diversity of parts that record, process and transmit information and energy in response to environmental states with intelligent action and awareness of self and other.

We are that. Our biological systems are that. Cells exhibit these same properties. Intracellular systems do as well. Does this pattern continue in both smaller and larger dimensions of scale? Could it be that these attributes of consciousness permeate all scale, as do cosmic patterns and musical harmonics?

With these attributes in mind, let's explore how the fractal-hologramic-synergetic model offers a premise for the inevitable emergence of consciousness, and especially self-awareness as in our case. We need to begin a bit technically to establish a foundational context.

In our general model of cosmic wholeness, we have a primary ground state at the Planck scale — the electromagnetic matrix of Planck Spherical Units (PSUs) in zerophase equilibrium. According to Haramein's unified physics theory, this ground state is the unified aether field in which all dynamics of energy, form and flow emerge as fractal manifestations. Protons, atoms, molecules, minerals, crystals, liquids, cells, organs, bodies… everything is composed of and in intimate relationship with this prime state.

The PSUs are proposed to be the base "pixel" resolution of our universe, meaning that they are the fundamental medium through which the information content of all atomic-to-universal systems is received, recorded and transmitted. As such they comprise the prime "bits" wherein all information of all events throughout all time is stored, very much in the same manner as the electrical and magnetic processing and memory storage aspects of computers occurs but with one very important difference — the PSU matrix is entirely hologramic, with all of the information of the entire cosmos present at every point. This is the Absolute Hologram described in Chapter 11. Everything that manifests within this universal hologramic medium is then a localized expression of energy, form and flow with a specific set of information pertinent to itself — i.e. the Relative Hologram. The Relative and Absolute are always-and-only in continuous reciprocal relationship (Bohm's Implicate and Explicate orders), and it is this reciprocal exchange of local and universal information that provides the feedback/feedforward function introduced in Chapter 18. Every local entity (integrated system as *relative* hologram) both informs and is informed by the cosmic totality (universal wholeness as *absolute* hologram) with the information exchange occurring every Planck Time ($\sim 5.39 \times 10^{-44}$ seconds, or 10^{44} times per second). This information flow is fractally transferred and increasingly localized up in scale as it in→forms the atoms, molecules, intracellular, cellular and biological systems in all living organisms. This is the biological Nested Rhythm Network described in the previous section; the harmonic system of light, sound and information that permeates all spacetime in a unified diversity of parts.

To say all this in simpler terms... There is a universal field of electromagnetic energy that receives, records and transfers information about every event such that, at every moment, each event informs the universal field and the universal field informs each event about every other event in an ongoing reciprocal exchange.

The very idea of time is predicated on one essential attribute, the lack of which would make the comprehension of time impossible — memory. No memory = no time.

It is this field of information storage and communication that Haramein and his research colleagues, William Brown and Amira Val Baker, call the Unified Spacememory Network (USN). Obviously, we have a new term here to define — spacememory. In modern physics the term used to describe the unified nature of space and time is spacetime. One does not exist without the other. As Haramein observes, the very idea of time is predicated on one essential attribute, the lack of which would make the comprehension of time impossible — memory. No memory = no time. Therefore, to deepen our understanding of the nature of spacetime, the word spacememory is substituted so as to highlight the vital systemic role memory plays in the cosmic structure. In order for there to be memory at all, there must be a physical function for it within the structure itself, and it is the PSU matrix that is proposed as the prime source of this function, forming a unified network of information storage (memory) and transfer (communication). Just as information about an object is stored holographically on a glass plate to create a visual hologram, information is stored hologramically throughout the entire cosmos to create a cosmic hologram, though in this case it is ubiquitous and continually updated throughout the whole rather than frozen into a static image as with a simple visual hologram.

In contemporary physics, theories of the holographic principle put focus on the surface features of an object, the so-called 2-dimensional hologram analogous to a holographic plate. In the generalized spacememory network model, the surfaces (of, for example, protons) are composed of the tiny "bits" of PSUs, encoding the relative information of the object that can be observed and measured as its local mass, size, color, temperature, etc. In this way the contemporary 2D surface model is congruent with the generalized USN model, describing the literal interface between the internal and external hologramic totality relevant to a given object. It is at this interface that Haramein and colleagues propose the presence of a Planck-scale "wormhole" network that connects all physical matter into a unified information system that communicates at superluminal (faster than the speed of light) rates of transfer — essentially instantaneously. This ubiquitous information network is seen to be the mechanism for the experimentally verified phenomenon of quantum entanglement, wherein two or more particles (such as photons) are linked across vast distances with no lag time for a change of state from one to the other. Change the spin of one photon and the other changes simultaneously, even if they're millions of miles apart. While current analysis suggests that one, a few or many particles can be entangled, the USN model proposes that all particles are always-and-only entangled, hence forming a cosmically unified network of quasi-instantaneous information exchange.

What does all this have to do with consciousness? To head down this road, we'll start with a quote from Haramein, Brown and Val Baker's paper, *The Unified Spacememory Network: From Cosmogenesis to Consciousness*,[113] that offers an overview perspective:

> *"Underlying the matter that comprises living systems, there may be memory imprinting into the planckian wormhole-spacetime structure, in which time is a function of information on the structure of space during the universal evolution. Memory and recursive information feedback/feedforward processes of the quantum vacuum allow for learning and evolutionary behavior. This applies not only to the mesoscale of the biological organism, but also to physical systems ranging from the planckian to the cosmological scale, and the universe as a whole. As such, the process of cosmogenesis can be equated with a living, or biological process of iterative evolutionary development — biological cosmogenesis. In this sense, there are living processes occurring at all scales of the universe, and with memory and learning being functions of awareness, life and consciousness are intrinsic ubiquitous characteristics, embedded in the very dynamics and mechanics of physical processes of the quantum vacuum structure and thus, the universe itself."*

Take in that last sentence again… **Life and consciousness are intrinsic ubiquitous characteristics, embedded in the very dynamics and mechanics of physical processes of the quantum vacuum structure and thus, the universe itself.**

Let's just pause with that thought for a minute. Close your eyes and contemplate it, remembering that you actually are an expression of a conscious living universe.

This idea flips the current model of consciousness being an epiphenomenon of the brain (i.e. it only exists because our brain exists) completely upside down and inside out. **The very attributes of consciousness that we began this chapter with are now seen not as special-case qualities unique to us higher-order intelligent beings but as inherently present characteristics found throughout the entire cosmos, from Planck to Universal scales.** From this perspective, the emergence of self-awareness as we experience it is an inevitable outcome of universal information feedback/feedforward processes of what we call intelligence that combine through ever-increasing fractal complexity into a synergetic whole called (in our case) a human being. It makes the scientific name, *Homo sapiens sapiens*, even more prescient; in that inherent in the double sapiens is recognition of the very feedback-loop attribute that underlies the cosmic evolution of consciousness itself! **We know that we know, and the more that we know, the more we will know in synergetic wholeness, and this is how the entire universe is learning and evolving as a living, conscious entity at every scale.**

Rather than the phenomenon of consciousness arising from within us (as in the current brain-centric theory), what the USN model suggests is that consciousness is present throughout the universal field and that our biophysical systems of brains, nerves, tissues, organs, cells, biomolecules, etc. are functioning as a fractal antenna that is receptive to this field. As stated in Haramein and Brown's paper, *Unified Physics and the Entanglement Network of Awareness:*[114]

"As a complex component of the spacememory field, the biological system is innately "plugged" into the universal wormhole information network. Following this paradigm, the intercommunication of information through the universal network is occurring constitutively during the normal functioning of every biomolecule and cell of the biological organism — an intrinsic awareness and ordering mechanism. From the smallest to the largest scales, the components of the biological system are fundamentally transmitter/receivers, like antennae. This signal transmission of the biological system occurs locally via mechanical and electromagnetic resonances (orbital rearrangements during chemical bonding change the electronic resonant structure of biomolecules, a primary signaling mechanism), and nonlocally through the quantized spacememory wormhole network.

Under this model, the macromolecular and cytoarchitectonic structures of the brain are not so much involved in producing a virtual re-creation of the "external" environment, but receiving the information and recording it, as well as orchestrating responses. In this sense, the brain-body system operates much more as a receiver and transmitter antennae with reply-back operations, recording the information in spatial configurations of myriad neuronal synaptic, subsynaptic, and supramolecular assemblies.

However, this type of behavior may not be restricted only to the brain, but more so that the brain arises from such behavior of physical systems in general. These developments generating bio-oscillator antennae (the body) are a highly refined and paramount example of such intrinsic spacememory mechanisms being present at the more basal level where there is a continuum between the "external" interpretations of the field, which is fed-back through the "internal" nonlocal spacememory network (read beyond spacetime) in a continuous feedback/feedforward ubiquitous principle. It's not the chicken first nor the egg, it's not matter first nor consciousness; it is a continuous information flow in a unified quantum network generating evolutionary systems.

*Just as the recurrent information feedback/feedforward processes of the planckian micro-wormhole network are integral in the general formation and organization of matter, so too in the dynamical interaction within the biological system, which involves tens of millions of chemical changes every second, the unified spacememory network may be an integral component and ordering influence. **As such, the intrinsic awareness of this universal system is present at the most basal level of function in the*** *biological system, from the atomic and subatomic Planck network, and not merely an emergent result of it. From that perspective, the biological structures are an extension of the fundamental field of awareness defined by the feedback structure of the spacememory network."* [Emphasis added]

Biological structures are an extension of a fundamental universal field of awareness that evolve through continuous feedback into greater degrees of complexity and more encompassing levels of wholeness.

This brings us around to the important role that synergy plays in the evolutionary process, and the characteristic of synergy that itself makes it hard to define something like consciousness when attempting to do so by analyzing the "parts" that comprise it. By definition of synergy, the whole is *greater than* and *not able to be predicted from* the sum of the parts when taken separately. There is nothing in a biological system of neurons linked together like an electrical grid with a central operating system called a brain that can predict self-aware sentience. The emergence of consciousness at every level of complexity is synergetic. It is an effect of wholeness that is greater than and unpredictable from the parts that comprise it. When we include this natural principle of emergent wholeness into models of cosmogenesis, biogenesis and the advent of self-awareness, the progression of evolution towards sentient beings such as ourselves becomes evident as an inevitable synergetic outcome of an innately unified, intelligent and self-reflective cosmic energy-matter-information system. Again, from Haramein's, et al, *The Unified Spacememory Network* paper:

> *There is nothing in a biological system of neurons linked together like an electrical grid with a central operating system called a brain that can predict self-aware sentience. The emergence of consciousness at every level of complexity is synergetic.*

> *"…nonlocal information dynamics, intrinsic to the properties and behavior of material systems and uniquely harnessed by the natural nanotechnology of supramolecular systems of the brain (similar to the Hameroff-Penrose model of orchestrated objective reduction (Hameroff & Penrose, 2014)) are involved in producing the sentience, awareness, and memory of cognitive processes. Moreover, we propose that nonlocal influences across spatial and temporal domains, communicated through the micro-wormhole network of the Planck-scale geometric structure of spacetime, may play an instrumental role in the evolution and development of physical systems, thus engendering an ordering dynamic as well as directionality towards higher levels of complexity and organizational synergy. This ordering dynamic is the same, from the evolution and development of physical systems to biological systems, and in fact, may serve as a defining characteristic of life itself. In this sense, the conception of a living system extends beyond the normal consideration of only the biological organism (e.g. evolution and synergism are not merely products of the biosphere, but are present in the interactivity of systems in general leading to the*

emergence of the biosphere) and properties of sentience and awareness are involved in the directed (non-random) generic evolution of matter and the universe."[115]

Dutch researchers, Dirk Meijer and Hans Geesink, hold a similar view, stating in the abstract of their September 2017 paper, *Consciousness in the Universe is Scale Invariant and Implies an Event Horizon of the Human Brain*:[116]

"Our brain is not a "stand alone" information processing organ: it acts as a central part of our integral nervous system with recurrent information exchange with the entire organism and the cosmos. In this study, the brain is conceived to be embedded in a holographic structured field that interacts with resonant sensitive structures in the various cell types in our body. In order to explain earlier reported ultra-rapid brain responses and effective operation of the meta-stable neural system, a field-receptive mental workspace is proposed to be communicating with the brain. Our integral nervous system is seen as a dedicated neural transmission and multi-cavity network that, in a non-dual manner, interacts with the proposed supervening meta-cognitive domain. Among others, it is integrating discrete patterns of eigen-frequencies of photonic/solitonic waves, thereby continuously updating a time-symmetric global memory space of the individual. Its toroidal organization allows the coupling of gravitational, dark energy, zero-point energy field (ZPE) as well as earth magnetic fields energies and transmits wave information into brain tissue, that thereby is instrumental in high speed conscious and sub-conscious information processing. We propose that the supposed field-receptive workspace, in a mutual interaction with the whole nervous system, generates self-consciousness and is conceived as operating from a 4th spatial dimension (hyper-sphere). Its functional structure is adequately defined by the geometry of the torus, that is envisioned as a basic unit (operator) of space-time. The latter is instrumental in collecting the pattern of discrete soliton frequencies that provided an algorithm for coherent life processes, as earlier identified by us. It is postulated that consciousness in the entire universe arises through, scale invariant, nested toroidal coupling of various energy fields, that may include quantum error correction. In the brain of the human species, this takes the form of the proposed holographic workspace, that collects active information in a "brain event horizon", representing an internal and fully integral model of the self. This brain-supervening workspace is equipped to convert integrated coherent wave energies into attractor type/standing waves that guide the related cortical template to a higher coordination of reflection and action as well as network synchronicity, as required for conscious states. In relation to its scale-invariant global character, we find support for a universal information matrix, that was extensively described earlier, as a supposed implicate order as well as in a spectrum of space-time theories in

current physics. The presence of a field-receptive resonant workspace, associated with, but not reducible to, our brain, may provide an interpretation framework for widely reported, but poorly understood transpersonal conscious states and algorithmic origin of life. It also points out the deep connection of mankind with the cosmos and our major responsibility for the future of our planet."

In the context of the conceptual premise presented in this book, I find the model proposed by Meijer and Geesink to be highly congruent with all three components of our working model of wholeness: cosmometry, unified physics and music. While there is much to explore in depth, here are highlights of why this is so:

- They view the brain as a component of an integrated fractal antenna system interacting with a universal meta-cognitive holographic structure, just as in the Unified Spacememory Network model. In both models, the zero point energy field [ZPE] is considered to be the prime information substrate of energy, matter and consciousness.

- They propose that the field-receptive mental workspace of the brain and entire nervous system generates self-consciousness from an underlying 4-dimensional information framework. In Fuller's Synergetics and the cosmometry model, the zerophase Vector Equilibrium (VE) and extended Isotropic Vector Matrix (IVM) is just such a 4-dimensional geometric framework, from which our 3D geometric field of perception emerges (as quantum to cosmological scale electromagnetic and acoustic waveforms). Further in the paper they state, "That we cannot directly perceive this information aspect is traditionally ascribed to a hidden 4th *spatial* dimension (not the dimension of time!)." Being the zerophase geometry, the 4D spatial model of the VE/IVM "will never be seen by man in any physical experience," as Buckminster Fuller pointed out (see page 45). This suggests that perhaps the VE/IVM is the universal informational substrate of consciousness, informing even our own mind-body experiences.

- They reference the torus as the functional structure of the field-receptive mental workspace, stating "*consciousness in the entire universe arises through, scale invariant, nested toroidal coupling of various energy fields.*" The prime cosmometric form of flow process, the torus, is integral to the interaction between physical biological systems and the individual and universal domains of consciousness. Energy-matter-information as "one thing" embeds fractally in toroidal dynamics from Planck to Universal scales.

- They refer to "*discrete soliton frequencies that provided an algorithm for coherent life processes, as earlier identified by us.*" Though not explicitly stated in the abstract above, this is described in Chapter 39 as a set of life-sustaining frequencies that pertain directly to the 12-tone music system, which in→forms our harmonically organized universe.

The research and theories presented by Geesink and Meijer offer an in-depth analysis of the ideas presented here worthy of great consideration.

It is with the perspectives shared in this chapter that we will explore the rest of the topics in this section, bearing in mind that the attributes of awareness, intelligence, reflexivity, purpose, volition and self-awareness, sum-totally called consciousness, are intrinsic to cosmic wholeness as energy-matter-information in fractal-hologramic-synergetic unity. The three lenses of cosmic geometry, unified physics and musical harmonic resonance are not describing a mindlessly random and statistically improbable miracle, they are the observable result of an innately intelligent system that is aware of itself at every level, in→forming every aspect of manifestation with a unified integrity that we, as the inevitable "lucky ones," can actually discern. In the words of the great Max Planck himself:

The three lenses of cosmic geometry, unified physics and musical harmonic resonance are not describing a mindlessly random and statistically improbable miracle, they are the observable result of an innately intelligent system that is aware of itself at every level, informing every aspect of manifestation with a unified integrity that we, as the inevitable "lucky ones," can actually discern.

> *"There is no matter as such. All matter originates and exists only by virtue of a force which brings the particle of an atom to vibration and holds this most minute solar system of the atom together. We must assume behind this force the existence of a conscious and intelligent mind. This mind is the matrix of all matter."*

Let's now explore the Human Experience of this awesome and beautiful cosmic being that we are.

CHAPTER 44
HOLOGRAMIC BLUEPRINT

Imagine this… You're sitting here, reading these words, eyes scanning the page as information streams through photons of light in the form of alphabetical symbols, the synergetic wholeness of which is telling a story and imparting meaning that informs your thoughts, feelings and state of being. In turn, you reflect upon the story and meaning, adding your own interpretation that is itself informed by your life experiences, the education you received, the beliefs you hold true (and many other factors) and projecting your state of mind, emotion and being back into the story. There is an intimate feedback loop between the story told by these word symbols and the story you overlay upon them, the combined result of which is the story you are currently living by as you sit here reading these words.

Now imagine this… The same thing is happening between you and the cosmic information field — the unified field of energy-matter-information in which you exist at all times. This field is the cosmic hologram composed of electromagnetic and acoustic standing wave patterns that are the literal information comprising your physical and metaphysical self being expressed locally and the totality of information being expressed universally, and between your self and the universal field there is occurring an ongoing story. The universal field is the book of symbols and you are the interpreter of those symbols, and what you interpret gets projected back into the story that is being told by the universal field.

And now imagine this… When you were conceived in your mother's womb, there was a blueprint laid down upon which your emerging being developed, cell by cell, to form the infant that was born into this world, free of all of life's experiences yet to come (though informed in part by your parents' experiences, and their parents before them). The 64 codons of DNA that comprise the chromosomes found in every cell are a literal hologramic blueprint that informs the entire development process from conception to this very moment. (It's hologramic because the whole (DNA code) is present in every part (cell).) When you were born, this blueprint was as close to pure as can be conceptualized — a master code of wholeness that, when ideally expressed, forms a beautiful, healthy baby that begins life with a fresh, innocent and largely untainted outlook. The information of your DNA lays the foundation of a story of what it means to be a human being, and from the day you're born, that story begins to be influenced by your personal experiences both internal and external. The hologramic blueprint story and your own personal story begin an ongoing interplay in a dynamic feedback loop that results in the story you live by in each moment, whether conscious of it or not.

From the perspective of holofractal physics, every form in the universe has a standing wave blueprint by which the atoms and molecules organize into coherent structures. This "whole information" or "holo-gram" is what all form is based upon, and the fundamental blueprint of a form's hologram is directly in→formed by the universal unified field at the quantum level. Rupert Sheldrake calls this blueprint a morphic field, defined as *"A field within and around a morphic unit* [e.g. an atom, molecule, crystal, cell, plant, animal] *which organizes its characteristic structure and pattern of activity."* [117]

In Sheldrake's theory of formative causation, morphic fields have an inherent collective memory informed by a process he calls morphic resonance:

> *"The hypothesis of formative causation states that the forms of self-organizing systems are shaped by morphic fields. Morphic fields organize atoms, molecules, crystals, organelles, cells, tissues, organs, organisms, societies, ecosystems, planetary systems, solar systems, galaxies. In other words, they organize systems at all levels of complexity, and are the basis for the wholeness that we observe in nature, which is more than the sum of the parts* [i.e. synergetic].
>
> *According to the hypothesis of formative causation, morphic fields also contain an inherent memory given by the process of morphic resonance, whereby each kind of thing has a collective memory. For example, crystals of a given kind are influenced by all past crystals of that kind, date palms by past date palms, giraffes by past giraffes, etc. In the human realm this is similar to Jung's theory of the collective unconscious.*
>
> *In the realm of developmental biology the morphic fields that shape the growing organisms are called morphogenetic fields; in social organization they can be called social fields; and in the organization of mental activity they can be called mental fields. But all these kinds of fields are particular kinds of morphic fields, and all are shaped and stabilized by morphic resonance."* [118]

In a harmonically organized fractal-hologramic universe in which there is an inherent feedback/feedforward memory network permeating all scales, we can see how a given form's morphic field (i.e. standing wave hologram) is an expression of resonance with a specific pattern of information inherent in the memory structure of space. Like Anirban Bandyopadhyay's **Nested Rhythm Network in the Living System** (see page 270), and Bohm's **nested scales of mutual influence**, *"even between macroscopic processes and those at the atomic level, indicating the complexity of the pathways through which the qualitative infinity of nature may manifest"* (see page 114), Sheldrake's morphic fields in→form biological systems at every scale of complexity from the whole organism to the organs, cells, molecules and atoms that comprise them. This is the same premise as we saw in the previous chapter regarding the fractal flow of information from the Planck-scale spacememory network into the atoms, molecules, cells, organs and organism, transferring information from the universal hologramic field into the localized hologramic or morphic field as a ubiquitous system of intrinsic intelligence. And as well, Sheldrake's process of morphic resonance is congruent with the feedback/feedforward model as a self-reinforcing and regenerative information blueprint, in→forming both the manifesting individual and evolving collective morphogenetic fields.

Considering the ideas of formative causation and morphic resonance in relation to the "story of our lives" that we live by in each moment, we can see that there is an ongoing process of information flow moving through us that is in reference to a personal hologramic blueprint, i.e. the morphic fields of the DNA, cells, tissues, organs, etc. that comprise our bodies. And not just our bodies but as well our thoughts and beliefs are informed by and inform a mental field, as Sheldrake proposes, and these physical and mental fields inform each other in a reciprocal feedback loop. This extends into the social field around us, which influences our thoughts and emotions, as well as into the environmental field of food, water, nutrients, pollutants, toxins, radiation, etc. that we are in relationship with all the time. It quickly becomes evident that there are numerous factors at many scales of complexity that impact and influence our morphic field, some of which cause imbalances in the harmonic wholeness of our original blueprint that we experience as disease.

In a harmonically organized fractal-hologramic universe in which there is an inherent feedback/feedforward memory network permeating all scales, we can see how a given form's morphic field (i.e. standing wave hologram) is an expression of resonance with a specific pattern of information inherent in the memory structure of space.

My friend and colleague, Dr. Beth McDougall, who is founder of the CLEAR Center of Health in Mill Valley, California, has investigated for over twenty-five years the nature of the blueprint and how we can restore our body's energetic patterning back to its original state of wholeness. In her words,

> *"Our degree of health depends on the degree to which we resonate with the patterning of our pristine blueprint in the unified field, and thus our ability to extract energy and correct information. As we go through life, things happen to us. We may get exposed to toxins, we may develop infections, we may have traumatic experiences. Since everything has a corresponding geometry that contains information, we start to accumulate misinformation.*
>
> *The chaotic energetic signatures of these misinformed patterns are out of harmony with the body and create dissonance. Like static on the radio, when the body communicates back to the blueprint, the chaotic signatures of these things are also communicated back as distorting patterns that begin to disrupt the coherent translation of the blueprint in the feedback loop with the body. The misinformation decreases the fidelity of the pristine blueprint's coding. This then leads to entropy, breakdown, aging and disease."*

Remember, we're exploring this in the context of a ubiquitous system of harmonic wholeness (Music) that in→forms the pattern relationships of resonant structures (Cosmic Geometry), which manifests through energy-matter-information dynamics as the world around us and cosmos as a whole (Unified Physics). Natural systems, from atoms to cells to organisms to planets, are all based upon harmonic relationships that inform their original hologramic blueprint, and that harmonic blueprint is still present at every scale, even if it has been distorted by life's journey with all its accidents, traumas and pathogenic intrusions. This original blueprint is literally an orchestra of electromagnetic, acoustical and rhythmic pulsation and frequencies that, when in its optimal well-tuned state, plays a harmonious symphony that we experience as health and well-being. And just like a musical orchestra, the instruments of our bodies often need tuning in order for the whole to act in a coherent and harmonious way.

Eileen McKusick, author of *Tuning the Human Biofield*, puts it this way:

> *"Since everything jiggles, or jitterbugs, everything, therefore, has a frequency. Each organ, each system in our body, resonates at a particular frequency, and these generated frequencies propagate or move away from their source point. Our heart frequency, or heartbeat, is perhaps the easiest to relate to regarding this concept. We can often hear our heartbeat, especially when we are scared or have just exerted ourselves. However, every part of the human body, including the brain, has its own rhythm, its own optimal frequency range. In this way the human body is like a symphony with many instruments. Ideally, everything is in tune and in harmony, but stressors can cause different parts of our being to lose their coherent frequency. Just like the way a car or an instrument can get out of tune, so can the human body. And tuning forks, by offering a coherent frequency by which the body can attune itself, offer a very simple and non-invasive way to get back 'in tune.'"* [119]

McKusick is pioneering research into the therapeutic effects of sound vibrations on the human body, with special attention on the field of energy and information that surrounds and penetrates the body — the biofield. [120] Through a diagnostic use of the coherent frequencies of sound generated by tuning forks, she has mapped out the anatomy of the human biofield, describing how our memories and associated energetic experiences are stored in the field surrounding our physical bodies.

> *"In addition to our memories, the biofield contains the blueprint that the physical body organizes itself around. Traumatic experiences on the physical, mental, and emotional levels give rise to pathological oscillations in the standing waves that act as a sort of noise in the signal and can cause a breakdown in the order, structure, and function of the physiology.*
>
> *The tuning forks are used like sonar — as they are combed or passed through the field, their changing overtones reflect changes in the terrain of the biofield. Blockages of flow*

and distortions in the field show up as a dissonance that is readily perceived by both the therapist and client. In this way, they are used diagnostically. However, the coherent frequency of the forks also acts therapeutically in a very targeted way when the forks are held in specific areas of acute distortion, inducing greater order into the system.

Over eighteen years of clinical practice this method has shown itself to be beneficial for a wide range of symptoms: PTSD, anxiety, depression, pain, digestive disorders, vertigo, migraines, emotional discord, and more. It is gentle, noninvasive, simple, and efficient, and can be learned with relative ease. Its basic premise is that it assists the body and mind to relax out of habitual patterns of tension, imbalance, and stress response, and in doing so facilitates self-healing."

Self-healing, in this context, is returning to a state of harmonic integrity and wholeness founded upon the original hologramic blueprint of our biofield. Interaction with and communication about the state of this blueprint occurs all the way into the DNA level of our being as well. As described in the manual for the Metatron device invented by Russian researchers Dr. Vladimir Nesterov and Vera Nesterova:

"The research made it clear that DNA molecules, chromosomes and proteins are capable to generate coherent emission, just like lasers. In other words, they are original transmitters with a recustomized wavelength. At the same time, they act as receiving antennas. These very DNA properties ensure in an organism wave interchange of genetical information, which significant part, as it was established, is stored in the chromosomal device as holograms. It allows each biological cell to learn instantly, what is going on in any corner of the organism. Besides, it appears that DNA is also responsible for reception of the external information. Thanks to that, the organism constantly interacts with the fields of living beings and other material objects."

More than just a code upon which the genetic makeup of our physical bodies is based, DNA is, in this perspective, a transmitting and receiving antenna that hologramically communicates information about all internal systems instantly into every cell through coherent electromagnetic emissions (biophotons), while also serving as an information exchange interface with external fields of other beings and all of the world around us.

Additionally, developmental biologist, Bruce Lipton, describes how cells learn and retain memory about genetic information, such as antibodies that combat viruses:

"The cells retain the genetic "memory" of this antibody, so that in the future if the individual is again exposed to measles, the cells can immediately launch a protective immune response. The new antibody gene can also be passed on to all the cell's progeny when it divides. In this process, not only did the cell "learn" about the measles virus,

it also created a "memory" that will be inherited and propagated by its daughter cells.
This amazing feat of genetic engineering is profoundly important because it represents
an inherent "intelligence" mechanism by which cells evolve." [121]

From DNA to cells to organs to the body and the biofield that surrounds it, there are nested fields of information interacting with intelligence, learning and memory. At every level there is a blueprint upon which each entity is based, a morphic field that in→forms the entity's original emergence into form that is itself informed by the evolving collective morphic field of the entity (i.e. all giraffes). These morphic fields are the holograms of information, learning, memory and communication that permeate all of reality in ongoing reciprocal relationship. While we humans are just at the threshold of fully re-alizing this intrinsic intelligence and the ability to tap into these morphic fields with our consciousness and frequency-based "tuning" (a.k.a. healing) technologies, it seems that nature beyond the human realm has an innate awareness of fields of energy and consciousness.

CHAPTER 45
THE HUMAN-NATURE EXPERIENCE

Here we sit, you and I, on a beautiful living planet, flying through space at over a million miles per hour when accounting for the movement of the galaxy we're in, and yet my view right now is of a gorgeous summer day with a slight breeze and otherwise perfectly peaceful stillness. My perception of this peaceful stillness is entirely relative to my local experience, which is a subset of a much larger relative context that is moving at a speed unimaginable to me, a speed that I, in fact, am also moving. The scales of time and space between my breezy summer day slowly changing as the sun heads towards setting and the galaxy moving ~1,235,000 miles every hour are a potent indication of just how limited our human experience is relative to the cosmic totality. And that's a good thing! We need to have our attention on the literal matter at hand in order to be in synchronous relationship with our daily lives, and our primary perceptual framework is nicely designed to function this way. And yet, while this perceptual framework predominates our awareness, we are certainly not limited to it. Dreams alone show us images and events that are clearly outside of our daily perceptual experience. I recently had one that featured a white raven that was larger than me and telepathically giving me guidance, whose name turned out to be Judy Limits. Haven't encountered that in my day-to-day life before! Yet the dream image was as vivid as my external perception, with color, lighting, texture and details of the finest quality. It requires photons of light for our eyes to see anything in our external reality. Where are these dream photons coming from, and how are we seeing them?

This example is offered to highlight just how relative, limited and special-case our daily human perceptual experience is, which again is a good thing for our earthly functioning. It also highlights that our perceptual experience is *not limited by* our daily experience, and that our experience of consciousness is not necessarily the primary benchmark for the experience of (or existence of) consciousness in other realms. While it is *our* primary experience, this does not mean that the presence of consciousness beyond the human experience will or should "look like" our experience.

In the model proposed in Chapter 43, attributes of awareness that describe our experience of consciousness are suggested to be present throughout the structures and systems of the cosmos at all scales. The phenomenon of consciousness is said to be emergent from the very presence of these attributes in an intrinsic systemic intelligence that evolves in complexity from the simplest binary bits at the Planck scale, to atoms, molecules, fluids, crystals, minerals, metals, biomolecules, cells, organs, organisms, plants, animals, humans, ecosystems, planets, solar systems, galaxies… such that consciousness permeates the entirety of it all. If this is the case, clearly the human experience of it is not the same as what occurs at other frames of reference; therefore, it is wise to not solely look for our experience of it when considering the presence of consciousness and intelligence in other beings.

For example, I had the good fortune of living on the Big Island of Hawai'i for four years and swimming with the Hawaiian Spinner Dolphins that live there, along with my beloved ally, Teresa Collins, and a close community of fellow dolphin-loving humans. Obviously, dolphins don't exhibit the abilities to apply scientific principles to invent and engineer technologies that enable flight, or play tennis, or look deep into space. That is definitely unique to humans (well, only if you rule out the likelihood that there are others "out there" who are as capable or even more so than we are in this regard). And yet, it is also obvious that dolphins exhibit a highly developed state of conscious awareness, which is commonly held to be true in scientific analysis.

I believe that dolphins (and other cetaceans) have developed holographic consciousness, which is the ability to be aware of both the totality of their environment as well as the particulars within it.

They, along with orca whales, Asian elephants, orangutans, bonobos, chimpanzees, gorillas, Eurasian magpies, and even ants (!) have been experimentally observed to be able to recognize themselves in a mirror, knowing it's their own image rather than behaving as if it's another of their species.[122]

My direct experience of dolphins goes well beyond this, though. They have what we who have spent a good amount of time with them call pod consciousness. This is the ability to communicate with their entire pod simultaneously in a manner that appears beyond the basic use of vocalization. In one moment, they're swimming along slowly, being in a resting state, and the next they all kick into high speed at the same instant and swim off. (Always makes you look around to check if a shark is nearby when that happens.) Many of us have also had the experience of dolphins being able to read our minds (or perhaps our emotions) and respond accordingly. One day I was feeling particularly "off" in myself and was so wishing to have a little personal interaction with them, and in that moment of thought and feeling a dolphin that was about 25 feet below turned and swam right up to me. This communication beyond physical acoustic vibration of words was distinct and certain, and the dolphin clearly exhibited an ability to receive and respond to it. Many people I've shared that story with have had similar experiences with them.

I believe that dolphins (and other cetaceans) have developed holographic consciousness, which is the ability to be aware of both the totality of their environment as well as the particulars within it. Their sonar provides a mechanism for this, and yet it feels true that their ability to perceive in holographic totality is something greater than this — a synergetic development. It makes sense that this is possible given the ubiquitous hologramic information field we're exploring in this model of consciousness. It may well be that while we humans have been applying our intelligent awareness towards development of higher mental and logical faculties and their practical applications, dolphins have been applying theirs towards accessing the hologramic field for their context of daily living. Does this make them more advanced, as some would say? In one regard, perhaps this is so, yet we can say the same for ourselves in other regards, so that's not really the point. What is compelling is that there appears to be in dolphins an example of living in a perceptual framework that clearly has similar attributes of consciousness as ours, and as well exhibits qualities that go beyond ours in relation to a normalized accessing of the hologramic field within their environment. How might this work, and can we humans develop this capacity as well?

At the risk of sounding trite, it works because that's the way the universe is intrinsically operating, and yes, we can access it as well. The phenomena of psychic abilities, telepathy, clairvoyance, clairaudience and clairsentience, intuition, higher sense perception, remote viewing, to name a few, are indications of this capacity. While the scientific community has had little to no model to base such phenomena on for explanation, there is ample evidence of these abilities both in clinical[123] and many non-clinical direct experiences reported anecdotally. With the fractal-hologramic energy-matter-information model, we now have a physical context for how these abilities are possible. Information and intelligence is present at every level of reality in a superluminal hologramic communication network, therefore it is possible to attune to it in a practical manner (the tuning of consciousness to a specific frequency range correlates with the tuning of a radio in this context).

It seems that nature has a more innate propensity for accessing this information-communication field in general than do we humans. (Again, most likely because our minds are more focused on the logical, logistical and very "local" day-to-day mode of thinking and living, which is a valuable attribute unique to our experience.) I had another direct experience of this in nature that clearly demonstrated an act of collective communication and awareness, this time amongst butterflies. As briefly described in Chapter 24, it occurred the day I embarked on a vision quest in the Adirondack Mountains when I was 21 years old, wherein I saw the Phi Double Spiral pattern in my inner vision. At the onset of that journey I had a quick, ceremonially cleansing immersion into the cold waters of the brook I was at, then stood on the rocks to dry off where there was the only patch of early morning sunlight. As I

stood there, a black swallowtail butterfly came and landed on the rock next to me. Then another, and a couple more… and a few more, and even more… and they started climbing on my legs as even more came in. I ultimately counted twenty on my legs with nearly as many on the rock around me. After about a half hour of this remarkable experience it was time for me to embark on my journey, so I gently shook my legs and bid them well with deep thanks for the blessing they bestowed on me.

Kenneth Dwain Harrelson
CC BY-SA 3.0

How did 30-40 butterflies put the word out into the general area to say, "Hey, let's all go over to this human and drink water off of his legs while he stands in the morning sunlight." (And generally blow his mind while they were at it!) Clearly, they had an ability to communicate with each other that I can only imagine occurred beyond something like shouting to each other with their voices. Their behavior exhibited individual and collective awareness, spatial and temporal coordinating ("he's over here, come over right now!"), willful volition to fly from where they were to me, and an ability to transmit, receive and respond to specific information and choose to act on it just as we would with our own minds and an intelligent assessment of the information.

Without a pragmatic model with which to evaluate how this could be, we humans generally scratch our heads at this point with a degree of mystified amazement. How could such lithe and ephemeral little fluttery beings be so obviously intelligent and aware? Sure, dolphins have brains bigger than us humans, but butterflies? Aren't they just simple creatures that act purely on automatic instinct alone? This is the common viewpoint about the existence and functioning of mind and intelligence in nature. Could it be that the morphic fields of dolphins and butterflies are also serving a "non-verbal" communication role amongst their respective species? Viewing them as hologramic information fields that are unified with the universal information field offers a logical framework for such a possibility.

With a model of ubiquitous attributes of intelligence, awareness and that which we call mind existent throughout all energy, form and structure in the cosmos, we can consider another viewpoint — that of intelligence being an innate attribute of nature, and that every creature (and even inanimate rocks, crystals, metals, fluids, vapors, gases etc.) have their own experience of this intelligence with some degree of self-awareness and responsive relationship to their environment. Our human experience of these attributes is a pinnacle, which we primarily see similar, though limited, indications of also being present in higher-order animals such as chimpanzees, gorillas, orangutan, elephants, dolphins, whales, wolves, big cats, etc. The fact is, scientists see these same attributes of self<>environment awareness in single-celled organisms, and even within the dynamics of plasma — the state of matter composed of free electrons, protons, etc. that comprises 99% of the cosmos.[124] Physicist David Bohm was often struck by this latter observation, and was *"surprised to find that once electrons were in a plasma, they stopped behaving like individuals and started behaving as if they were part of a larger and interconnected whole. He later remarked that he frequently had the impression that the sea of electrons was in some sense alive."* [125] If you've seen videos of large flocks of birds flying together in a beautifully choreographed synchrony — called murmuration — this is what plasma's behavior is like.

"If you ask most people in science, they can't even define 'conscious' or 'aware' or 'intelligent' or 'learn' — all of these big words. And then we're so certain about where these things are and where they're not and what we should be looking into and what we shouldn't. It's almost discounting the fact that, when we have looked, the little bit that we have looked suggests that we should look further, we should look deeper. I've been talking to people who work with amoebas and the slime molds and it's the same all over. These guys, the critters, are amazing. They do stuff that we don't even dream of. And by not dreaming of it, we assume that it does not exist."

– Monica Gagliano, Research Associate Professor in Evolutionary Ecology at the University of Western Australia, on intelligence in nature at Forbes.com

Our human experience of consciousness is in large part predicated upon the general worldview we hold to be true about the nature of reality, and in recent centuries that worldview has become dominated by a scientific perspective that states we're separate from nature, that nature is merely an aggregate of atomic particles and chemical elements that can be analyzed by dismantling the things of the world, and that there is no consciousness as we experience it in nature. This material reductionist-based worldview has engendered beliefs of humans being superior to nature with our supreme intellect and abilities for innovation, invention and manifestation of technological civilization, putting nature's resources to use solely on our behalf. As a consequence of successfully escalating this belief and practice, we've rapidly brought many natural systems to the brink of collapse. We'd be very wise — doubly wise, in fact — to take a deep pause and rethink our relationship with nature.

We are, of course, just as much of nature as is all other life and matter in the world and cosmos. The hologramic totality is present in us and we have the ability to access it just as do dolphins and butterflies. Our logical minds have been taught for a long time to question, and even deny, this ability. Now we have a scientific model that can open the way for deeper inquiry into the reality of our consciousness existing beyond the brain, beyond even our physical presence as a human being. Let's explore a few basic aspects of this inquiry pertinent to the cosmometry of being human.

CHAPTER 46
COSMOMETRY OF BEING HUMAN

Tat tvam asi… A simple Sanskrit phrase essentially affirming: You Are That.

You, me, we are that. We are as much an integral aspect of the cosmos as is the galaxy we live in. The harmonic patterns that in→form one in→form all. We are Light and Sound converging into beings we call Human. The very atoms we are made of are "perfect musical instruments" vibrating in whole number harmonic tones, which in turn combine in geometric resonance to form the biomolecules, cells, organs and systems of our bodies. From atom to biomolecule to cell to organ to body, harmonic information is seamlessly transferred as scalar continuity in a unified system of intelligence, creativity and awareness, the synergetic totality of which is called (speak your name here). Yes… I Am That, I Am.

While there's a wide range of ways to venture into exploring the human experience, for the purpose of this chapter we're going to look specifically at the cosmometry; that is, how do the patterns, structures, processes and systems we find present throughout the cosmos in→form our being? The holomovement that animates everything is doing so in, as and through us, right now. Interference patterns of the cosmic hologram ripple throughout our being as electromagnetic and acoustic waves of energy-matter-information — Light-Sound-Consciousness — just as they do throughout all else.

We've seen already how the Phi ratio is present within our skeletal structure and DNA molecules, and that Fibonacci spirals comprise the structure of microtubules within our cells, the pinecone-like double spiral pattern of the pineal gland in our brain, and the Phi spiral pattern that defines much of the curvature around our eyes and nose (as well as the curvature of our ears, as is well known). These physiological characteristics of cosmometry show us that our bodies are just as much in→formed by the same dynamics found in nature and the cosmos in general.

The pineal gland is especially fascinating due to its shape resembling that of a pinecone, hence its name. Having this shape indicates that it is highly resonant with the fundamental Phi Double Spiral field pattern basic to the cosmometry of form and flow found throughout nature, as we saw in Section 4. It may well serve a kind of calibration role within our physiology and consciousness, aiding in our alignment and resonance with the greater fields around us. The pineal also contains photoreceptors similar to those found in our eyes, which are primarily held to be integral to the sleep cycle, sensing when it's dark and releasing melatonin from the pineal to support relaxation and rest. Apparently, these photoreceptors point inward towards a center point, an interesting fact when we consider the possibilities for what other functions they may serve. Researchers have also discovered tiny magnetite crystals in the tissue near the pineal gland. These magnetically sensitive crystals are similar to those found in various birds and mammals and suggest a functional interaction with Earth's magnetic field. While magnetite crystals in nature are almost always octahedral in shape, the ones found in our brain are actually cuboctahedral[126] — the very shape of the Vector Equilibrium! Perhaps between this resonant symmetry with the zerophase aether field, the photoreceptors of the pineal "looking within," and its double spiral pinecone shape, the pineal is physically capable of peering into the cosmic hologramic information field itself. I often wonder if this is where the light of dreams is actually being seen, as well as the physiological mechanism for psi phenomena such as remote viewing, clairvoyance, etc.

In Section 4, Richard Merrick describes how the Phi ratio damps down frequencies (of light, sound, quantum activity, etc.) below a threshold Fibonacci ratio of 13:8 (the octave threshold) to create coherence, and heterodynes frequencies above this ratio into standing wave resonance that defines the 12-tone harmonic structure of music. The octave-scaling system of music is found in sound, light and within the zerophase structure of space itself. As is extensively written about in many esoteric, new age and energy healing texts, we also have this same harmonic system in our energetic structure, called Chakras. The Sanskrit word, chakra, translates as a wheel or spinning vortex, and it is said that there are seven such vortices that comprise an essential architecture of our energy body. Here is a simple illustration using Phi Double Spirals to depict the chakras:

The circular "wheels" are defined by the Phi Boundary Condition, with the surrounding aura emerging from the extension of the double spiral field pattern beyond the body. Think of them as torus vortices, rather than as flat discs. As is commonly the case, the chakras are shown in a spectral sequence, correlating with the octave spectra of light and sound, which makes sense when we consider that our energetic system is arising from the same harmonic structure that in→forms the entire cosmos.

In a model of consciousness arising from (and as) a universal field of information permeating all space and form, we can see how such a harmonic structure creates a more fundamental level of coherence of consciousness at a purely energetic level; that is, as a non-physical or metaphysical presence localized in space. When we view our body's systems as a fractal antenna, we can see how it exists within a subtler energetic field that is our cohering consciousness in→forming our local physical experience as human beings. This system is in resonance with the same harmonic dynamics found in the electromagnetic atoms that make up our bodies, the rhythmic cycles of electrical information that flows through biomolecules, cells and organs, and the acoustic resonance of sound that harmonically in→forms the physical universe.

When we view our body's systems as a fractal antenna, we can see how it exists within a subtler energetic field that is our cohering consciousness in→forming our local physical experience as human beings.

As mentioned, much has been written about the levels of consciousness that the chakras correlate with, which can be readily found online. I had the good fortune of studying with Barbara Ann Brennan in the late 1980's and highly recommend her books and courses of study on this subject.

Next, I want to bring attention to another level of our energetic being, the knowledge and awareness of which has been of the greatest value in my life.

In Section 3, I introduced the concept of the One Point, which I first learned about when I studied Aikido in college. It is an energetic center located in the middle of our belly. Knowledge of this point has been present in Asian cultures for centuries, referred to as tan t'ien in Chinese (or dantien, for appropriate pronunciation), and held to be a seat of life force energy. It is essentially the central point of our physical being around which all movement takes place.

In Aikido they teach a very simple practice to activate this center — simply put your attention on it and imagine it radiating energy in all directions, like a star. By "extending ki" in this way, we immediately and effortlessly become coherent in our body/mind/ energy integration. The powerful stability that we gain from this one simple practice is remarkable, and it's absolutely natural and available to us all the time. It brings coherence to our physical sense of self in a way that is both empowering and relaxing. There is not one person I've shared this practice with who did not immediately experience such strong stability that it became difficult to push them off balance, whereas beforehand it was quite easy. Just drop your mind into the one point when you're lifting objects, doing sports, dancing, etc. and you'll feel the coherence integrating your body and mind with the movement of the action.

There are two other tan t'ien points in the space of our bodies as well, both of which engender the same kind of coherence within different levels of our being. These two are the middle tan t'ien, located in the higher heart area, and the upper tan t'ien in the center of the head. I'm quite certain that these three points are in a Phi ratio relationship, as seen in this illustration:

Just as we did with the lower tan t'ien in our belly, we can bring our attention into these points and radiate energy. When we do so with the middle one in the heart area, we bring coherence to our emotional body. When we do so with the upper one in the center of the head, we bring coherence to our mental body. Again, as simplistic as this practice seems, it really is this simple to engender coherence in our energetic being. By doing so we stabilize our minds and emotions, just as we do our physical body, and we begin to reside in our higher mental and emotional bodies. In the same way that it becomes difficult (even impossible in the case of a trained master) to be physically pushed "off center" when we're focused in the One Point, we remain much more stable mentally and emotionally when we're centered within these energetic points and radiating life force. This practice actually allows the dynamics of mental and emotional experiences to pass through us without getting stuck, helping us to keep clear in our consciousness amidst the challenges of life.

From the perspective of cosmometry and unified physics, when we activate these centers, we're tapping into the zero point field present in the center of everything. We're literally accessing a flow of life force emanating from the source itself, and as such it is inexhaustible. We're activating a free energy technology that's always present within our physical, emotional and mental being. It will never be depleted from too much use.

It is also effective to bring energy from the cosmos *in* to these centers, especially when sitting quietly or resting. It's like we're returning back to the zero point, centering ourselves into the stillness and silence. Doing so into all three centers at once is a great meditation (as is radiating them simultaneously).

It's good to remember that when we're bringing our attention into these points and centering in the stability they engender, we're not going somewhere else that's not us. In the field of consciousness that we are, these points and the chakras are as much who we are as is the physical body. We are energy beings as much as we are physical beings. We are these centers, therefore becoming conscious of residing in them is to be more fully conscious of our whole selves.

One of the most important aspects of bringing our world into greater harmony is to establish coherence in ourselves, in our relationships and families, and in the human family as a whole. The practice of centering ourselves in these three energy points and radiating life force is one of the best, most accessible and readily available methods I am aware of. As I said earlier in this book, I feel this practice ought to be taught in every school starting at a young age. Give it a try the next time you're waiting in line somewhere or stuck in traffic and start to feel impatient. One of my favorite times for practicing it is while driving, centering in my One Point and extending ki up the road ahead of me so that my body and mind are intimately connected into and integrated with the flow of life as it moves towards me.

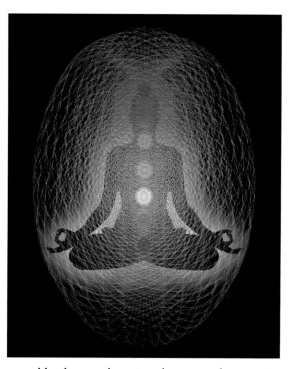

Establishing coherence in our physical, emotional and mental bodies, and tuning the octave harmonics of the chakras for optimum balance and wholeness brings vitality to our torus energy field and our physical body that resides within it. Finding the places we are experiencing constriction and releasing the blockages allows for a free flow of life force, opening the channels for harmonic information to transfer from the Planck-scale spacememory network throughout all levels of our being… and beyond.

Embodying our radiant ki energy is what I call being in the Joy Body. I'll share more about the important role Joy plays in engendering balance in our lives and world shortly, but in the context of the cosmometry of being human, I want to bring attention to this vital aspect of our true nature.

Many years ago I was introduced to a very simple practice for calling forth the realization of our Joy Body — an experience of being that is in alignment with the source blueprint, and that when embodied, brings this alignment into our physical body at all levels. This practice is taught by one of the Masters in the deeply insightful book series, *Life and Teaching of the Masters of the Far East*,[127] written by Baird Spalding in the 1930's as an account of actual expeditions by him and a small group of Americans at the turn of the 20th century in which they were invited to experience, learn from, and document the lives of the living Masters in India, Nepal, Tibet, China and other locations. It is an affirmation that is repeated at night while falling asleep that says, "*I now realize that there is within me a spiritual joy-body, ever young, ever beautiful. I have beautiful, spiritual mind, eyes, nose, mouth, skin—the body of the Divine Infant, which now, tonight, is perfect.*" In the morning, upon awakening, we feel the presence of a "divine alchemist within" that has transmuted the body into evermore youthful realization.

For me, radiating ki energy throughout my energetic and physical being feels like the experience of being in my Joy Body. I imagine every cell radiating this spiritual light from its center and my whole body being filled with the rejuvenating presence of "the body of the Divine Infant" that activates the regenerating capacity of stem cells to restore wholeness in alignment with the original blueprint. I highly encourage you to try it for yourself.

Practicing ki energy radiance in these ways has also brought to my awareness a dynamic sense that I call the Feeling Body.

CHAPTER 47
THE FEELING BODY

As has been expressed many times in this book, an essential feature of evolutionary processes in the cosmos is feedback. At every scale, the hologramic whole is informing the parts and the parts are informing the whole. This reciprocal relationship assures a continuity of integrity at a fundamental level of existence, providing a coherent means for the entire cosmos from micro to macro to evolve in simultaneous unity and diversity. The attribute of feedback is at play all the time in our lives, informing our experience at every level of our being — in our bodies, in the chakra energy system, through the tan t'ien — as well as in the world around us. Our presence, words, behaviors, actions etc. inform our environment and we receive feedback from what's around us back into our personal experience. In the simplest of terms, this is the process of karma as seen through the eyes of physics.

In Chapter 19 we saw how the torus flow process serves as a good model of this feedback dynamic, with the inflow and outflow co-existing in relationship to a shared center point.

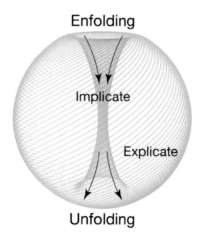

As we go about our daily living, is there a way that we can become more conscious of the feedback dynamic and ideally put it to beneficial use in our lives? We certainly experience it through our emotional and mental reactions to people and events in ways that can be both exciting and uncomfortable. There is another simpler and less dramatic means by which we experience feedback, though, and that's through what I call the Feeling Body. This is an aspect of our being that is in responsive relationship with our emotional and mental experiences but is not either of them. Our minds and emotions tend to be involved in the saga of the human drama as it unfolds within and without us, and they serve as excellent mirrors of our personal state of being, reflecting our beliefs and patterns of behavior quite well. The feeling body is different, though, because it is more involved in the purity of feedback itself without dramatic investment into the circumstances. This feedback is essentially more physical than the mental and emotional levels; it is the body's response to circumstances that we can actually feel, and as such it is more direct, operating both responsively to and independent from the mental and emotional experience.

The experience of the feeling body's feedback is simple: it either contracts or expands. This expansion/contraction dynamic is how the body signals how it feels in a given circumstance, and while we're not always consciously aware of this level of feeling (often due to being easily distracted by the emotional and mental responses), we are nonetheless feeling it. In more extreme circumstances, this is similarly experienced as the familiar fight-or-flight response, triggered by a release of

> *The experience of the feeling body's feedback is simple: it either contracts or expands.*

hormones. Yet what I'm referring to is subtler, and by becoming conscious of it we can begin to use it as an ally in navigating life's experiences, even at the most mundane levels such as imagining what we'd like to eat. Think about some food and you'll feel whether there's a response of expansion or contraction. It can be very subtle, and easily overshadowed by addictions of the mind and emotions that just simply want something, good or bad, but it's definitely there. As with all things in life, the more we bring our attention to it, the more it becomes developed.

Another example of using the feedback of the feeling body is when we need to decide to do something. We think about it, have an emotional experience about it, and we also feel it in our body. By tuning into what the feeling body is indicating, we can benefit from its simpler responsive feedback and get a sense of contraction, constriction, withdrawal from, or expansion, excitement and attraction towards the circumstances we're considering. Sometimes it's as simple as not being the right timing to act on something and when we tune into our feeling body, we'll experience contraction, so we might choose to wait a bit. It's important to realize that contraction doesn't always equate to "bad" or "negative" experiences, as sometimes it's simply this kind of pure feedback. No doubt we all have had an experience of walking into a room and having an immediate feeling of either excited expansion or hesitant contraction. This is our feeling body providing feedback at a level different from and not dependent upon our thoughts and emotions.

I've been personally aware of and working with the feeling body since I studied Aikido and learned the ki radiance practice, which as described in the previous chapter is a simple technique for introducing an expansive energy flow. The feeling body responds to this immediately, releasing constriction that is often present from chronic states of contraction, commonly induced by mental and emotional reactions. This is why practicing ki energy radiance from our tan t'ien points is so beneficial, because it actually affects our physical being in this way. Stress from fear, anxiety, anger, depression, etc. is experienced as a contractive state in the feeling body, and by consciously choosing to reverse the flow into one of expansion we can engender a shift in the feeling body's state, which in turn shifts our physical, mental and emotional experiences. In the previous chapter I used the examples of waiting in line or sitting in traffic as times to practice ki radiance, both of which are prime circumstances in which we are likely to experience our feeling body going into contraction. We are not victims at the mercy of this feeling body contraction; we are co-creative partners with it and can consciously engage it as the feedback ally it can be for us.

I've long wondered what is actually happening physiologically when we experience the feeling body? Having been in conscious relationship with it for forty years, I've come to have experiences that are much subtler than the more visceral feeling of expansion and contraction we have in our muscles and tendons. In recent years I've begun experiencing subtle yet powerful waves of excited energy moving through my body, much like an electrical current but not as might be experienced in our nervous system. It's more like a shimmering of energy. The image I get is similar to the description of the behavior of plasma (free electrons not bound to atoms) made earlier; like a large flock of birds flying in synchronized waves of murmuration. This is very much what it feels like in my body when this experience happens. Although not as yet scientifically analyzed, here's what I've come up with as to what may be occurring…

Most everyone is familiar with the fact that our bodies are predominantly composed of water, which accounts for roughly two-thirds of our body mass. What is quite remarkable, though, is that when the molecular content of individual cells is tallied, water molecules make up ~98.73%.[128] From a molecular perspective, our physical biological being is about 99% water! While typically considered more as a background medium in which the physical structures of cells, organs and biological systems exist and function, the presence of this much water in our molecular makeup suggests that it may in fact play a greater role than just providing a liquid medium for cells and their component structures to float in.

Water is, of course, a readily conductive medium for electromagnetic and acoustical impulses. Electrical current flows easily through water, which is essential for the body's energy transfer and communication systems to function effectively. Electrochemical processes are foundational to the operation of biological systems at all scales, from chemical interactions and cell signaling, to neuronal synapse and nervous system electrical flows that communicate information and trigger biochemical responses (some of which are directly correlated with resulting emotional experiences). All of these electrical flows are made possible by the vast reservoir of water molecules that comprise the environment in which the cellular systems reside.

The atomic structure of water is also geometrically resonant with the tetrahedral geometry of the isotropic vector matrix (IVM) — the zerophase state of equilibrium at the center of all oscillating dynamics. As such it has an atomic propensity towards the superfluid mutability of the IVM, making it such a predominant element in many chemical processes of dilution, dissolution and transformation. The reason it is so mutable is due to the water molecule's readiness to let electrons move from one molecule to another, be it with other water molecules or different chemical elements. In other words, the movement of electrons in water molecules is free enough to potentially exhibit behavior like plasma — a murmuration of electrons flying through the medium of water. In a paper entitled

Super-Conducting Liquid Crystalline Water Aligned with Collagen Fibres in the Fascia as Acupuncture Meridians of Traditional Chinese Medicine,[129] researcher Mae-Wan Ho states:

> *"The really special thing about water is that the coherent oscillation occurs between the ground state and an excited state at 12.06 eV, just below the ionizing threshold of water at 12.60 eV. In liquid water, the [coherent domain] of about 100 nm in diameter contains millions of water molecules, and hence some millions of almost free electrons—forming a plasma—that can be readily donated to electron acceptors."*

With this in mind, when I tune into the shimmering feeling that courses through my body, I'm coming to the conclusion that it is the water that is creating the experience. But it's not the water alone; it's directly tied into my consciousness. I often feel this shimmering in the morning when I'm stirring myself from sleep, beginning to reactivate thoughts about life in a new day. With these thoughts can come emotional feelings of happiness, or anxiousness, or frustration, and when they do, I've begun to shift into ki radiance — and then the shimmering kicks in full on. I believe I'm feeling a flow of consciousness within the water of my body that's moving like birds in murmuration because it's actually electrons behaving as plasma. Given that plasma comprises 99% of the physical universe, and the premise that consciousness permeates the cosmic totality, perhaps this is indeed what is happening in our bodies. Experiments have shown that water holds the memory imprint of a DNA molecule long after the molecule is removed, even to the point where the DNA can be replicated later from the information within the water alone.[130] In this way, water behaves much like the hologramic aether field that holds the memory imprint of all events in the cosmos (known in metaphysical literature as the Akashic Record of Hindu and Theosophical cosmology, and written extensively about in the context of contemporary science by Hungarian philosopher of science and systems theorist, Ervin László).

As we consider this in relationship to the feedback role of the feeling body, it becomes plausible that the expansion/contraction that we feel is actually occurring in the water first, then transferred into our nervous system. Perhaps the water in our body is as much an antenna as are the brain, heart and nervous systems? Perhaps the water is an even finer level antenna than these systems, attuning more so to the electromagnetic and acoustical impulses of our greater environment, as well as the greater field of consciousness itself? The experience of the feeling body may well be a physical attribute of the geometry of water molecules either expanding or contracting in their collective arrangements, or possibly a signaling medium that informs the nervous system to contract or expand the muscles, tendons and tissues. These are my conjectures and there is much as yet to explore here.

Whatever may be the biophysics of it, we have a built-in feedback mechanism in the feeling body that offers instantaneous and unfiltered information about our experience of the environment around us. Bring your attention to it and see what it has to say as you move through your daily life.

And speaking of attention…

CHAPTER 48
INTENTION, ATTENTION, LOVE AND JOY

The feeling body operates through an experience of a fundamental principle of energy dynamics in the cosmos — the interplay of expansion and contraction. This cosmic polarity is essential to all things manifest, universally exemplified as electromagnetic radiation (radiance of light) and gravitational tension (tensegrity of matter); the always-and-only-co-existing expansion-compression of energy-matter-information that creates our sensorial universe. While we experience this as a physical sensation in our feeling body, we also are in constant relationship with this dynamic in the realm of our consciousness; a metaphysical relationship of mind, emotions, intuition, etc. engaging with the physical cosmos in ongoing creative play through the attributes of Intention and Attention.

The first thing we notice about these words (in the English language) is their similarity to the word "tension", which is referenced above as the gravitational attraction dynamic of tensegrity. As such, we can restate them as In-tension and At-tension, with the latter also possibly stated as Out-tension so as to highlight its role in the inward-outward dynamic interplay. With tension as a primary component of universal manifestation, it makes sense that consciousness would have a direct relationship with this dynamic since the physical and metaphysical universe are viewed as a unified whole in our exploration. Tensional integrity is what brings energy dynamics into physical form, and with a model of consciousness as a ubiquitous presence, this inward tension is quite literally a universal attribute of in-tension, referred to in the human experience as intention. From this perspective, it could be said that there is intent at all levels of universal processes, an idea that Arthur Young proposed when he said, "The universe is a process put in motion by purpose."[131] While the notion of purpose is generally withheld from scientific analysis of the physical universe, Young sought to include it as a causal imperative within all processes, atomic to universal.

Merriam-Webster Dictionary defines purpose as:

1. ***a :*** something set up as an object or end to be attained **:** intention
   b : resolution, determination

2. a subject under discussion or an action in course of execution —
   on purpose : by intent

As we can see, purpose and intent are intimately related linguistically. While the human experience of intention may appear to be different from the purposive cause of physical processes, in the context of our model of ubiquitous consciousness they are really one and the same thing. Human intending is our version of a universal attribute of the purpose-driven process of manifestation, and when we intend something, we're literally calling upon this process to tend the universe to manifest "in" our direction — what is often referred to as the Law of Attraction. We are influencing the tendency of the holomovement with our consciousness in co-creative interaction with in→forming energy-matter-information. Which brings us to the word tend.

Human intending is our version of a universal attribute of the purpose-driven process of manifestation, and when we intend something, we're literally calling upon this process to tend the universe to manifest "in" our direction.

"Tend" is the root of all words related to this particular exploration — intend, attend, pretend, extend etc. It is itself a word that speaks of action with a purpose. To tend to something is to apply oneself to the matters at hand with a purpose in mind. In order to do so we must do two things: Intend, which is to define the metaphysical purpose, and Attend, which is the physical act of showing up to fulfill that purpose. We can intend all we want, but if we don't attend to making it so, it's of little use. For example, I intended to write this book for many years, eventually sitting down to attend to the act of writing so as to fulfill the intention being manifest as these words you're reading right now. Intending alone does not manifest a book! The so-called Law of Attraction (in-tending) is only effective when we actively engage in the action of manifestation (at-tending) that is inherent in the universal process of creation. And here's the playful part of the process — pre-tending.

Before we commit to intending and attending, we are free to let our imagination run wild with any and every possible idea, to pretend that something can be so even if what we imagine is beyond the means of current reality to manifest (or is it?). Pretending is a vital component of the creative process, one which children are masters of, yet as we "grow up" we tend to diminish its role. In a more academic and therapeutic context, the eminent psychologist, Carl Jung, called this process Active Imagination.[132] By using this uninhibited process of creative play he personally transformed what had been overwhelming fears and depression, ultimately successfully applying this process of pretending in his professional client relationships.

Pretending — freely imagining any scenario and purposeful outcome in the creative process. **Intending** — attracting in specific elements of the creative process for manifesting a defined purpose (literally causing a tension inward towards us within the universal aether). **Attending** — showing up as an active participant in the creative manifestation process. Tending the garden of creation so as to bring seeds of imagination to fruition. Till the soil, plant seeds, water the garden, reap the harvest. Co-creative partnership with the universal process of creation is an inherent attribute of the cosmic hologram. With our brain, heart and nervous systems seen as receiving and transmitting antennae within the universal field of energy-matter-information that is our greater "self" in consciousness, we can see how there is indeed a co-creative physics of pretending, intending and attending. As said by Jude Currivan:

> *"Realizing that everything we call physical reality is the expression of the in-formation-al intelligence of cosmic mind completely reframes the question of human and indeed all consciousness and cognizance… the paradigm-shifting view of the cosmic hologram, which recognizes the actual immateriality of the physical realm and the ultimate unity of consciousness, is offering a new view of the brain and its purpose. By identifying the brain as playing an important role in the informational organization of the embodied awareness of human beings, it redefines each of us as a unique and microcosmic indi-viduation of the intelligence of the cosmic hologram of our Universe, literally making us co-creators of reality."* [133]

So, what are we in-tending in our lives? How are we showing up to at-tend to our garden of life on Earth? What are we pre-tending as we imagine the future? We are co-creators of reality supported by the vast creative potential of the cosmos to manifest our hearts' desires. We transmit our intention and receive feedback, and what we put our attention on grows, whether generated from fear and doubt or confidence and trust. The outcome is in→formed by our state of being — the thoughts, emotions, feelings that in-tend the process — as well as our behavior and actions — the manner in which we at-tend the process. In a world overwhelmed by fear, distrust, aggression, domination, etc. arising from centuries of believing everything is separate and scarcity is the true nature of things, we are compelled to deeply consider our personal and collective states of being at this time of critical transition when environmental, financial, social, medical and many other ecosystems are fragile and nearing collapse. We are far too powerful a species to carry on as if we're not responsible for the outcome, which clearly is the case. We are, in fact, more responsible at this time than ever in recorded history, given the potential dangers of nuclear contamination (whether through war or meltdown, and just plain toxic waste), chemical and electromagnetic pollution, a genetic engineering folly, unchecked artificial intelligence escalation, and many other newly emerging factors. What might provide a foundation for approaching these powers and their inherent dangers with appropriate caution, reserve, care and appropriate stewardship? For our part here in the context of exploring consciousness and the human experience, the most basic yet equally profound answer is:

Love and Joy.

Two simple words, Love and Joy, yet so vast in their implications. It is not my intention to attempt to define these words and intellectually examine the many layers of meaning they may hold in our personal and shared experiences. Rather, I'd like to share a perspective about them that aligns with the balanced attraction and radiance dynamic explored above, bringing the metaphysical experience of consciousness into the physical processes of restoring wholeness within ourselves and our world.

We begin with a scientifically poetic insight from our elder guide in this journey, Buckminster Fuller… "Love is metaphysical gravity." Gravity as the force that binds energy events into physically sensible matter is the universal attribute of Love. Scientifically, Fuller is saying that the human experience of love is observed as gravity in the physics of the cosmos. It is fundamental to all manifestation, be it quantum gravity in atomic structures or cosmological gravity in celestial structures. Love is the metaphysical attractor that holds the whole in constant integrity. It permeates the entire cosmos as gravity with its innately attractive nature. Love is only half of the equation though. Gravity is but one expression of energy dynamics, complemented by its ever-present dance partner, Radiance.

In our human experience, Joy is a radiant feeling that bursts forth with inevitable levity. And here is where we find the great cosmic mind sneaking in yet another unanticipated wordplay in our language. Levity in physics is the opposite of gravity.

The radiance of Light permeates the entire cosmos as well, in equal measure as gravity's attraction (and perhaps slightly greater, given the observed expansion trend of the universe). What is the radiant metaphysical complement to Love?

Joy.

In our human experience, Joy is a radiant feeling that bursts forth with inevitable levity. And here is where we find the great cosmic mind sneaking in yet another unanticipated wordplay in our language. Levity in physics is the opposite of gravity. To levitate something is to counteract the effect of gravity. And the same holds true from a metaphysical perspective; to bring levity to a situation is to counteract the gravity of the situation. These words mean the same thing in both physical and metaphysical contexts. (Of course, since there's just one thing at play in this UniVerse).

When I was in college it struck me that, if this is the case, there must then be a complementary statement to Fuller's "Love is metaphysical gravity." What seemed quite obvious to me is that "Joy is metaphysical levity." Love and Joy are the metaphysical balance of forces that when present in equal measure bring equilibrium, which in metaphysical terms we call Peace. Therefore, **in order to establish a coherent state of Peace in our world, we must bring both Love *and* Joy into our experiences of relating, interacting, respecting, negotiating and resolving with each other**.

I am of a strong conviction that Love alone is not enough to carry us over the threshold to success during these challenging times. So much of the fighting that has consumed the human journey is in the name of love — of family, of tribe, of religion, of country, of dogma. We fight because we love something so much that we'll seek to eliminate that which is foreign to our personal experience of love. When joy is lacking, love can become distorted into expressions of anger, aggression, etc. And here's where it really gets interesting… these expressions are actually the radiance dynamic of joy still being expressed, but without the joy. The attraction-radiance dynamic is always co-existent, so when there's an imbalance of love without joy, the radiance comes out in these distorted and extreme ways. Hatred, anger, aggression are symptoms of a lack of joy in the equation. (Conversely, a lack of joy can also be expressed as depression when the radiance is withheld.) Imagine bringing joy in as a conscious choice as much as we call upon ourselves to do so with love. Imagine world leaders sitting together in joy to come to terms in the negotiations for that which they love. It's hard to hold mutual animosity when both parties are experiencing a true state of joy. Quite the opposite, it's so much easier to find mutually beneficial solutions when the gravity of the situation is balanced by the levity of joy in the pursuit of resolution.

It has become apparent to me that we humans often need to give ourselves permission to be in our joy. There's so much heaviness in the world and it's all too common to feel the weight of it precisely because we love the world. We might even feel a bit guilty thinking we could be in our joy in the face of it. I believe it is essential that we do

Love and Joy are the ingredients of Compassion, restoring wholeness in our being and embodying Peace as a way of life.

so, though, for the reasons stated above. I feel it is the true nature of compassion to bring both love and joy into our relationships with each other and our beautiful world. Compassion feels the gravity deeply while releasing the feeling with radiance. Compassion does not collapse under the weight of circumstances. It shines a loving light into them. Love and Joy are the ingredients of Compassion, restoring wholeness in our being and embodying Peace as a way of life. It is through establishing this ongoing state of compassion in ever-increasing numbers that we will create coherence in the human sphere of consciousness on this planet — the noosphere.

CHAPTER 49
COHERING THE NOOSPHERE

"There is obviously only one alternative, namely the unification of minds or consciousnesses. Their multiplicity is only apparent, in truth there is only one mind."
- Erwin Schrödinger

Erwin Schrödinger (1887-1961) was a Nobel Prize-winning physicist whose seminal works on wave mechanics provided what are considered to be foundational aspects of quantum mechanical theory. (He's also famous for having a cat that was both alive and dead at the same time, at least until someone peeked in the box it was kept in to see which state it was actually in, thus causing the collapse of the very wave function that he was heralded for defining — go figure...) It is quite fascinating that someone with his level of rigorous analysis of physical properties would come to the conclusion stated in the quote above — in truth there is only one mind.

"There's only one of us here" is a popular phrase in gatherings of spiritually minded groups, giving a nod to acknowledging this sense of unity of mind and consciousness. "Collective consciousness" and "group mind" are common terms for the phenomenon of experiencing a greater synergetic intelligence emerging from a group of individuals who are in a state of resonance and coherence in thought and feeling. There is a palpable relationship between the individual personality minds that make up the group and the shared group mind they comprise that both includes and transcends the individuals present. When such a group begins to catch hold of how the group mind is informing the shared objective of the group and the common interests of the individuals, a new level of wholeness emerges wherein everyone begins to see their own personal perspectives in relation to a unified one. This is group synergy, wherein a shared perspective that is greater than and unpredictable from the individual viewpoints comes into form, which is also the fulfillment of the views and objectives of the individuals. It brings to mind Arthur Young's description of a flashlight's purpose only being realized when the parts that make it up are assembled and operating as a unified whole, a purpose that the parts cannot fulfill when separated out.

Extending this idea to the planet as a whole, we can consider the field of human consciousness in its totality, what is called the noosphere. *Merriam-Webster Dictionary* defines this as "the sphere of human consciousness and mental activity especially in regard to its influence on the biosphere and in relation to evolution."[134] Often referred to as "the thinking layer" of Earth, the noosphere can be envisioned in a similar manner as the atmosphere and ionosphere that surround the planet. In fact, there is growing evidence that these geophysical layers, especially the ionosphere, are intimately connected with the noosphere. It is well known that the electromagnetic and acoustical pulsations of our brain, cardiovascular and central nervous systems are synchronously congruent with the Schumann Resonances, which are electromagnetic oscillations in the space between Earth's surface and the ionosphere. The base Schumann frequency, for example, is 7.8 hertz, which is a predominant frequency in brainwave rhythms.

HeartMath Institute's Global Coherence Initiative (GCI) has studied the relationship between geomagnetic fluctuations and physical, mental and emotional changes in us humans for many years. (For an in-depth paper on their findings, see *Synchronization of Human Autonomic Nervous System Rhythms with Geomagnetic Activity in Human Subjects*, published 13 July 2017.[135]) Using data from their Global Coherence Monitoring System of magnetometers that record changes in Earth's magnetic field, GCI is researching correlations between solar and geomagnetic activity and the collective behavior of humanity. As quoted from their website:

> *"The following GCI hypotheses guide our ongoing collaborative research:*
>
> 1. *Human and animal health, cognitive functions, emotions and behavior are affected by solar, geomagnetic and other earth-related magnetic fields.*
>
> 2. *The earth's magnetic field is a carrier of biologically relevant information that connects all living systems.*
>
> 3. *Every person affects the global information field.*
>
> 4. *Collective human consciousness affects the global information field. Therefore, large numbers of people creating heart-centered states of care, love and compassion will generate a more coherent field environment that can benefit others and help offset the current planetary discord and incoherence.*
>
> *Related to all of the above hypotheses is that* **human emotions and consciousness interact with and encode information into the geomagnetic field and this information is distributed globally. We believe there is a feedback loop between human beings and the earth's energetic/magnetic systems... We are suggesting in essence that this encoded information is communicated nonlocally between people at a subconscious level, in effect linking all living systems.** [Emphasis added] *Magnetic fields act as carrier waves for this information, which can influence all living systems — positively or negatively — within the field environment as well as our collective consciousness."*[136]

This description offers a scientific model for the physical presence of the noosphere as an actual unified electromagnetic field around the planet. GCI's hypotheses regarding the encoding and global distribution of information within this field correlate well with the Unified Spacememory Network (USN) model of ubiquitous information and consciousness presented in Chapter 43. It offers evidence that the information network *within* our bodies, communicating fractally from sub-atomic to biological scales, continues *beyond* our bodies, essentially forming the next level of synergetic wholeness in our human experience — the noosphere. As well, the non-local communication and feedback loop effects at this level correlate with the same universal effects proposed by the USN model, suggesting quantum entanglement of information within the entire global system of humans, Earth and all life. The magnetic fields of our brain, heart and nervous systems (as receiving and transmitting antennae)

> *The information network within our bodies, communicating fractally from sub-atomic to biological scales, continues beyond our bodies, essentially forming the next level of synergetic wholeness in our human experience — the noosphere.*

are in resonant relationship with the magnetic field of Earth in a unified noosphere of consciousness. We are deeply interconnected, with each one of us influencing the whole, and the whole influencing each one of us.

Another ongoing study of the collective field of human consciousness by the Global Consciousness Project (GCP) at Princeton University[137] has experimentally observed such effects. Over the course of many years, GCP has been monitoring a network of 60-70 random number generators (RNGs, also called "eggs") that have been situated all around the world. Each RNG generates a random event every second, with the data collection of the entire network being accurately synchronized to assure a consistent correlation of data. With over fifteen years of research and in depth analysis of anomalies in the RNG data that occur when global events happen that have an emotional effect on a large proportion of the human population (such as the death of Princess Diana, for example), the GCP has come to this simple conclusion:

> *"The behavior of our network of random sources is correlated with interconnected human consciousness on a global scale."*

They go on to say; *"There is a highly significant overall effect on the GCP instrument during special times we identify as global events when great numbers of people experience shared emotion. The effect is a tiny statistical deviation from an expected randomness, but the patient replication of tests has gradually created very strong statistical support for the reality of a subtle correlation of human consciousness with deviations in random data. The probability that the effect could be just a chance fluctuation is less than 1 in a trillion, an impressive bottom line statistic that is composed of small effects accumulated in more than 450 tests."* [138]

In over 450 events considered to have a global impact on human consciousness, GCI has seen a deviation from the expected randomness of RNGs at a statistical level that indicates a correlation between the field of human consciousness and the RNGs. While a scientific model to theorize the physics of these statistical results is not yet proposed by the GCP, the data clearly portrays a period of correspondence within the RGN network when a global event causes a shared experience in the collective field of consciousness — the noosphere. It is theorized that during such punctuated events a period of coherence and resonance occurs, wherein a large number of people are experiencing a similar emotional response at the same time. The effects of this coherence and resonance are not spatially dependent either, meaning that they are not greater within the RNGs that are closer to the actual location of an event, which suggests that the field of the noosphere is globally connected with equal influence throughout.

What is highly compelling about the GCP's observations of their data across many events and many years is that they see *"stronger effects when events embody or evoke deep feelings of compassion, but smaller effects when the level of fear is high. [This] point seems counterintuitive to many, but upon consideration, the relationships make sense and they bear strong implications for us. Compassion is an interpersonal, connecting emotion, while fear drives us toward personal survival; it separates us."* [139]

The implications of this are indeed worth considering as we look ahead in our quest for harmonization as a species with the Earth and cosmos. Coherence and resonance are more readily engendered when compassion is the emotional content of our individual and shared experience of consciousness. Events that evoke a fearful emotional state are weaker in their effects. While it is obvious that engendering compassion, understanding and mutual benefit is humanity's only viable option for making it through this critical transition period, the GCP's research shows that there is a real and tangible physical effect when these are the emotional signatures of our global state of being.

Imagine the potential for resonance and coherence when our global systems in all sectors are oriented towards restoring wholeness, balance and wellbeing for all people and all life on Earth. We can see indications from the GCP research that the results are indeed guaranteed as we align with the cosmic wholeness that already permeates all of reality (except where our gift of free will throws wrenches of pollution, environmental destruction, warfare, fear-based media, political and economic control, etc. into the mix). Returning to the words of HeartMath's Global Coherence Initiative, excerpted from their article *Coherence: Bridging Personal, Social, and Global Health*, by Rollin McCraty, PhD and Doc Childre:

> *"Most people know what it feels like to be in harmonious state, the place where our hearts, minds, and bodies are united in a feeling of wholeness. We speak of this variously as "the zone," "flow," "oneness," etc. When we are in this state, we feel connected not only to our deepest selves but to others — past, present, and future — and to all living plants and creatures and even to the cosmos itself. We call this state of internal and external connectedness "coherence." Increased personal coherence can be achieved as people learn to more consistently self-regulate their emotions from an intuitive, intelligent, and balanced inner reference. When more individuals in families, workplaces, and communities increase and stabilize their coherence baselines, it can lead to increased social and global coherence, which is further stabilized through self-reinforcing feedback loops. Being responsible for*

and increasing our coherence baseline is not only reflected in our personal health and happiness but also in the global field environment, which helps strengthen a mutually beneficial feedback loop between human beings and the earth itself." [140]

As we consider again the premise of a unified network of intelligence throughout the cosmos from which our experience of human consciousness arises as one expression, we can begin to see how the Global Consciousness Project and Global Coherence Initiative experiments indicate the reality of a unified noosphere of human minds that encompasses our planet in a localized synergetic field of consciousness, embedded in a larger cosmic totality of consciousness. We might say that our great "test" as a species at this time is to achieve a state of coherence within the noosphere, which can be seen as a natural evolutionary process of a globally awakening and organizing species like ourselves. It is this process that I refer to as "normalizing cosmic consciousness."

We might say that our great "test" as a species at this time is to achieve a state of coherence within the noosphere, which can be seen as a natural evolutionary process of a globally awakening and organizing species like ourselves.

The idea of cosmic consciousness has been around for a long time in spiritual contexts, primarily realized by a rare few individuals who expanded their awareness to include a sense of cosmic wholeness within their experience. These consciousness pioneers became the teachers, seers, prophets, yogis, mystics, priests and a host of other spiritually sanctified "blessed ones" who were tapped by divine grace to impart cosmic wisdom. What appears to be happening in an accelerated manner is that human consciousness as a whole is expanding at this time as "the conscious awareness of cosmic phenomena" — cosmic consciousness — becomes increasingly accessible and shared. Whether it's through psychedelic and meditative states, or through seeing the physical phenomena of the cosmos captured in Hubble Telescope images, or through the ubiquitous availability of spiritual and esoteric knowledge, or through a scientific understanding of the fractal-holographic nature of energy-matter-information in wholeness, we are rapidly expanding our apprehension of cosmic phenomena, and with this comes the realization that we are all an integral component of this phenomena and we're bringing this into our everyday experience en masse. The process of normalizing cosmic consciousness seems to be an inevitable step in our evolutionary journey as well, perhaps portending the time when humanity is prepared to venture beyond our planet and join the greater galactic community that many feel is ready to welcome us (and already is in many cases right here on Earth — a topic of consideration beyond the intended scope of this book).

In our current times, we are inundated with images and statements that serve only to stir up emotional drama in the noosphere. Mainstream news channels are obsessed with politicians who are obsessed with fighting… and round and round it goes, 24/7. Terror, death, natural disaster, conflict between (you name it) is the prime agenda to suck in viewers eyeballs and keep them twisted into a fearful state (with an occasional fluff piece thrown in for a feel-good moment). Given the insights from the GCP research, this is clearly contributing to maintaining a state of incoherence in the human population. While writing this section I saw a compelling video showing violent conflict between protestors and police in Germany during the 2017 G20 Summit juxtaposed with the (so-called) world leaders attending the summit listening to a transcendent performance of Beethoven's 9th Symphony at the same time. It was quite an exquisite video, really, with the magnificent music weaving a disparate narrative between the cavernous absurdities of the two simultaneous realities. We humans can and must do better than this, especially since the stakes are only getting higher by the day on all fronts.

The key to making this shift is found in the heart of Beethoven's genius — harmony. His understanding of the vast range of musical dynamism produced symphonies of beauty and power beyond words. As we've seen, this beauty and power is entirely sourced from the musical nature of the cosmos itself — the innate harmonic resonance that permeates all form and flow in every moment. This resonant harmony is literally right at our fingertips, waiting for us to recognize it, to tap it, to align with it. And when we do, we will fully realize our true nature and bring the already present coherence of the cosmos into our human experience.

CHAPTER 50
HARMONY

"The world is not to be put in order, the world is order incarnate.
It is for us to put ourselves in unison with this order…"
- Henry Miller [141]

A fundamental premise of our exploration is that the cosmos is an ongoing process of "undivided wholeness in flowing movement," as David Bohm describes it. This very moment as you read these words *is the Holomovement at play*, not some anomalous offshoot sitting in its own separate corner of space and time. As hard as we try to convince ourselves otherwise, we are absolutely integral to the entire cosmic phenomenon, because we *are* the cosmic phenomenon. The same patterns, structures and processes that underlie cosmometry, unified physics and music are that which we are made of at every level of our being. How could it be otherwise? How is it possible to be somehow not of the totality of manifestation in which we find ourselves? Like vortices in a flowing river, every atom, molecule, cell and organ of our body is in→formed by the same continuous source — the great cosmic river of energy-matter-information that courses through us and all of reality in every moment. Is it any wonder that we call it the "current" moment? We actually know this to be true and our language speaks of it as so. And yet, it's apparent that in the recent few centuries of humanity's journey we've forgotten this truth. We've forgotten that we are riding the flows of "current reality" as integral and intimate co-creators, instead thinking that we're somehow distinct from, objectively related to, and "above" it all, especially in our intelligence and capacity for innovation.

David Bohm referenced the dynamic flow of music as an analogy to describe the nature of the Holomovement and the reciprocal interplay of the Implicate and Explicate Order. From the vast reservoir of cosmic energy arise notes, rhythms and harmonies that play their parts in a song before returning to the silence from which they emerged. The tempo and meter of the song are implied — the Implicate Order of time — and the notes, rhythms and harmonies ride on the current of this implied order to form a sonic landscape upon which a melody is expressed — all of which are the Explicate Order in a flowing movement of wholeness.

In our exploration of the cosmic song, the sonic landscape is the "acoustic" component of matter and form that is manifesting based upon the exact same harmonic system as what we call music, as is proposed in the previous section on Music and the Harmonic Interference Theory of Richard Merrick. Which brings us to Henry Miller's quote.

The world, the universe, the cosmos, is order incarnate. We do not need to put it into order. We need to put ourselves in unison with this order. This brilliant and potent statement, expressed by Miller in a mere two sentences, offers us the most succinct guidance when it comes to approaching the path ahead at every level of our current reality. We simply need to tune our instruments, listen for the tempo and rhythm, align with it, and start playing along with the cosmos, and before we know it, we'll be singing and dancing with a whole lot more joy than the world presently has moving through it.

We simply need to tune our instruments, listen for the tempo and rhythm, align with it, and start playing along with the cosmos, and before we know it, we'll be singing and dancing with a whole lot more joy than the world presently has moving through it.

We are the one species on our planet that is not in alignment with the flow of energies. No other species is behaving in such an unharmonious way towards the rest of life, let alone its own kind. And given the magnitude of our impact upon the delicate balance of natural ecosystems, we are rapidly and dangerously creating disharmony and the inevitable consequences of degradation of wholeness and the strife that comes with it. The good news is that we now have enough scientific knowledge about fundamental principles and processes intrinsic to the generative flow of manifestation that we can return to a state of operating in harmony with nature and the cosmos, rather than imposing conflicted and destructive behaviors as we're predominantly doing at this time.

This is the process of coming into Harmony with the cosmos, and achieving this state is the primary evolutionary imperative that informs all of our choices and actions. As stated earlier in this book, while the experience in our lives of such a state often seems rare and fleeting, and it may appear to be an idealists fantasy that it could be achieved on a global scale, when we have the understanding of how it is achieved in nature and the cosmos, we have only to choose to apply that knowledge with the conviction that it will inevitably evolve us towards that outcome.

As it is in music, the key to engendering harmony is found in resonance. Just as when one tuning fork causes a sympathetic vibration in another of the same frequency, we can devise (and are devising) technologies that resonate with the cosmic plenum of energy-matter-information that flows throughout all things at all times, and in so doing harmonize with the natural patterns and processes that will restore wholeness to our bodies, Earth's ecosystems, and the consciousness of humanity as a whole. This is both a deeply personal process and a wholly shared one. It is essentially one of starting to sing the same song as the rest of the Uni-Verse — the One Song — that is revealed through understanding the cosmometry and physics of our innately musical cosmos. And since we *are* that, we have this same harmony already within us, obscured only by the limited perceptions of a worldview that has us believe we're not that. In the words of my brother Hal's song, Indian Drum… *"Just might take a lot of singing and dancing to chase our demons away!"*

Thankfully, we humans are waking up in ever-larger degrees to the "insanity of humanity" playing out blatantly before our eyes and realizing that there has to be another way. Thankfully again, many people are innovating technologies and social systems that apply cosmomimicry in their design on behalf of providing healthy, clean and safe alternatives as the old systems collapse, which they inevitably will and already are. As suggested in Section 3, imagine again an economic model based upon the dynamic principles of a Torus, wherein the flow of resources, information, knowledge, etc. is shared equally throughout the whole social system in a balanced reciprocal exchange; such a system is being devised by a team of business and economic professionals, originating in Brussels, Belgium.[142] Imagine a growing database of whole-system solutions that can be accessed by anyone, ultimately providing a collaborative network of financial, technical and legal experts to guide implementation; the foundation for this is already established by the Buckminster Fuller Institute as an Idea Index, stemming from their Fuller Challenge program.[143]

These and many other innovations are steps in the direction of harmonizing with nature and the cosmos. As the current systems reach their limit of efficacy, it is vital that alternatives are in place that can be readily adopted and implemented. It is not for us to fix the dying systems but rather to design new ones that will replace them. As Fuller himself said, "You never change things by fighting the existing reality. To change something, build a new model that makes the existing model obsolete."

What will life on Earth be like when we bring ourselves into unison with the innate cosmic order? Given the magnitude of imbalance we are experiencing in social, economic and environmental systems, is it possible to imagine such a time within the foreseeable future, and soon enough to mitigate the tendencies towards systems collapse that appear to be increasingly prevalent? I personally believe we are at the threshold of achieving this state of unison on our precious, small planet, and that this process is a natural and inevitable consequence of the tension and pressure that is compelling the intention of humanity towards the pursuit of harmonization across all areas of life.

As we complete of our journey here, let's allow ourselves to "pre-tend" what such a future world may be like when we've crossed that threshold and come into unison with the "order incarnate" of the cosmos at The Next Octave.

Section 7 Endnotes

110 Haramein, Nassim, Hyson, Michael, Rauscher, E. A., *Scale Unification – A Universal Scaling Law For Organized Matter*, see Figure 2A.
https://resonance.is/research-publications/

111 https://www.merriam-webster.com/dictionary/conscious#h1

112 Haramein, Nassim, Brown, William, *Unified Physics and the Information Network of Awareness.*
https://www.researchgate.net/publication/309680981_Unified_Physics_and_the_Information_Network_of_Awareness

113 Haramein, Nassim, Brown, William, Val Baker, Amira, T*he Unified Spacememory Network: from Cosmogenesis to Consciousness; Neuroquantology*, Vol 14, No 4 (2016).
http://www.neuroquantology.com/index.php/journal/article/view/961

114 Haramein, Nassim, Brown, William, *Unified Physics and the Information Network of Awareness.*
https://www.researchgate.net/publication/309680981_Unified_Physics_and_the_Information_Network_of_Awareness

115 Haramein, Nassim, Brown, William, Val Baker, Amira, T*he Unified Spacememory Network: from Cosmogenesis to Consciousness; Neuroquantology*, Vol 14, No 4 (2016).
http://www.neuroquantology.com/index.php/journal/article/view/961

116 Meijer, Dirk, and Geesink, Hans, *Consciousness in the Universe is Scale Invariant and Implies an Event Horizon of the Human Brain; Neuroquantology*, September 2017.
https://neuroquantology.com/index.php/journal/article/view/1079/852

117 http://www.sheldrake.org/research/glossary#morphic

118 http://www.sheldrake.org/about-rupert-sheldrake/frequently-asked-questions

119 McKusick, Eileen Day. T*uning the Human Biofield: Healing with Vibrational Sound Therapy*, Inner Traditions/ Bear & Company.
http://www.biofieldtuning.com

120 Rubik, Beverly et al. "Biofield Science and Healing: History, Terminology, and Concepts." *Global advances in health and medicine* vol. 4,Suppl (2015): 8-14. doi:10.7453/gahmj.2015.038.suppl.
https://www.ncbi.nlm.nih.gov/pmc/articles/PMC4654789/

121 Lipton, Bruce H. *The Biology of Belief 10th Anniversary Edition: Unleashing the Power of Consciousness, Matter & Miracles*, Hay House, Inc.

122 List of Animals That Have Passed the Mirror Test.
http://www.animalcognition.org/2015/04/15/list-of-animals-that-have-passed-the-mirror-test/

123 "Plasma, Plasma, Everywhere", NASA Science.
https://science.nasa.gov/science-news/science-at-nasa/1999/ast07sep99_1

124 Jahn, R. G. , Dunne, B. J. , Nelson, R. D. , Dobyns, Y. H. , and Bradish, G. J., *Correlations of Random Binary Sequences with Pre-Stated Operator Intention: A Review of a 12-Year Program*, Princeton Engineering Anomalies Research (PEAR) School of Engineering and Applied Science, Princeton University.
http://noosphere.princeton.edu/papers/pear/correlations.12yr.pdf

125 "David Bohm, Implicate Order and Holomovement", by David Storoy, August 2014.
https://www.scienceandnonduality.com/david-bohm-implicate-order-and-holomovement/

126 "Biomagnetism and Bio-Electromagnetism", The Academy for Future Science.
http://affs.org/biomagnetism-and-bio-electromagnetism/

127   Spalding, Baird T. *Life and Teaching of the Masters of the Far East*, Volume 1, Chapter 5; Devorss & Co.; Revised Edition (June 1, 1964)

128   Freitas, Robert A. Jr. *Nanomedicine,* Chapter 3. Molecular Transport and Sortation, Table 3-2. Estimated Gross Molecular Contents of a Typical 20-micron Human Cell; Foresight Institute. http://www.foresight.org/Nanomedicine/Ch03_1.html

129   Ho, Mae-Wan, *Super-Conducting Liquid Crystalline Water Aligned with Collagen Fibres in the Fascia as Acupuncture Meridians of Traditional Chinese Medicine;* Forum on Immunopathological Diseases and Therapeutics, pages 221-236; Institute of Science in Society, 29 Tytherton Road, London N19 4PZ, UK. http://www.dl.begellhouse.com/journals/1a654bf03faf67ac,744ec0d724b32947,0ec99b70090562bf.html

130   Montagnier Luc, et al, *Transduction of DNA information through water and electromagnetic waves;* (2015) Electromagnetic Biology and Medicine, 34:2, 106-112, DOI: 10.3109/15368378.2015.1036072 https://doi.org/10.3109/15368378.2015.1036072

131   "The Theory Of Process 2", by Jack Saloma. http://www.arthuryoung.com/the2exc.html

132   "Active Imagination", GoodTherapy.org. https://www.goodtherapy.org/blog/psychpedia/active-imagination

133   Currivan, Jude (2017-02-16). *The Cosmic Hologram: In-formation at the Center of Creation* (Kindle Locations 3466-3469). Inner Traditions/Bear & Company.

134   https://www.merriam-webster.com/dictionary/noosphere

135   McCraty, R.; Atkinson, M.; Stolc, V.; Alabdulgader, A.A.; Vainoras, A.; Ragulskis, M., *Synchronization of Human Autonomic Nervous System Rhythms with Geomagnetic Activity in Human Subjects; Int. J. Environ. Res. Public Health* 2017, 14, 770. http://www.mdpi.com/1660-4601/14/7/770

136   "The Science of Interconnectivity", HeartMath Institute. https://www.heartmath.org/research/global-coherence/

137   Global Consciousness Project website: http://noosphere.princeton.edu/index.html

138   IBID http://noosphere.princeton.edu/introduction.html

139   IBID

140   McCraty, Rollin, PhD and Childre, Doc, *Coherence: Bridging Personal, Social, and Global Health;* Altern Ther Health Med. 2010;16(4):10-24.) https://www.heartmath.org/assets/uploads/2015/01/coherence-bridging-personal-social-global-health.pdf

141   Miller, H. (1969). "Creation," The Henry Miller Reader. New York: New Directions Publishing Corporation. p.33.

142   WiseHolding – http://wiseholding.net/en/
Club of Brussels – http://clubofbrussels.org/

143   Fuller Challenge Archive, Buckminster Fuller Institute. https://www.bfi.org/challenge/archive

SECTION 8
THE NEXT OCTAVE

SECTION 8
THE NEXT OCTAVE

As a musician I've had the lifelong pleasure of listening intently to, and feeling deeply into, the harmonic effects of sound. The experience of music is first and foremost a feeling one, with our bodies being literally moved by the acoustical impulses of sound in harmonic relationships, and in that movement comes recognition of when the music lifts and inspires us, or makes us feel disturbed and sad, or soothes us into a balanced and calm state of being. Our bodies' central nervous system, organs, tissues, cells all operate with a rhythmic synchronicity of frequencies and pulses that innately "know" the harmonic nature of things, even if our minds have not yet intellectually learned it through the study of harmonic science or music theory.

One of the more compelling experiences of harmonic relationship is that of feeling the "beating" effect when two notes sound that are just slightly different from one another. While this effect is present in all harmonic relationships, it is most obvious when the notes are close to each other, such as when B and C are played simultaneously on a piano. A great way to learn about harmonic relationships is to start with a low C note and another C one octave higher playing together, then slowly move the lower note up in half-step increments while continuing to play the higher C note. You can feel a visceral tension and release in your body with each step in the progression of intervals — the settled beauty of the major 3rd, the uplifting feeling of the 4th, the unsettling and restless dissonance of the minor 5th tritone interval and the blissful relief of resolving it to the "perfect" 5th... As we move the lower note ever closer to the higher one, the interference pattern of the combined frequencies of the two notes creates a sonic beating effect that becomes most apparent when we're at the interval just before the notes come into unison, playing B and C together a half step apart. (Unison is when the two notes are the same, therefore fully resonant with each other, i.e. playing the same C note.) Playing this half-step interval repeatedly for too long will cause anyone to feel very unsettled as the dynamic tension innately craves its final resolution — unison.

It is just this kind of frequency shift from one octave to unison at a higher octave that I feel is playing out in the harmonic relationships of humankind at this time. We are at the threshold of arriving to unison, wherein we will experience a deeply settling resonance in our beings, and it is at this threshold just before unison that we are experiencing the most apparent "beating effect" in our world — a great dissonance that precedes and anticipates the inevitable resolution into harmonic resonance. While this

345

may seem to be a metaphorical perspective on our current times, it may in fact be quite literally true.

In a harmonic model of cosmic evolution, it is plausible that there may be literal frequency shifts as the dynamics of energy and consciousness progress from one state of being to another, i.e. from one octave to another. Whether influenced by physical dynamics of galactic and solar energies, or by a presence of "higher beings" guiding the evolution of consciousness (or both, perhaps one and the same in spirit), it feels evident that just such a shift is at hand and that we're seeing and feeling the effects of dissonance that precedes resonance. The noosphere of magnetic, electrical and consciousness dynamics may well be experiencing the chaos before the calm as we make the last step in the harmonic progression towards the next octave of life on Earth. It may be that in such an evolutionary progression of consciousness, a "next octave" of thought, feeling, visionary knowing, intuitive insight and scientific discovery becomes present in the noosphere as a kind of "visionary's call", and that the inevitable direction is towards this next octave for those that hear the call and live into it. Often described as the "ascension" of humanity in a spiritual context, such a progression will only be fully "realized" (made real) when it manifests into our physical world and daily experience.

> *The noosphere of magnetic, electrical and consciousness dynamics may well be experiencing the chaos before the calm as we make the last step in the harmonic progression towards the next octave of life on Earth.*

What might such a next octave reality look like? Are there signs of it present now in consciousness and manifestation such that we can orient ourselves towards the call and engender its full realization? Let's go on a short visioning adventure and see what we can find.

The visionary's call sounds something like this…

> *"Hey humanity, you're awakening to cosmic consciousness, intuitively knowing the truth of wholeness, unity and connectedness of all things, and scientifically understanding this unified wholeness across all disciplines. You're realizing that all energy-matter-consciousness is one phenomenon of vibration in harmonic synchronicity and discovering the science and technology to monitor, diagnose, manipulate and harmonize with the unified field of "all that is". You now have the opportunity to either live into and create a world in harmony with all that is or perpetuate the current dissonance that is an expression of the erroneous beliefs, choices and actions of an earlier phase of your conscious evolution. You have the knowledge, scientific and technological know-how, societal capacity, and spiritual inspiration to engender this process of harmonization with full support of the cosmic plan, which is always-and-only operating on the same fundamental principles that are the basis of your path to harmony. You're at the threshold of tension just before coming into unison at the next octave. All you*

need do to resolve the turbulence you're experiencing at this vibratory threshold is choose to come into resonance with the natural harmonic order."

As briefly described in the previous section, cosmic consciousness is in the process of becoming normalized in humanity at an accelerating pace. Barring a few cosmic idiots pushing the wrong nuclear buttons and blowing the whole show, it appears to be inevitable that humanity will move in the direction of resonance and harmony and stabilize our world "just in time". With the looming potential collapse of contrived economic systems and compromised ecosystems, it seems that there really is only one choice here, and thankfully with the emergence of cosmic consciousness comes the skills, technologies, systems designs and moral bearing to act upon that choice and cross the threshold from dissonance into resonance and harmony.

The first phase of this transition is to stabilize our physical, emotional, and mental states of being through self-mastery practices such as found in heart coherence and centering ourselves in the three tan t'ien (as described in Chapters 46 and 49), as well as fully assuming personal accountability within our relationships. We are both autonomous beings and an integral part of the world we live in, an inherent characteristic of existing in a fractally-embedded toroidal universe. Embodying self-sovereignty and supporting each other to thrive within a coherent societal environment that upholds protection of natural rights of person and property and eliminates laws that engender authoritarian control by an elite few (as currently dominates our societal structures) will establish an innate "universal morality" required to cross the threshold we are presently called to traverse. This is putting the science of Love and Joy into everyday practice!

On the other side of this threshold is a world wherein people, animals, plants, social systems and ecosystems are co-existing in balance, wholeness and integrity — fundamental features of every healthy living system. Through the ongoing application of cosmomimicry towards the resolution of problems, we humans will take responsibility for our part in the great play and wield our magnificent power with compassion and honesty, finally realizing our role as stewards tending the garden of life in conscious reciprocal relationship. By marrying the intuitive knowing of indigenous spiritual mind with the logical knowing of modern scientific mind, we will integrate our own being and restore the Whole Being that is our true nature.

This is not a pipe dream puffed up by new age utopians (well, maybe in some ways it is; cosmic consciousness is neutral as to in whom and how this process unfolds ;o). Scientific realization of the nature of the unified field of energy and consciousness is rapidly establishing a new paradigm of theory and application based upon the simple principles of resonance and harmony. Understanding that all is vibration and oscillation — from cosmological cycles of galaxies and solar systems, to the nested rhythmic network of biological systems and precise musical harmonics of finely tuned atoms — we now have the Master Code in the palm of our hands. That code is what we call Music, though what we experience as music is but a micro-fraction of what the totality of this code holds. The code is also called Cosmic Geometry, the energetic relationships that define form and fractal manifestation. Putting this musical geometric code into application through Unified Physics yields results that may at first seem like something beyond science fiction, yet when the basic principles of fractal-holographic resonance and energy-matter-consciousness as one thing are the foundational framework of logic, it becomes much easier to grasp what is actually occurring in the cosmos and in the applications that mimic the cosmos.

Imagine a world in which the source of electrical energy is unlimited, clean, free and safe. Remember the ever-spinning proton? Never decays, according to current scientific analysis.[144] That which is a prime physical unit of the universe (comprising 99.9999% of the mass) demonstrates without question that the true nature of reality is vast abundance. While our current sources of energy are inefficient and limited, engendering a paradigm of scarcity and all that comes with it, new technologies based upon tapping the same unified field from which protons derive their energy to power our world will usher in a paradigm of abundance beyond anything yet imagined. These technologies already exist and are poised to enter into the electricity-generating infrastructure on a global scale. Imagine cars, boats and planes that never need fueling; electrical appliances that don't need plugging in; mobile phones, computers and tablets that never need recharging; commercial refrigeration and computing infrastructures (two of the most energy-demanding sectors) that utilize unlimited, clean and safe energy. Imagine no longer being dependent upon an energy grid that is vulnerable to major storms, solar activity and acts of war, instead having each home, neighborhood and town supplying their own power needs autonomously.

This change of energy source alone completely transforms the basis upon which we define an economy, shifting from a model of scarcity of energy resources that informs and dictates market prices, distribution and wealth equality, etc., to a model of abundance wherein all people and industries have equal access to unlimited and clean energy. Every sector of society depends on energy in our modern world; therefore, the entire economic system will undergo a reformation of economic valuation within and between sectors. Economic and health impacts of energy related pollution are largely eliminated as well when exhaust from automobiles, trucks, planes, coal and gas power plants, as well as the lethal threat of nuclear waste contamination, is no longer present on our planet. Unsightly power lines can be removed, making urban and rural vistas more aesthetically pleasing.

How do these technologies work? By combining harmonic frequencies and geometric configurations of magnetic field fluctuations that are in resonance with the zero-point unified field geometry (Planck-scale electromagnetic aether) such that a density differential is created that draws a current from the field into our level of physical activity, supplying a greater amount of energy than is required to run the device — what's called over-unity (unity = 1:1 energy in:out; over-unity would be 1:1.5 energy in:out, for example). Thankfully, the science and engineering know-how for "new energy" technologies (ironically, the oldest source of energy in the universe!) has been around for a century in modern times and numerous devices have been built, but sadly it's been repressed in academic and industrial sectors by those who gained power and control through the current scarcity-based economic paradigm.

Along with understanding the source of energy and how to tap into it with these devices, the model of unified physics also defines the source of gravity, making it possible to design new technologies that can manipulate this force and change its behavior from being directed towards the center of Earth to being directed away from Earth. In other words, we now have the knowledge to engineer devices that will levitate. When combined with propulsion derived directly from interaction with the unified field, this is also a fundamental paradigm shift in an essential sector of human need — transportation. Imagine planes that never need fueling, use energy that is clean and harmless, operate silently, lift off and maneuver with ease and precision, maximizing the safety of passengers and cargo and not polluting the environment… that's going to be what the next phase of transportation technology is built upon. And it goes beyond low-orbit planes (and other transportation vehicles). Extraterrestrial travel becomes a practical reality, no longer having to burn fossil fuels to thrust our way through the gravitational constraints of Earth, but rather coming into resonance with gravity and directing its force to lift us outward into interplanetary (and interstellar, eventually) space.

While our current sources of energy are inefficient and limited, engendering a paradigm of scarcity and all that comes with it, new technologies based upon tapping the same unified field from which protons derive their energy to power our world will usher in a paradigm of abundance beyond anything yet imagined.

Sound like UFO tech? If you have any open-mindedness to the possibility that ET civilizations have been to Earth before (as depicted by numerous ancient cultures through art, architecture and mythology), or that they may be doing so in our current times (as deemed to be the case by many people from all sectors of professional, academic, military, commercial and civilian society[145]), then it would make sense that such advanced civilizations who would be able to travel light-years through spacetime to get here would have just such technologies. It is also said by many that these very technologies are already in existence as human-made gravity control vehicles that are kept confidential in covert military projects. Given that the science of unified field dynamics, zero-point energy, gravity and thrust control has been around (and suppressed) for at least a hundred years since Nikola Tesla and others cracked the door open, this is a highly plausible likelihood.

This is what the "next octave" looks like in energy, transportation and economic aspects of society, at a very high level of course. Let's continue this visioning with environmental restoration. We saw above how switching to abundant and clean energy sources eliminates the vast and highly detrimental pollutants from burning fossil fuels and nuclear fission. Imagine how quickly the skies will clear in Los Angeles, Beijing, Delhi and everywhere around the planet when these pollutants are no longer being spewed into the atmosphere. It won't take long for the hydrocarbons to be sequestered by plants and oceans once and for all when they're not being constantly renewed by our technologies. Imagine also using resonant frequencies at atomic and sub-atomic scales (quantum technologies, as they're called) to neutralize lethal radiation from nuclear waste and accidents at sites such as Fukushima. Sadly, there are those who say with certainty that such technologies already exist but are not yet allowed to be utilized, again simply because once they're known by the mass public the entire paradigm of science, and therefore economics and power dominance, changes.

Imagine also frequency and resonance-based technologies that restore wholeness to natural ecosystems such as oceans and rivers, as well as agricultural environments. At the source of every elemental manifestation, such as water for example, lies a blueprint of wholeness that is in resonance with cosmic geometry and harmonic integrity. Water ecosystems that are polluted with chemicals, plastics, biological waste, etc. have a distorted blueprint that compromises the integrity of the ecosystem's functioning, inhibiting effective natural processes and negatively impacting the health of plant, fish and animal species in general. Understanding that energy, matter and information are one thing, it is possible through resonance with the field to reintroduce the appropriate information at the quantum level (through frequencies of energy carried by safe and natural nano-particles of matter) that will restore the original blueprint of water in an entire ecosystem, and thus restore the innate wholeness and integrity of the ecosystem. Being an effect of information rather than matter, the restoration process becomes rapidly shared throughout the quantum field through harmonic resonance and the effects of balance and wholeness being restored can be seen almost immediately. With the application of such quantum technologies we can foresee a day when all of Earth's water systems are restored to a pristine and healthy state, as long as we also stop introducing the pollutants that cause the imbalances in the first place. The same holds true for terrestrial ecosystems and agricultural environments. When water, air and earth are restored to a state of innate wholeness in their quantum-atomic-molecular information blueprint through harmonic resonance with cosmic geometry, life will thrive and disease will be minimized, allowing for these ecosystems and environments to become the healthy living systems they originally were.

The same holds true for us humans. We too have an original blueprint at every level of our biological systems that has been compromised by pollutants and toxins of all kinds, be they industrial, agricultural and pharmaceutical chemicals, electromagnetic radiation, mental and emotional stresses, natural toxins, etc. The same principle applies: restore the information blueprint — the original hologram — and wholeness will be restored to our DNA, cells, tissues, organs, nerves, hormones, etc. While such technologies that can establish this hologramic restoration may sound beyond our wildest dreams, they're actually at our fingertips.

The next octave of health diagnosis and treatment is frequency and resonance based, working in harmony with the natural information blueprints at every scale. Every system in our bodies, from macromolecules like DNA to whole organs like the liver, has a specific vibratory state that is its unique keynote, its own song, we might say. Even vitamins, minerals and chemicals ring out their specific vibrational signatures. These vibrations are transferred throughout our body in one big symphonic orchestra of frequencies, converting from electrical signals to acoustic impulses that travel through nerves and tissues,[146] ultimately converging in the vagus nerve (the largest nerve pathway located in our chest). With the vagus nerve being directly connected to the larynx, it turns out that our own voices carry this entire symphony of frequencies, and that when we speak, they are all expressed within the vibration of sound that is our words. Sound is holosonic — the vibratory states of every system in the body are present in the frequencies of the voice. These frequencies can be digitally analyzed and referenced to a database to identify, evaluate and diagnose the state of any given system, such as the liver.

350

By comparing the signal (i.e. information) of the liver to its baseline healthy state, pathological conditions that may otherwise be as yet undetectable can be revealed. And not only revealed but treated with frequency and resonance-based technologies that can strengthen weak signals, introduce needed ones (such as a specific mineral's vibratory information), and eliminate pathogenic frequencies through phase cancellation specifically applied to a given condition. Sound like Star Trek's tricorder device? This technology already exists in a variety of offerings[147] that can not only diagnose and treat conditions of physical biological systems but as well the surrounding and interpenetrating subtle energy field — the aura and chakras — that comprise the metaphysical torus of consciousness through which we interact with the local and universal unified field.

By simple application of cosmomimicry — utilizing harmonic resonance, Phi ratio damping, geometric integrity, rhythmic synchronization, and unified physics principles — we can (and will) rapidly make our technologies become clean, efficient, quiet, minimally polluting, and even therapeutically beneficial when tuned to the "algorithm of life" frequencies.

By simple application of cosmomimicry — utilizing harmonic resonance, Phi ratio damping, geometric integrity, rhythmic synchronization, and unified physics principles — we can (and will) rapidly make our technologies become clean, efficient, quiet, minimally polluting, and even therapeutically beneficial when tuned to the "algorithm of life" frequencies described in Chapter 39. I once stayed at a beautiful, high-end retreat center that was obviously designed for great aesthetic and physical comfort; except when I woke up in the mornings I felt seriously hung-over, even though I didn't drink alcohol. My intuition told me that it was likely caused by the continuously humming drone of large refrigeration and air conditioning units outside my room that were probably putting out frequencies that are detrimental to biological systems (as also identified in the same algorithm of life study just mentioned). Imagine engineers of such technologies incorporating knowledge of these frequencies and methods of reducing fan noise[148] to both make quiet and tune these appliances (and, of course, run them with their own unlimited source of energy). "We have the knowhow," as they say.

The good news is that we each have the knowhow inherently within us, for we are all expressions of the one cosmic presence that informs all. As many an indigenous and modern energy healer has done, we can tap directly into the unified field of consciousness through attuning our biological antenna with the hologramic information that is whole at every point, tune in specifically to a person or a state of a biological system, inquire of their condition, and call into action the appropriate frequencies and harmonies that can restore intrinsic balance and resonance. We are equally a free-energy harmonic resonator as are the devices we create, for in fact they are extensions of our consciousness made manifest, based upon fundamental principles common to all form and flow and always-and-only in→formed by the universal holomovement.

How can we engage in this process right now, in our daily lives, attending to the mundane demands of life while engaging in the exquisite possibilities at hand? First and foremost is to remember, and really take in and embody, that we are the unified field become manifest in this human experience.

Being hologramic and universally entangled, our consciousness and the greater field of consciousness are intimately reciprocating an exchange of information in the form of thoughts, emotions, words and deeds, and the "external" feedback that comes back to us from the reality around us. So what are we putting into the field? Are we introducing turbulence, dissonance, stress? Or are we contributing to engendering coherence in the noosphere?

By using our imaginations to pre-tend a vision of our future, we catch a glimpse of the beauty and wholeness to come, in-tend our choices to call forth this vision into form, and at-tend to do our part as co-creators of ever-emerging reality.

Each one of our relationships and the world around us is a "sacred mirror" offering a reflection in an ongoing feedback loop of consciousness. While there is much about the current state of the world that we may feel is not a reflection of whom we personally are, it is a reflection of the noosphere in which we live and into which we inform the whole with our presence. In the spirit of Aikido, we have the opportunity to blend with current reality and re-direct it towards a state of harmony and peace in every moment. By centering ourselves in the "One Points" in our belly, heart and head, we establish a coherent stability that says to the noosphere, "I've got this. I'm a conscious agent of coherence on behalf of "real-izing" the resonant unison that is our destination and destiny at the next octave of human civilization. A tuning fork emanating beneficial frequencies and canceling out detrimental ones, inspiring those who can feel the clear tones in their soul to resonate with me and with the cosmic field and restore the natural blueprint within the hologram of human consciousness, present now."

By using our imaginations to pre-tend a vision of our future, we catch a glimpse of the beauty and wholeness to come, in-tend our choices to call forth this vision into form, and at-tend to do our part as co-creators of ever-emerging reality. We have both the opportunity and responsibility to do so, for once we've peered through the veil of contrived human systems and see the vast potential of cosmic harmonization, there's really no turning away and heading back into our TV-infused (and confused!) world and returning to unconscious complacency. We are truly at the threshold of choice — rush headlong into catastrophe from irresponsible implementation of ever-growing technological capacity (unconscious evolution), or embrace the full import of the opportunity we have to harmonize with life on Earth and in the cosmos and move deliberately and responsibly towards manifesting the next octave of resonant technologies based upon harmonic integrity, with full conviction that doing so assures success (conscious evolution).

Thanks to the synergetic nature of Wholeness, we can't predict what the outcome will look like, for it's a mystery greater than what we can as yet imagine. Yet we can hold the ideal in mind, steady and true, and take every step each day towards seeing that outcome with our own eyes, and in the eyes of all generations to come.

Cosmometry is a piece of this cosmic puzzle, offered here as a thesis to be poked at, challenged, corrected, verified and utilized as may best benefit the path ahead. I'm grateful you took the whole journey to these final words and look forward to engendering coherence in the world with you in every moment.

Joy is the Outward Flow of Pure Energy

Love is the Inward Flow of Pure Energy

Peace is the Harmonious Stillness present in the

Balanced Union of these two Opposites

∞

Section 8 Endnotes

144   https://en.wikipedia.org/wiki/Proton_decay

145   http://www.disclosureproject.org/

146   "The thermodynamics of thought: Soliton spikes and Heimburg-Jackson pulses" by John Hewitt, Medical Xpress, September 12, 2013.
https://medicalxpress.com/news/2013-09-thermodynamics-thought-soliton-spikes-heimburg-jackson.html

147   For example, Soniphi Vitality App: https://soniphi.com/soniphi-vitality/

148   http://paxscientific.com/fansblowers/

ADDENDUM
COSMOMETRY SUMMARY

A Bell Rings

ॐ

Universe

The words above convey in the simplest of terms the essence of what has been explored in this book — the vibratory nature of the entire universe is exactly the same as that of a bell ringing. It is, in fact, the ringing of a bell that creates the universe of form and flow, as we know it. The bell, in this case, is the spherical/toroidal tensegrity surface membrane of the universe that defines a resonant cavity in which harmonic relationships emerge, resulting in all dynamics of energy-matter that we observe and measure. Within the vast space of this cosmic bell is a constant interplay of tones, overtones and undertones, the sum total of which ringing in eternal presence we call Om — ॐ — the source of all that is. It is this vibratory harmonic interplay that we hear with our ears and eventually discovered operates as a 12-tone system of relationships, which we named Music. This system of relationships in-forms all vibratory phenomena as Acoustical pressure/compression within a universal field of Electromagnetism — Sound and Light as one cosmic whole. The dodecahedral pattern of temperature variations in the Cosmic Microwave Background (CMB; see page 249) is a cymatic attribute of this sound-light interplay, exhibiting the underlying harmonic influence of resonance upon the manifestation of form at the largest scale.

All form in the universe is an *acoustic* expression arising from the radiation/gravitation dynamics of electromagnetism, and as such it is **in-formed by the harmonic system of music**. The system of music, therefore, is the prime implicate "information" that is carried within the waves of sound and light that comprise all that is. This is one reason why David Bohm referenced music as an analogy for his concept of an Implicate Order out of which emerges the Explicate Order we experience, perceive and measure. Bohm was correct, though it's not an analogy. **The harmonic system of music that we discovered is an implicate system intrinsic to the entire cosmic field of acoustic vibration and electromagnetic oscillation**. If it weren't we wouldn't have discovered it.

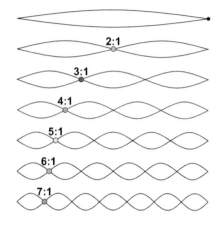

The system of music is a higher order organizing framework that is emergent from the fundamental quantized nature of the cosmos. All vibratory states transfer packets of energy in discrete quanta, with the magnitude of energy being directly correlated to the frequency of vibration/oscillation. The higher the frequency (smaller wavelength) the greater amount of energy there is present. **It is this spectrum of quantized energy that is the source of the fractal aspect of the cosmos, wherein patterns of form and flow are repeated across scales in a self-similar manner**. Music is just such a pattern with its 12-tone system repeated in a frequency doubling structure called Octaves. Octave doubling is the basis for the first of **three fundamental number systems** — the **2:1 ratio Binary** (2 4 8 16 32 64 128 256…). As we'll see in a moment, the Binary number system is inherent in the most basic geometry of space.

Complementary to and co-existent with the Binary system is another number system that is inherent in and emergent from the quantized nature of the cosmos — the **1.618:1 ratio Phinary**, based upon the Golden Ratio of Phi. Since all quantized action is expressed in whole-number quantities, the Phinary number system is represented as the Fibonacci sequence (1 1 2 3 5 8 13 21 34 55 89 144…). Fibonacci quantities and Phi ratio proportions are found throughout nature across all scales of the cosmos. (The dodecahedral geometry within the CMB described above is an example at the universal scale.) It is through the interaction of the Binary and Phinary number systems (or more appropriately, their ratios) within standing wave interference dynamics of sound and light that the third number system arises — the **Dodecanary** (1 2 3 4 5 6 7 8 9 10 11 12). This is the 12-tone harmonic resonance system of Music that is emergent from the always-and-only co-existing interplay of the Binary and Phinary systems. The self-similar Phi ratio (Phinary) serves a simultaneous frequency damping and resonance heterodyning function that carves a 12-tone harmonic interference pattern (Dodecanary) within the fundamental spatiotemporal container of the octave (Binary). Music, then, is a synergetic (higher order) organizing framework emergent from Binary and Phinary quantization ratios that in-forms energy-matter frequency dynamics in patterns of fractal resonance. All atomic and molecular geometric resonance is emergent from this implicate framework.

The entire cosmic phenomenon is frequency dynamics of sound and light in standing wave interference patterns. These interference patterns exist everywhere and are, in the case of laser light, what are captured as "information" in the photosensitive emulsion of a holographic plate. The resulting holographic image appears to the naked eye as a pattern of overlapping rings, much like we see when pebbles are thrown in water. When coherent laser light illuminates the plate, a 3-dimensional image appears depicting the object's image. The holographic image is not solely a phenomenon created by the coherent laser light, though. Rather, **the holographic information of the object is already present in the general field of light itself** and the holographic image captured on the plate is simply a very low-resolution version of what is already present as an extremely high-resolution hologram located in the space where the plate is placed. When we place our eye in the same location instead of the photographic plate, we're seeing the high-resolution hologramic information that's present. That information is present at every point in space, as evidenced by moving your eye 1 inch or 1 foot in any direction and still seeing the image. This is the **Relative Hologram**, since the image seen is relative to the angle of perception. In cosmometry, **the hologramic principle is stated simply as: The information of the whole is present in every point**. The entire field of light and sound — therefore the entire cosmos — is hologramic (not just the surfaces). It is a fully unified interference pattern of harmonic resonance and enharmonic damping expressing the innate and natural laws of Music in a grand Hologramic Symphony.

All vibration and oscillation is centered by one thing — zerophase equilibrium. It is the silence before sound, the stillness before movement. It is the one thing that is common to all things, for although there are myriad modes of vibration and oscillation, there is only one zerophase. As such, all things are unified in the zerophase; therefore, all things always and only comprise one whole. Just as the zerophase is silence and stillness, it is also prior to the concepts of time, size, rotation, perception, experience, etc. — *"The zerophase of conceptual integrity inherent in the positive and negative asymmetries that propagate the differentials of consciousness,"* as Buckminster Fuller describes it. Since it is not ruled by the limits of time and space, **when all information about all vibratory modes throughout the entire cosmos crosses the zerophase as it oscillates, it becomes instantaneously and simultaneously present everywhere**. The zerophase always and only knows itself as one whole, informed at every moment and in every point by the totality of all that is expressed as "the universe as we know it." This is the **Absolute Hologram**, the totality of information present in every point, inclusive and transcendent of all past, present and future phenomena.

In the cosmometry of energetic relationships **there is one geometric form that fulfills the criteria of zerophase equilibrium, wherein all vectors are of equal length around the circumference and to the center — the cuboctahedron or Vector Equilibrium** (VE), as Buckminster Fuller named it. In Fuller's energetic-synergetic geometry system, this represents the perfect balance between explosive radiation and implosive gravitation.

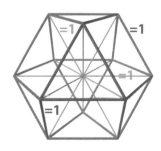

The VE is derived by close packing of twelve equal size spheres around one central sphere, either tangentially (as Fuller did) or in an overlapping "flower of life" arrangement (as Haramein did; see page 58). With its obvious correlation to the 12-tone system of music, the VE represents the intrinsic potential for harmonic relationships when in the zerophase state of silence, stillness, no-thing-ness. All vibratory phenomena (i.e. the entire known universe) are an expression of this system in the disequilibrious dynamics of harmonic relationships we know as music.

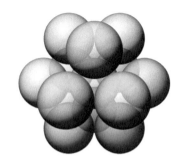

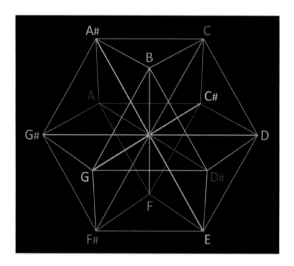

The equal-vector symmetry of the VE can be extended as an Isotropic Vector Matrix (IVM), creating a 60° triangulated array of energy relationships in equilibrium. In Fuller's synergetic geometry, the IVM is the universal field of zerophase equilibrium, with every point in the matrix being a potential center point of a "local" Vector Equilibrium. **Inherent in this matrix is the Octave doubling relationship, the source of the 2:1 Binary number system**.

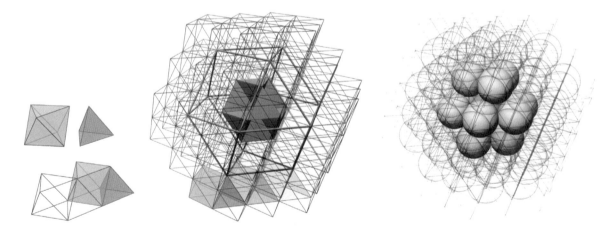

In Haramein's unified physics model, this is the geometric arrangement of **overlapping electromagnetic oscillators at the Planck scale** — what he calls **Planck Spherical Units (PSU)**. It is this equilibrium "ground state" of all energy-matter dynamics that Haramein describes as **the fundamental information pixel of our quantized universe**. This zero-point Planck-scale matrix imparts a granular characteristic to the structure of so-called empty space, and its zerophase equilibrium makes it a superfluid, superconducting liquid-crystal medium.

It is within this cosmic sea of superfluid, superconducting "aether" that all observable (as well as presently unobservable, i.e. what is currently called dark matter and dark energy) **phenomena becomes manifest in the same manner as do vortex structures in a river of water**. The vortices are all made of the same medium, though for a time they appear distinct and semi-autonomous. The PSU-IVM is the aetheric medium (e.g. the water) that all energy-matter dynamics (the vortices) are made of. Haramein's holographic mass solution for the proton and electron demonstrates that the atomic elements are composed of this quantized PSU field and that through this field all particles are universally entangled.

The shift from zerophase equilibrium to manifest disequilibrium (or dynamic equilibrium) occurs when the VE/IVM experiences a spin (a vortex), which introduces tension in the matrix. This tension pulls the twelve vertices of the VE towards the center point, creating disequilibrium between the outer gravitational force (the circumference vectors) and the inner radiational force (the radial vectors). In what Fuller calls the Jitterbug motion, the VE oscillates between both spin directions as its vertices spiral inward, and as they do they form symmetries of tension and resonance that we call the Platonic Forms. **The IVM, and the VE's jitterbug motion within it, are the source of the most basic tensegrity symmetries of form in the cosmos — the tetrahedron, hexahedron/cube, octahedron, dodecahedron and icosahedron.** All of these geometries have Phi ratio relationships within and between them, which defines their form and interrelatedness as harmonically resonant tensegrity structures. These geometries are the cosmometric ingredients that combine to form all atomic, molecular, crystalline, cellular, biological, planetary, solar and galactic structures and systems — the music of form.

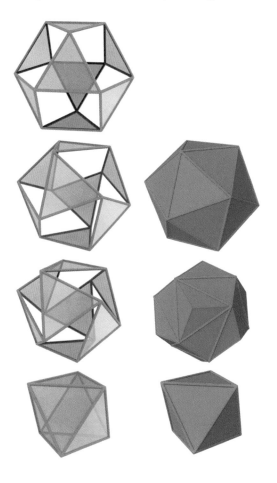

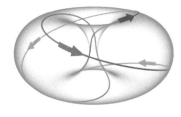

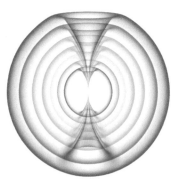

The oscillating jitterbug motion creates a dynamic flow process in space, swirling the local PSU field into the fundamental fractal energy flow form of a Torus. Whether at the scales of a proton or a galaxy or everything in between (and beyond), the energy dynamics of balanced flow in healthy systems are toroidal, and more specifically double toroidal for all rotating systems (which introduces coriolus forces). **The torus flow process provides the essential feedback/feedforward reciprocal information exchange between the zerophase equilibrium and the dynamic equilibrium of energy-matter in motion.** It also allows for seamless fractal embedding of dynamic systems across Planck to Universal scales, integrating localized information (such as a person) into a fully connected network of information flow such that the localized space (i.e. person, place, planet) is informing and informed by the cosmic space (i.e. atomic, molecular, cellular… solar, galactic, universal). **Cosmic information flow is whole and seamless, like an ocean, within which apparent divisions emerge in toroidal forms in the same manner as do vortices in a river of water.**

Rather than thinking of a torus as an object, think of it as a dynamic flow process that is made from the medium in which it exists. For example, a smoke ring is a torus made of air and smoke. The smoke makes visible the torus flow, which is still there even if you blow a ring without smoke. In simple terms, a proton is a torus made of Planck Spherical Units, according to Haramein's theory, with the PSUs being akin to the air molecules of a smoke ring torus. **It is because the protons are made of this superfluid aether medium that continuously supplies them with energy that they are observed to never decay. This one fact tells us about the true nature of the cosmos — it is absolutely abundant.** Scarcity is a fictitious concept being held as real in the minds of those who do not understand the true nature of the cosmos. When we realize (make real) the ability to tap into the cosmic abundance through zero-point technologies, our entire basis of perception of reality will change, resulting in a fundamental worldview shift that will in-form the design of our economic, medical, educational, governance and communications systems, our spiritual beliefs, and all other areas of human endeavor from the perspective of abundance. The torus provides a model upon which to design sytems for maximum efficiency, stability and harmony.

Most torus flow dynamics are not visible, such as magnetic fields, ecological and economic processes (the latter of which is presently not toroidal), weather patterns and respiration cycles in plants and animals. We can, though, find visual evidence of the dynamic action of toroidal energy flow in the patterns of nature, the most visibly apparent of which is the **Phi Double Spiral**. This pattern can be

seen in plants, cacti and trees, and in the flow of water as it interacts with more dense media, such as sand on a beach. **The Phi Double Spiral can be viewed as the cross-section pattern of a torus energy flow**. While the double spiral can be represented as a 2-dimensional pattern, it is actually a 3D standing wave within the general field of spacetime — a fundamental toroidal field pattern within the magnetohydrodynamics of energy-matter-information across all scales, whether visible or invisible.

The Phi Double Spiral creates a boundary condition that defines the limits of physical form, such as is readily seen in pinecones, sunflowers, the bark patterns of trees, etc. Phi's energy damping role provides the necessary limits within which harmonic resonance of form can exist. For example, the space between the seeds of a sunflower is Phi damping that provides the boundaries in which the seeds can resonate in form. This is exactly the same as Phi damping and heterodyning of sound frequencies to create musical tones. Sunflower seeds are denser musical tones within a background pattern of energetic damping.

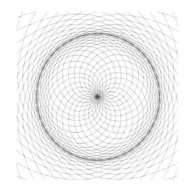  

The three fundamental energy dynamics described above — the Vector Equilibrium, Torus and Phi Double Spiral — combine into the **Unified Model of Cosmometry**, which depicts the integral relationship of these forms and patterns as a basic reference model of wholeness in both zerophase and dynamic equilibrium aspects. When looking at this image, imagine the VE jitterbugging (oscillating), creating the dynamic equilibrium of the torus and phi double spiral pattern.

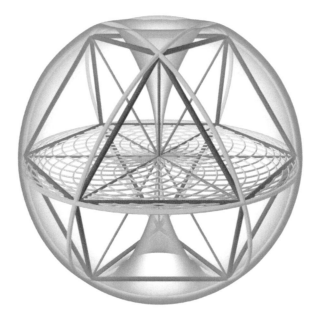

There are three essential components that comprise cosmic reality — **Information, Energy and Matter (or mass)**. While they can be seen as unique phenomena unto themselves, in our exploration here they are viewed as one thing. We can consider them as individual components for the sake of discussion, but in reality they are unified as one phenomenon — Universe. While Energy and Matter can be observed and measured as physical attributes, Information is the metaphysical data of the *qualities* of energy and matter as it's expressed in form and flow. It can be said that Information is the universal mind aspect of physical reality, providing the essential basis upon which manifest reality knows itself in its totality. In this way, **Information precedes its expression as Energy and Matter**. "Mind is the matrix of all matter," as Max Planck stated.

In order for there to be information in the structure of space there must be a mechanism by which it is stored as memory and shared throughout the whole. According to Haramein, William Brown, Jude Currivan and others, the Planck field of electromagnetic oscillators is the information data storage and transfer medium. As described above, this field contains the whole of all information in every point as a zerophase cosmic hologram. This hologramic information then transfers up from the Planck field into the atoms, molecules, cells, organs, organisms, ecosystems, planets, stars and galaxies of the unified cosmos. Since all of these things are made of the Planck field, it introduces an intrinsic feedback/feedforward information exchange between the local entities (the things) and the cosmic hologram's ubiquitous information totality. The entire universe is simultaneously and instantaneously informing and informed by every entity in it in a toroidal reciprocal exchange at every scale. **It is this dynamic feedback/feed-forward flow process that we experience as self-awareness, the prime attribute of consciousness.**

With this process occurring throughout the entire cosmos as local and universal information memory, transfer, perception, reflection and response, we can assume that the qualities of self-awareness and consciousness as we know it have their roots in the very structure of space itself; that in fact self-awareness and consciousness is present throughout and *emergent* as *Homo sapiens sapiens* — those who know that they know — due to the synergetic wholeness of our higher-order complexity of information, energy and matter. Our brains, hearts, solar plexus and central nervous systems are a fractal antenna that is interacting with the local and universal information field of consciousness, which we experience as a localized "self". We are, in fact, both that local self and the universal field of consciousness.

The only reason that consciousness can even observe and communicate about all that is described above is because it is all consciousness. Consciousness cannot experience something that is not consciousness. Light and Sound and all that manifests through them in the cosmic hologram are not sterile artifacts that "higher-order beings" are uniquely fortunate to perceive through evolved physical apparatus, they are consciousness itself permeating the entire universe in a unified field of mind and matter. Descartes' original mind/matter "duality" is an artifact of limited perception — mind cannot be something separate from the physical universe, and vice versa. While the polarized nature of energy dynamics is fundamental to the manifestation of physical reality and our experience of it (*the positive and negative asymmetries that propagate the differentials of consciousness*), the underlying state is always and only unified.

There is only one thing going on in the cosmos
and you are that, reading about yourself.

It is my wish that this summary provides a means to see the wholeness that is represented throughout all the pages of this book; an overview narrative that ties the pieces together in such a way that the underlying simplicity can be seen even while exploring the complexity that arises from it.

Thank you for taking this journey with me and being an advocate for advancing our shared understanding of the true nature of life for the benefit of all beings on Earth and throughout the cosmos.

363

About the Author

Photo by Pete Longworth • www.theartofseeing.life

"Intrepid Actualism Will Exist Forever..."

Marshall Lefferts has been a student of Nature since the age of five when he made his first trip to a remote cabin in the deep wilds of the Adirondack Mountains with his parents and brothers. Fifty-five years later, he still goes to that cabin and listens intently to what Nature wishes to teach him, and much of what is shared in this book has come from those magical and insightful experiences. He also began studying music at the age of eight and is now a multi-instrumentalist, performer and composer.

In his first year of college in 1978, following a spontaneous epiphany of awakening (where the quote above came from), he began studying the martial art of Aikido and became inspired by the writings of R. Buckminster Fuller, having the good fortune of meeting Bucky the following year. Veering away from traditional academia into the indigenous education of the great Universe-ity, Marshall has traversed an unconventional path in service to the bigger picture of what's going on here on planet Earth during this time of critical transition.

Along the way he became a Producer of media projects, starting with *Star Trek*® CD-ROMs in the early 1990's, then co-producing a short film about Mars Pathfinder for the Jet Propulsion Laboratory in 1997. In 1998, he met Barbara Marx Hubbard and subsequently became Co-Director of the Foundation for Conscious Evolution from 1999-2004, launching evolve.org in 2000. During these same years he produced internet media projects for the Buckminster Fuller Institute, then located in Santa Barbara, CA, where he was living. From 2005-2009 he lived on the Big Island of Hawaii, immersing in the study of "pod consciousness" with the Hawaiian Spinner Dolphins, and composing, recording and producing a collaborative album of original music, called *Mystery of Souls*.

Marshall served as Board President of the Resonance Science Foundation from 2006 to 2019, as well as co-designing, writing curriculum for and launching the Resonance Academy in 2014, for which he continues to serve as a member of the faculty. From 2007 to 2012, Marshall served as Associate Producer for the documentary film, *Thrive: What On Earth Will It Take?*, which is now the most widely viewed long-form independent documentary film, and is collaborating again with the Thrive team as Co-Director of Visual Effects and Post-Production Supervisor for *Thrive II: This Is What It Takes!*

Index

W

Y

Z

Made in the USA
Middletown, DE
27 April 2020

91231388R00221